Astronautics for Science Teachers

EDITED BY: John G. Meitner, Stanford Research Institute

THE AUTHORS:

Nicholas Rosa
Stanford Research Institute

Myron G. H. Ligda
Stanford Research Institute

Daniel B. DeBra
Lockheed Missiles and Space Company

Poul Anderson
Author and Lecturer

Phil Adamson
Hughes Aircraft Company

Egan J. Rattin
Aerospace Corporation

Lawrence D. Ely
Aerospace Corporation

Kurt R. Stehling
Electro-Optical Systems, Inc.,
a Subsidiary of Xerox Corporation

Arthur L. Costa
National Aeronautics and Space Administration

JOHN WILEY & SONS, INC., New York · London · Sydney

Library of Congress Catalog Card Number: 65-16419
Printed in the United States of America

Preface

The field of astronautics has rapidly grown to an effort which is both one of the biggest and one of the most fascinating undertakings of our nation. An unprecedented engineering effort—consuming currently more than 7 billion dollars per year—has been built upon every discipline of science, and the demands for new information have, in turn, considerably increased our total scientific effort.

The relation of astronautics and science is that of a mutual impact: at first we noted a rapid expansion of scientific efforts under the pressure of astronautics' needs for new basic information. In turn, the practical realization of astronautics has already yielded a large amount of new scientific data, collected from outer space; this information is now providing the background for a large and new body of scientific theory. It is in fact quite likely that the total extent of scientific knowledge gathered throughout history will be exceeded manifold within a few decades, by expanding our field of view from the surface of the earth to the near and far regions of the universe.

These mutual impacts of science and astronautics deserve appropriate study and exemplification at all levels of science instruction. Because space exploration is the most adventurous and romantic undertaking of mankind, it has already sparked many high school students to take a new interest in science and technology. Their enthusiasm should be appropriately rewarded in their science instruction.

The problem of reaching this objective is one of professional specialization: the men who are most familiar with astronautics, i.e. the scientists and engineers who are now pursuing this effort, are not qualified to instruct high school students. The teachers, who *are* professionals in science instruction, may not be sufficiently conversant with some aspects of the complex science and technology of space exploration.

   This book was, therefore, prepared by space scientists and engineers in order to bring teachers up to date in astronautics, so that they can introduce some of its facets into their science classes. The first two chapters of this book rapidly introduce the entire field of astronautics in a narrative fashion, sweeping across its history and accomplishments without introducing technical details. The scientific background of space missions and some of the apparatus and equipment required to explore space are subsequently presented in some technical detail in Chapters 3 through 8. Chapter 9 provides a fascinating but factful outlook of astronautics for the next decade—a chapter which indeed roused the mirth and enthusiasm of even those of us who have been practicing scientists in the aerospace field since its inception. We hope that this projection may also provide a spark of enthusiasm for the science teachers who impart the mirth and wonder of science to those who are now their students and who will later become our colleagues and successors. The last chapter is designed to assist teachers in transferring astronautics to the classroom; this chapter was prepared by an educator-scientist who has taught science in high school, and who is now directing educational efforts in the aerospace field. In addition to a series of suggestions to teachers, the author also provides a very extensive list of references, aids and other assistance available for props, models, movies, charts and exhibits.

   I should like to take this opportunity to thank the authors of this book for accomplishing a difficult task with patience and with dedication; let me assure the readers whose professional interests are focused elsewhere that the authors of this book are pioneers and respected experts in their field: I should also like to thank Mr. Kenneth Brown of John Wiley and Sons, whom we first knew as an excellent aerospace engineer; we now find him a talented publisher who has provided much guidance and assistance in the preparation of this book.

Menlo Park, California   JOHN G. MEITNER
December 1964   Editor

Contents

CHAPTER 1

Introduction to Space Exploration

John G. Meitner
Stanford Research Institute

Contents

Introduction to Space Exploration

1.1 ASTRONAUTICS AND SCIENCE

This book deals with the exploration of space. The subject has become of extreme importance in the lives of all of us; it represents not only a very large national effort, and therefore has great economic consequences—it is undoubtedly also the greatest adventure in the history of mankind.

As science teachers, you are, of course, aware of the great impact of astronautics upon all fields of science. This is a chain reaction: astronautics is an application of all fields of fundamental science and of all fields of applied engineering. By straining all scientific knowledge and all skills of engineering, astronautics has recently become a reality for the first time in human history. Its achievements, its impact, its demands, and, perhaps most of all, its fascination have in turn made a great impact on all scientists and engineers. This fascination also affects others, and as science teachers you can take advantage of the mirthful interest and excitement of your students about space exploration. It is not quite so obvious as you may think, to account for this general fascination with astronautics. Let us, therefore, examine astronautics itself and realistically examine some simple facts.

It is interesting to note that astronautics has only become of importance during the very last few years. It is also interesting to note that since this very recent inception it has become one of the most important topics throughout the world; we also know that a significant fraction of our entire national income is devoted to the pursuit of astronautics. Accordingly, one may well ask why this is so, and one may, in a more reflective mood, also ask why we undertake this effort altogether, what the expected returns are, and what constitutes, after all, this large field of space exploration, or astronautics.

The very recent coming of age of the field—and not perhaps a thousand years ago nor a thousand years hence—is not a mere historical accident. Rather, astronautics became a practical field in the late 1950's because the various engineering skills had reached during

and after World War II a practical level sufficient to permit man
for the first time the actual exploration of space. It had always
been a dream of man to do so, at least ever since history has
been recorded. If a single factor can be cited which is perhaps the
most important for the realization of space travel in 1957, it is the
success of rocket propulsion; this resulted from military missilery
during World War II. Simultaneously, electronics had grown rapidly
to the level required for the control of space missions; this is also
in part due to military World War II technology, for example, radar.
With these means at hand to propel a robot payload—and ultimately
a man—into space, and with the necessary electronic control available
to assure that the payload will indeed reach the target of its mission,
no decision weighing was necessary for men to proceed.

Once the means appeared to be finally available, man's *curiosity*
was presumably not the paramount reason for the immediate decision
to explore the universe. It is interesting to note, however, that this
particular reason for the exploration of space has been consistently
minimized; although I am aware that more practical and economically
more sound arguments must also be made—because large funds are
required from the taxpayers to support the astronautics effort—I do
not wish to pass the motivation by curiosity or by interest too lightly.
Man has since time immemorial been curious, and he has wondered.
I am sure that when aboriginal man came to the shore of a lake
or to the seashore he has gazed and he has wondered what lay beyond.
Ultimately he learned to build a boat and to cross the waters. Similarly, men have wondered what lay beyond a barrier of mountains
and eventually they have conquered the mountains and explored the
valleys beyond. It can be shown quite scientifically that man's curiosity is as factual and as a real part of him as some of his physical
attributes. It is quite likely that aboriginal man has gazed at the
stars, at the moon, and at the comets and that he has wondered.
We too gaze and we wonder. However, unlike our ancestors we now
have the means to go out and to look closely at the bright and
at the dark sides of the moon and to find out just what it is that
makes the stars twinkle.

This particular motivation-by-curiosity is also one of the three
major relationships between space exploration and science: the motivation of a scientist (his oft-quoted "search for knowledge") is curiosity—he gathers individual facts and data without any justification

Figure 1.1.   What Is Space?

other than that it is interesting to note and to know individual facts about birds and bees and that it is interesting to know all about particular colors and reflections and about specific waves and sounds. The scientist also connects these facts by general theories and hypotheses, again by a motivation of curiosity toward understanding—merely for the simple satisfaction of understanding *why* all birds and bees fly, what *all* colors have in common, and what the *general* aspects of waves are.*

The other two major relationships between science and astronautics are based upon the two directions of their interchange: (1) astronautics engineering has made new demands upon scientific facts and theories in order to build the necessary hardware items for space

* Like astronautics, science is not directly concerned with applications; however, engineers and physicians, following up the discoveries of science and those of astronautics, do of course apply the facts and theories and are thus motivated not by curiosity, but by the objective of concretely creating something new and useful, for example, a new machine or a new drug.

exploration; in this process much expansion of scientific endeavor has recently been created; and (2) as astronautics engineering has progressed to the point of having already accomplished many space missions, new facts and data were provided from outer space for science. Scientists can now expand existing theories or perhaps formulate entirely new hypotheses, based on the new scientific knowledge (see Chapter 2).

1.2   WHAT IS SPACE?

Obviously, the explorer of space must examine first of all what we already know about our destination—outer space. For our purposes it may suffice to define space as "everything beyond the atmosphere of the Earth" or "space is that which extends outward from any point that is vertically about 100 or 200 miles above our sea level." Thus space contains all heavenly bodies—the moon, the planets, the sun and the stars—and it contains their debris—the meteors, comets, meteoroids, and dust.

Space—or more properly the vast regions which are not occupied by celestial bodies—also transmits radiations; or we can equally well state that space *contains* radiations—those that are made up of elementary particles such as protons and electrons (e.g., the Van Allen Belts) and those that are transmitted in wave form (e.g., X-rays, visible light, radio waves and others). The transmission of electromagnetic radiation (e.g., light) through an otherwise empty medium (i.e., deep space) is not yet completely understood, in spite of the mathematically precise fashion with which we can describe radiation phenomena. Similarly, we know that elementary particles (between the celestial bodies) exist only in fantastically low concentration, so that deep space is indeed largely "empty"—we know, in fact, that deep space represents a very fine vacuum; and, a vacuum is of course that which contains nothing at all. Yet, space *does* contain radiations, which apparently transmit or propagate through this "nothingless." While it is well to recall these limits of our understanding, it is also well to recall two other points: (1) many facts relating to astronomy and to the physics of space are known and provide sufficient guidance for designing our astronautics missions (a relevant review of these facts about space is presented in Chapter 3) ; (2) where facts are known but not properly related, future exploration of space will likely provide the additional data necessary to permit new theories and a more complete understanding of space and of the universe. The hope for such understanding is indeed the scientist's motivation for undertaking astronautics.

1.3 WHY EXPLORE SPACE?

The curiosity of all mankind and the never-ending search of scientists for new facts and for greater and more unified understanding are only *one* expression of our motivation to explore space. Several other motivations exist, which are applied or practical. For example, the United States has military objectives in space which can be grouped into two categories: (1) those objectives for which a clear military advantage of entering space is already known, e.g., a satellite that observes the enemy continuously ("spy-in-the-sky") and periodically radios back to the earth what it has seen, or an orbiting defense system which automatically attacks invading enemy weapons; and (2) those objectives where further knowledge is required to decide whether a military advantage does indeed exist and, if so, to ensure that the United States will then be in control of that advantage, e.g., a military base on the moon; since we do not know what the surface of the moon is like, we do not know yet whether it is an advantage to have a base there or not. However, if ultimate inspection of the lunar surface should reveal something to indicate that a military base would be advantageous there, we should certainly like to deny this advantage to our potential enemies and we can only ensure this by being there first. Similarly, precise knowledge of basic scientific facts—for example, how does a man function for prolonged periods of time in space—is also of importance to the military so that they can make the proper choice in possibly placing men into space for defensive or offensive purposes during future wars. Most military objectives in space are as yet quite subordinate to civilian interests, but the military interests nevertheless form another ingredient of our total motivation for exploring space.

Noting that our military interests in astronautics are as yet fairly small, it is apparent that our paramount expectations from the exploration of space are based upon civilian objectives. Several interesting projects exist indeed which interact directly with our civilian technology; for example, the satellites which predict changes in weather, the international communications satellites, and those that are navigational aids. These projects are in an area in which the payoffs of space exploration can be directly predicted; for example, the economic effect of accurate weather forecasting can be and has been calculated. To the extent to which a satellite-borne meteorological instrumentation permits a great improvement in the accuracy of weather prediction, the economic payoff of such a meteorological satellite system turns out to be very much worthwhile. Similarly, the economic effect of extending present world-wide communications by satellite relays can also be estimated. These and other projects are discussed in more detail in Chapter 2, but their existence and the fact that their predictable returns form a concrete element of the total motivation for the undertaking of space exploration should be noted here.

Other returns, which we expect but cannot yet describe, also add to the total anticipated payoffs from our astronautics effort. For example, we cannot predict directly just what it is that will accrue to us by exploring the moon, but as scientists we feel fairly certain that the exploration of an entirely new domain will undoubtedly yield new facts for new applications in our civilization. While we do not know what these facts will be, the probability of achieving valuable returns is rather overwhelming.

Let me explain this apparently paradoxical argument of a high probability of extremely valuable returns in an area in which we have not even explored our universe, in some detail: the argument is based on two premises from which the prediction follows. The first premise relates to the many elements of our civilization, each of which is in some way based upon a previous scientific discovery. Most innovations of our civilization—in fact all innovations throughout the history of mankind—are either engineering developments or medical developments. Neither of these can be undertaken without prior knowledge; no medicine, no drug, no medical treatment, no warmth, no instrument, nor any book can exist without prior knowledge of fundamental scientific facts. The second premise relates to the source of gathering and connecting these scientific facts; all knowledge and all science of mankind, all facts and all data, have been obtained by observations within our somewhat restricted field of view, that is, from an observation platform no greater than the surface of our

TIROS VIII Weather Satellite
(Courtesy of National Aeronautics and Space Administration.)

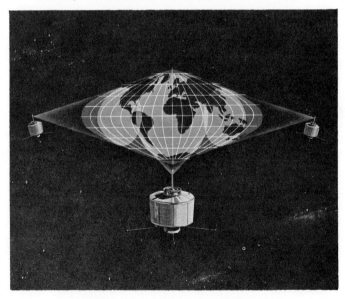

Syncom World-Wide Communications Satellite System
(Courtesy of Hughes Aircraft Company.)

Figure 1.2. U.S. Application Satellites.

earth. The exploration of the universe and travel into space enlarges this field of view by a tremendous factor, which literally has infinity as its upper limit. In the light of these premises, the argument presented above is one of simple connection and extrapolation: if indeed the field of view from which previous facts have been gathered is enlarged manyfold and if, on the other hand, all advances of civilization are based upon the discovery of such facts, the number of applications and benefits to our civilization will similarly increase by a manyfold factor. Therefore, a scientist can also confidently look upon material payoffs of space exploration in those areas in which we are as yet ignorant in pointing to specific accomplishments.

In summary, it is interesting to note that the Director of the National Aeronautics and Space Administration, the Hon. James E. Webb, has expressed these and other motivations for the American space effort under the following five desiderata:

1. The international leadership by the United States.

2. The support of our national security where it depends upon mastering advances in technology.

3. The expansion of scientific knowledge to be gained from space exploration.

4. The achievement of the anticipated material uses of space technology for the benefit of mankind.

5. The stimulation of these challenging efforts upon our society, especially the young.

1.4 HOW DOES ONE GO INTO SPACE?

The Purpose of Missions: Payloads and Spacecrafts

At present, the only purpose of space exploration is reconnaissance; according to current science fiction, other purposes may eventually include celestial mining, military outposts in space, low-gravity hospitals, observation and experiment stations, transfer points, and perhaps even permanent, general living space for humans on extra-terrestrial ground. This may all come true, but keep in mind that this is as yet only fiction and that at present the only real objective of all space exploration is observation; we collect and analyze samples of the far region of the atmosphere, we take pictures of the far side of the world's cloud formation, we measure radiations beyond the atmosphere, we "take the temperature" of Venus, we determine magnetic fields in outer space, and we wish to look at the surface of the moon and determine the quality and composition of the lunar soil.

Much of this reconnaissance can be accomplished by instruments, but we also send men into space. There has been considerable debate on the necessity or even the desirability of manned missions. On the side of the proponents of unmanned-missions-only, it can, of course, be said that these missions are frequently simpler and they avoid possible loss of human life. Many observations in space can indeed be made by automated instruments which take specific measurements at the distant location and radio back the desired information on temperatures, radiations, meteorites, magnetic fields, compositions, etc. Instruments are frequently more compact than humans, and since they are also hardy and require less temperature- and atmosphere-conditioning than men, the total weight of an instrumented mission is usually much less than that which includes a human observer; this makes it in turn much simpler and cheaper to loft an unmanned mission than a manned mission. The chief *limitation* of unmanned missions is their restriction to follow through on a specific, preprogrammed task and their inability then and there to look elsewhere, as a human being can: for example, if an instrument lands on the moon and is preprogrammed to measure the color and the temperature of the lunar surface, it may do so with complete accuracy. However, if it happened to land, say, within a small black field which was an unusual spot within a huge green-and-gold area extending from horizon to horizon, the instrument would not "know" that it was measuring a very particular field and *we* would not know that the information we receive as to the nature of the lunar surface was not general. Contrarywise, a human observer would immediately recognize the problem of obtaining "relevant" surface measurements. In short, the human observer is the only instrument that can be *generally* programmed, that is, he can be told to "go there and tell me all about it." But the human observer is heavy, and he cannot live in outer space unless he is completely encapsulated and presupplied with his entire earthly environment of appropriate climate, atmosphere, and food. This requires a good deal more weight than an instrument requires and, until recently, we simply did not have the rocket power to launch such a big package.

The controversy between manned and unmanned missions has subsided—it is now obvious that we will undertake both types and extract the most usefulness from each.

Regardless of unmanned or manned types of missions, the first item to consider among space exploration gear is the *payload,* that is, the item that conducts the reconnaissance. The payload in unmanned missions is an instrument (or a series of instruments) and their accessories; in manned missions the payload consists of the passenger and his personal gear and rations. These payloads are usually packaged in a shell, structure, cabin, or other housing which also contains all accessories for their function (power, atmospheres, communications gear, etc.) and the total packaged assembly of payload, accessories, and housing is called a *spacecraft.* Understanding then, that the purpose of a mission is reconnaissance, the spacecraft is the final and minimal package which must be placed on the target in order to conduct the reconnaissance. Depending on the type of mission, the spacecraft may be a satellite (i.e., for orbiting missions, and it may be unmanned or manned) or it may be a re-entry container (i.e., for near-space ballistic missions, and, again, it may be unmanned or manned). Spacecraft are described and discussed in Chapter 8.

The System: The Space Vehicle and Ground Support

To ensure placing even a small spacecraft on target requires a truly gigantic amount of complicated gear. A *space vehicle* is usually defined as the entire assembly leaving the earth and it contains by and large two elements: (1) The *spacecraft*—which it is to deliver onto its target—and (2) the rocket power required to hurl it towards its target—the *launch vehicle* (see Figure 1.3).

There are other elements, primarily those concerned with keeping the spacecraft on proper course toward its target (guidance), those electronic items that maintain contact with the vehicle while it is in flight (tracking and communications), and the vast stationary complexes associated with these tasks and the launching (ground support).

It is quite difficult to develop these complicated items and at the same time to keep a proper overview so that the individual components will all work in the same direction. For example, the payload size and mission target define the power required by the propulsion system in the launch vehicle; but if the payload is sensitive to large accelerations, for example a human passenger, the propulsion power must also be dispensed at a given *rate,* which then becomes quite as important as the total power itself. In turn, such a narrowly specified propulsion power rate will then make requirements on the guidance instrumentation over and above those of ensuring the simplest path from the launch site to the target. This particular guidance complex may, in turn, make additional demands on an otherwise satisfactory communications and ground support arrangement.

The complicated, total arrangement resulting from this strong interdependence of individual and complex components is generally called a *system.* In astronautics the systems concept merely calls attention

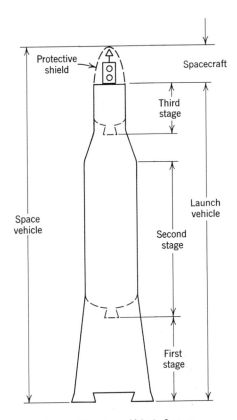

Figure 1.3. Space Vehicle System.

to the fact that much and complicated work must be conducted on an interdisciplinary level in order to ensure that all effects of all components mesh properly and represent an over-all optimization of the desired end result: to place a spacecraft most reliably and most efficiently on its target within a minimal expenditure of time and money.

In order to enter space and to place a spacecraft on its target, a large space vehicle must be launched from the surface of the earth, generally from a very complex ground station. This space vehicle consists of the spacecraft (see above) and the launch vehicle; the latter contains the rocket power required to lift the entire vehicle assembly and propel it into space, and the electronic and mechanical devices which ensure that the space vehicle will proceed on the proper course. In order to launch such a complicated and very large space vehicle, the ground complex must contain the pads for launching, an array of equipment which can interact from the ground station with the guidance and control electronics in the space vehicle, and numerous support stations such as assembly, loading, fueling, transfer, check-out, and others—many of which are in turn operated by remote control (see Figures 1.8 and 1.9). Beyond these local ground stations supporting the launching of the space vehicle are a globally extended series of tracking stations which observe electronically the positions and trajectories of the spacecraft, and which provide radio control and communications for the postlaunch phase of space missions. Again, the complexity of the entire space vehicle and its ground support recall the interdependency of large systems.

The Launch Vehicle and Propulsion

In order to overcome the gravitational effect of the earth, that is, the weight of the entire space vehicle, a force greater than this weight must be provided in order to lift off. This power is supplied by one or several stages of rocket power.

A rocket is a heat engine which delivers forces, or *thrusts*, entirely by reaction. By combustion of chemicals within the rocket motor, heat engines of the rocket variety generate large amounts of hot gases under high pressures, which are subsequently exhausted through a nozzle affixed to the aft end of the rocket motor; the impulse of the gas molecules departing rearward causes a forward impulse of the same magnitude to be imparted to the rocket motor, and the sum of these impulses is equal to the forward thrust of the rocket motor (see Figure 7.1). These underlying principles and several examples of rocketry are explained in considerable detail in Chapter 7.

The greatest amount of rocket power is employed during lift-off; after these launch rocket motors have exhausted, the launch vehicle is usually jettisoned and the detached spacecraft proceeds toward its target by itself. Some propulsion power may still be required later

Figure 1.4. Rocket Ascent (APOLLO Test) (Courtesy of National Aeronautics and Space Administration).

for corrective maneuvers, landing, docking, return, etc. Such auxiliary rocket power is, of course, placed in the spacecraft.

Guidance and Control

Space exploration has become possible primarily because the necessary rocket power for lofting the instrumented and manned spacecrafts has become available during the last decade; however, equally important to the success of space exploration are the recent means for proper targeting of these spacecrafts—their guidance and control.

The task of placing a spacecraft into a predictable orbit, or of impacting a payload on a distant celestial body, requires truly fantastic accuracy. It may be interesting for students—and it will be surprising to you—to express such accuracy in some analogy which deals with objects more familiar to us in ordinary life. For example, you may pose the problem of defining the size of a clock in relation to an ordinary 22-caliber rifle bullet, and then define the distance from which a sharpshooter must hit the sweep-second hand in order to exhibit an accuracy similar to that achieved by an Earth-launched spacecraft impacting within a prespecified 100-square mile area upon the moon; you will find that the size of the clock is small and that even if the clock and the sharpshooter were placed upon fast jet aircraft moving in opposite directions, the distance at which he were to hit the target would be many miles, were he to duplicate the feat of current astronautic guidance requirements.

In essence, space missions require either the achievement and maintenance of a predictable orbit or they require the rendezvous of a spacecraft (or its docking) with a rapidly moving distant target, for example, another spacecraft or a celestial body (of which the moon, at a distance of approximately 250,000 miles, is our very nearest neighbor in space!) The paths for such a mission can be determined relatively easily; these trajectories and orbits follow, of course, the laws of motion which govern the natural celestial bodies—the stars, planets, and comets. Accordingly, once the mission target is defined, the trajectory can be very accurately calculated; by employing modern computers, the lengthy mathematics involved for the determination is reduced to practical terms. In general, several paths or trajectories may be possible to achieve a given mission, and a choice among such trajectories will be made according to the minimal power requirements (i.e., that requiring the least amount of propulsion). The background of orbit and trajectory determinations, their efficiencies, and some of the details of determining them are discussed in Chapter 4.

It is the purpose of guidance and control units to ensure the proper achievement of the desired trajectory of the spacecraft. In principle, the guidance of the spacecraft requires two operations, and the control units translate the results into appropriate steering maneuvers in order to keep the spacecraft on its course.

The two guidance operations involve respectively (1) navigation, that is, a continuous determination of the exact position of the spacecraft, and (2) a comparison of this actual location with the position the spacecraft *should* occupy at this particular time, according to the trajectory (or orbit) originally calculated. This process of comparing *actual* positions with those *required* according to the planned trajectory is continuous and is accomplished by means of a miniaturized computer in the space vehicle. The control units—basically a steering device for the space vehicle—are inactive whenever the guidance unit is zeroed (i.e., when the difference between the desired and the actual positions is zero). However, whenever the spacecraft position deviates from its planned course (for whatever reasons, i.e., error during launch, faulty deployment of propulsive thrust, meteorite impact on the spacecraft, or deviations caused by the minute drag of residual atmospheres in relatively low orbits, etc.), the guidance unit will determine the difference between the actual and the desired positions and provide an appropriate signal to the control units; these will in turn provide a corrective maneuver to the spacecraft. The corrective maneuver continues until the guidance unit determines again that there is no difference between the actual and the desired position of the spacecraft. At this point the guidance instrumentation provides another signal to the control unit and the corrective maneuver is terminated. Several means for control maneuvers are available; for example, short bursts of auxiliary rocket units may be employed.

It should be noted that guidance and control operations proceed during the initial lift phase (i.e., involving the entire space vehicle) and also subsequent to the jettisoning of the launch vehicle (i.e., involving only the spacecraft). Accordingly, some guidance and control gear is replicated in these two major positions of the space vehicle, while other functions are combined for both phases and are operated from the spacecraft. The elements of electronic guidance and control units and of auxiliary control rockets, are discussed, respectively, in some detail in Chapters 6 and 7.

Communications and Other Auxiliaries

One of the principal requirements for electronics aboard a spacecraft is the need to record and to transmit to earth the information which has been acquired aloft; in a manned expedition this information consists largely of the observations of the personnel in space, who remain essentially in two-way radio communication with ground personnel.

In unmanned spacecraft, electronic sensors are programmed to observe the phenomena which the mission is designed to study. For example, a temperature measurement or a series of such measurements may be made, or optical observations by still or motion picture photography, or by television, may be arranged. In each case a record of the observation is made, scanned electronically, and stored (e.g., on a magnetic tape). Communication then requires that at certain prearranged times the tape is read through a scanning device which radios the information back to earth. A reverse process of this type permits ground personnel to submit commands to the spacecraft. For example, a radio command signal of a given frequency may be transmitted from the ground to a specially designed radio receiver on the spacecraft; this receiver will then electrically actuate a device which may control various operations, for example, the firing of a small rocket in order to carry out a corrective maneuver which places the spacecraft back on its course; or, the command signal may control the opening and closing of a chamber in order to trap an atmospheric sample, or it may cause initiation of a television camera, etc. Details of communication elements are described in Chapter 6.

In addition to the command and control devices and the communication and telemetry devices discussed, there are many observational, controlling, and conditioning devices which are operated electronically. For example, some equipment—electronics itself is a good example—can operate only within given ranges of temperature, say, between −100 and +100°F. Whenever the external temperature exceeds these limits, arrangements must be made to shield the sensitive equipment from such temperature extremes. Two examples by which such temperature protection can be afforded are (1) an arrangement of external

louvers of which one side is painted white and the other black, or
(2) an ordinary heating/air-conditioning system. In the first scheme,
the louvers are turned white side out whenever the temperature is
near the upper limit, so as to reject the solar heat radiation impinging
on the spacecraft; when the temperature drops close to the lower
limit, the louvers are, conversely, turned to expose the black side
to outer space so as to absorb solar heat radiation. The heater/air-
conditioning arrangement resembles closely that provided in an ordinary thermostatically controlled household. In either method electronic sensors and control devices provide automatically the required
internal thermal environment.

In order to increase our store of knowledge, much record keeping
is also required on the function of the spacecraft, its equipment,
and its occupants. Accordingly, the current and relatively simple
missions serve as a test basis for future and more complicated missions.
The present missions therefore contain a great deal of instrumentation,
which continuously records the various states, temperatures, electrical
charges, moisture content, chemical composition, and similar events
of a large variety of the equipment on board. Such instrumentation
also automatically and continuously records a variety of biological
measurements conducted on the human astronaut. For example, the
early American manned spaceflights continuously provided temperature readings at several locations on the body of the astronaut and
also recorded his heartbeat, pulse rate, EKG, and a variety of other
measurements. These data are continuously determined and recorded
and again communicated (or "telemetered") to the globally dispersed
tracking stations on the ground.

Other auxiliaries required on board a spacecraft include sources
of power, sources of materials to provide such power, life-sustaining
equipment for the astronaut, and interconnecting circuitry and control
devices. Electric power on board for these auxiliaries can only be
provided from two sources (except for the briefest of journeys, in
which case electric storage batteries may suffice); these primary power
sources are either a nuclear power reactor on board, or the sun.

Nuclear reactor power has not yet been employed in space but
will undoubtedly form one of the sources of primary energy in future
space experiments. Derived nuclear sources (i.e., synthetic radioactive materials, which decompose under the liberation of heat which
is used as an energy source) have already been employed. To date,

Figure 1.5.   Solar Cell Array on PIONEER V.   (Courtesy of National Aeronautics and Space Administration.)

the energy required for powering the large number of auxiliary devices described has usually been collected from the sun.

Whether nuclear or solar energy is used as a primary power source, it is always necessary to convert this primary energy form into electricity; after all, most auxiliary devices, and particularly the electronic devices, require electric power. The conversion of solar energy into electric power can be accomplished in several fashions. To date this has usually been accomplished through the "solar cells," or *photovoltaic* cells. These are solid-state devices, which generate a small amount of electricity when exposed to light (an example of such photovoltaic cells is found in photographic light meters). Since the amount of current generated in a cell is small, large arrays of such cells are required in order to produce even a relatively small amount of power. These are the "paddles" which stud many spacecrafts (see Figure 1.5).

Since these devices can obviously only operate when exposed to direct sunlight, it is necessary to provide a separate orientation means so as not to cast the cell arrays in their own shadow, if the space-craft should turn. Moreover, since the spacecraft may be in the shadow of the earth or some other celestial body for a part of its time, it is also necessary to provide a storage battery which collects and stores a portion of the power from the solar cells and can thus provide electrical energy during the dark time, when the solar cells are inoperative. Other means of converting solar energy to electric energy employ such schemes as rotating heat engines (turbo-generators which are energized by solar radiation), diodes of special (thermionic) design, and other devices still in the experimental stage. One of these is the fuel cell, which promises not only to be of considerable value as a power source in space, but which may eventually revolutionize terrestrial power economics—perhaps even replace the automobile engine.

In principle, a fuel cell is the ultimate of chemical batteries; like other batteries, it relies on a pair of chemicals, of which one is oxidized and the other reduced. Such "redox" cycles characterize all chemical batteries, and their electrical current output represents the flow of electrons accompanying chemical reduction/oxidation reac-tions.* Fuel cell generators may be powered by hydrogen (or other reducing agents) and oxygen; the chemical reaction partials and the over-all reactions are represented respectively by (a) and (b), and by (c):

$$H_2 \rightarrow 2H^+ + 2e^- \tag{a}$$
$$2e^- + \tfrac{1}{2}O_2 \rightarrow O^{--} \tag{b}$$
$$\overline{H_2 + \tfrac{1}{2}O_2 \rightarrow H_2O + \Delta H\dagger} \tag{c}$$

While these reactions represent only the familiar formation of water from its elements, it is now within the new fuel cell technology to channel the electrons, liberated by hydrogen (and subsequently captured by oxygen) through an external conductor and to produce thereby an electric current. At the present stage of development approximately one kilowatt-hour of electricity can be generated for every pound of water formed.

---

* By definition, a chemical oxidation involves the liberation of electrons from a material; these electrons are absorbed by another material (which is thereby—chemically speaking—reduced). The relation of these phenomena to electricity is the electric current, which consists of a flow of electrons through a conductor.
† ΔH is the energy liberated during the reaction—in this case, electricity and heat.

Life-Support Equipment

For all manned missions in space, a complicated and reliable provision must be made to insulate the space traveler from the inimical environment of outer space; moreover, a sufficient amount of atmosphere and food must be provided for him, provision for his waste must be made, and, in addition to the shielding against radiation and meteorites, his capsule must keep him at a comfortable temperature. These arrangements are complicated and heavy.

The primary concern is to provide adequate shielding from radiation, both solar and galactic. This may be accomplished completely by the capsule in which the astronaut travels; alternatively, the capsule may only provide partial radiation protection, and residual shielding is then provided locally or by a special space suit. Similarly, pressurization of his capsule (or cabin) with air must be provided and safeguarded. The air is supplied at ordinary atmospheric pressure from high-pressure bottles. The pressure seal against the vacuum of outer space is provided by his capsule; in order to protect the astronaut against sudden decompression if the capsule should be penetrated by a meteorite, his spacesuit provides a second safeguard. The pressurization of the spacesuit can be accomplished from the same storage system or by an independent auxiliary system. Exhaled air may be recycled or replenished, depending on the length of the journey. Complete recycling of air, as well as bodily wastes, has been extensively studied and will undoubtedly be practiced in the future during long journeys. Similar provision of food, or a possible recycling, again separates past accomplishments from future deployment.

The major elements of keeping an astronaut alive and several of the actual and future devices are described in some detail in Chapter 5.

1.5   PRESENT EFFORTS AND OUTLOOK FOR THE FUTURE

Our goals in future space exploration and our past accomplishments define our present efforts. Past accomplishments in American missions—manned orbital flights, unmanned impact on the moon, and a very successful Venus fly-by, to name only the most spectacular achievements—have provided (1) nearly all of the proved engineering technology, (2) most of the store of knowledge, and (3) a large amount of useful hardware items, which are required for currently planned, future space exploration. For quite some time to come, future hardware will therefore largely evolve from our past experience by scale-up and by refinement rather than by break-through. (4) However, new astronautics maneuvers—notably "docking," that is, the joining of individual spacecrafts in orbit—and extensive test work of new hardware on the ground and in space loom as monumental tasks in our present and future efforts.

Our present efforts in *new engineering technology* are accordingly expended in life sciences (e.g., recycling of environment, i.e., "closed ecology" systems), in electronics (e.g., greater accuracy and reliability), in new power applications (e.g., primary nuclear reactor power, more efficient solar-to-electric power conversion, electric means of rocket propulsion), and in a host of new materials and processes. Our present efforts in *new knowledge* continues in all disciplines of science, but it is *not* now assumed that the missions currently planned for the next decade (see below) will depend on new discoveries made in the present scientific effort now underway in life sciences (e.g., psychopharmacology, hibernation), physics (e.g., molecular electronics), chemistry (e.g., combustion, extreme high and low temperature phenomena), or astronomy (space physics). In the current effort of *hardware engineering* the biggest single objective is the provision of very large propulsion units, rockets like the Saturn stages which dwarf the present launch vehicles (e.g., the Atlas). Other hardware developments concentrate on refinements of electronics, design, and tests for specific space capsules and their life-support and communications systems. Similarly, gigantic ground systems complexes, both for launching and telemetry, are in development, new guidance electronics for specific missions are in test, and auxiliary power systems, including fuel cells, are in development.

A very large portion of the current effort concerns testing; in order to ensure proper functioning of hardware and to minimize risks of loss of life, full-scale tests in gigantic space-simulation chambers for spacecrafts and for rockets are under way. Such space-simulation chambers permit tests of simulated acceleration and deceleration in a temperature and pressure environment of outer space (-250 to $+250°F$; 10^{-12} mm Hg!), and they are truly impressive in their

Figure 1.6.   Space Simulation Chamber at Jet Propulsion Laboratory (with RANGER Spacecraft).
(Courtesy of National Aeronautics and Space Administration.)

size and array of cooling, heating, and evacuation accessories; they
also take a long time to build and put into proper operation and
they cost some 10 million dollars (see Figure 1.6) !

Related to testing are unmanned space missions, which are pre-
cursors of the manned missions of the future, in order to test without

possible risk of life new orbital and maneuvering techniques. For the past year most of these efforts have been successful and no serious doubts exist, therefore, that our plans and programs for the future can indeed be carried out, although some occasional delay in planned schedules may occur.

The magnitude of the present effort is staggering, and only a familiarization with the tremendous extent of the installations required and a look at manpower and expenditure figures can provide even a partial understanding of the gigantic size of this undertaking. At present, the biggest single U.S. effort consists of the many tasks required in pursuit of landing two men on the moon within this decade—Project Apollo (see Chapter 9). This project contains several areas of feverish and extensive development; the development and testing of the necessary rocket power for launching the space vehicle—the Saturn V launch vehicle—is the biggest task. This vehicle stands some 350 feet high, it is more than 30 feet in diameter, weighs

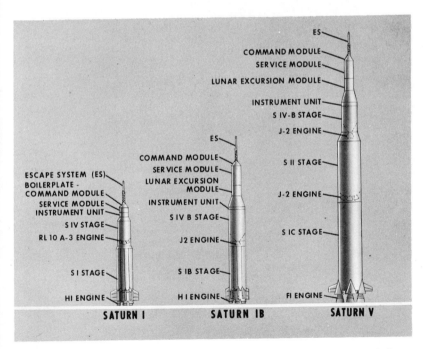

Figure 1.7. APOLLO Space Vehicles. (Courtesy of National Aeronautics and Space Administration.)

Figure 1.8.   SATURN Static Firing Test Stands.   (Courtesy of National Aeronautics and Space Administration.)

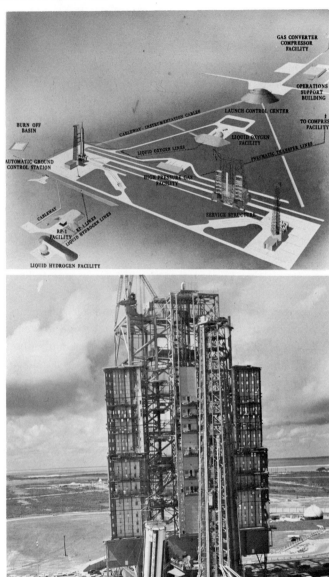

Fig. 1.9. SATURN Launch Facilities. (Courtesy of National Aeronautics and Space Administration.)

6 million pounds, and will provide the fantastic thrust of nearly 9 million pounds (the Atlas delivers less than 400,000 pounds of thrust). It contains 11 rocket engines (of two types, the F-1 and J-2 engines) in three stages, and the development, the testing, and the qualification of each engine type alone generally require the continuous work of several years and cost more than a half billion dollars! In order to provide power in the meantime for testing other components in similarly difficult development (e.g., guidance, control, and communication electronics), intermediate launch vehicles must be developed, for example, the Saturn I, and Saturn IB which employ different engines (see Figure 1.7).

These gigantic launch vehicles require tremendous launch facilities which also take a long time and large sums to build. A look at some of these major hardware items is more impressive than a brief review of their cost figures, but to mention at least some of them, it may be interesting to note that in 1964 about one billion dollars was expended on the development of Saturn and its engines. Other work on Apollo concerns the development of the spacecraft and its several cabins (one remains in lunar orbit with one astronaut while another cabin with two men descends to the moon and subsequently reascends to rendezvous with the orbiting ship; see Figure 9.5) and the many electronics, power, and life-support subsystems; this portion also represents an annual expenditure of more than 1 billion dollars. Another billion is expended annually on construction, subsystems, and management of this program.

Although Project Apollo consumes more than 3 billion dollars of current annual effort and will continue to do so for several years, this task represents less than half of the total United States space work. Some 1700 million dollars are expended by the Military, primarily in pursuit of (1) military satellites, (2) development of large solid space booster rockets (for future military launch vehicles), and (3) development work for manned space stations (and various subsystems for other future developments).

There remains currently, then, an effort of some 2 billion dollars expended by the National Aeronautics and Space Administration on (1) non-Apollo missions and (2) other scientific work. Within these areas, some of the most fascinating work is conduced in preparing future missions and in scientific research. Included are missions to the planets, thorough scientific investigations of the physics and biology of space, and the development of new electronics, new nuclear power hardware, and novel methods of propulsion.

The outlook for the future is indeed very promising, based on the progress of our present effort. Obviously, project Apollo has the highest priority, promises to accomplish one of the most fantastic achievements of mankind—and it costs the most money. Its success appears reasonably certain, based on its current status; its target date of "prior to the end of this decade" may be met narrowly or perhaps missed a bit. The outlook for gathering new information about the solar system and the universe beyond is excellent. New and major scientific data are now being continuously produced through the exploration of space, and major scientific theories are now formulated on the basis of these new data. As fascinating and as important as such progress in science is—think of the simple but far-reaching new knowledge in geomagnetics based upon the U.S. discovery of

Figure 1.10.   Artist's Concept of Manned Lunar Landing.   (Courtesy of North American Aviation, Inc.)

the Van Allen Belts, or the foundation laid for new theories of the origin of the solar system by our Venus experiments and the determination of the rotation and (absence of) the local magnetic field—the most intriguing scientific information to be obtained soon will be that relating to extraterrestrial life. Finally, there is an excellent opportunity to develop novel hardware in nuclear power, new sources of propulsive power and new—fantastically efficient—microelectronics. *All* of these projects in current development are making excellent progress and promise not only to further the exploration of space but to enrich our civilian technology and medicine. Such recent dreams of science-fiction gadgetry as wristwatch-size radios have through such work already been made obsolete and new forms of transportation, of life maintenance and of other health-giving and health-restoring aids, of forecast and ultimately of control of weather, as well as a vast expansion of communications, are all going to accrue to us within a relatively short time—based again, on a realistic appraisal of current technology within the far-out endeavor of astronautics. For a glimpse of a more fascinating picture of the future based on a similar analysis, this writer should like to recommend to the more mirthful members of his audience a book that he personally found to be most enjoyable: Arthur Clarke's *Profiles of the Future* (Harper and Row, 1963).

Restricted to astronautics, the outlook for the future sketched out above is presented in more detail here in Chapter 9.

CHAPTER 2

History and Accomplishments
of the Space Program

Nicholas Rosa

Stanford Research Institute

Contents

History and Accomplishments of the Space Program

2.1 THE DAWN OF THE SPACE AGE

Introduction

We see ourselves as living in a new age. Our times are, in fact, a new age of exploration—the exploration of interplanetary space. We tend to think that this age began on October 4, 1957, when the Soviet Union placed its Sputnik 1 into orbit. Actually, the probing of "near space" had begun at least a decade before that, when the United States sent instrumented rockets to heights between 100 and 200 miles.

A moment's reflection will remind anyone that the exploration of space really began in the year 1609, when a teacher of mathematics and science named Galileo Galilei first tilted a crude little telescope to the evening sky. Before Galileo's time men could look, and wonder, and spin fine theories and even make a few remarkably good measurements, but they could not really explore.

Perhaps the ultimate significance of Galileo's discoveries was that mankind was forced to realize it had some exploring to do. The exploring began at once—within the space of a year, Europe had sprouted a fine stubble of telescopes. Of course, it was going to be some time before anyone could add to Galileo's breathtaking collection of "firsts." But progress was rapid.

During the next 200 years improvements in telescopes made it possible for astronomers to look out beyond the Solar System to the universe at large. Before the end of the eighteenth century scientists were trying to measure the distances to selected stars by triangulation methods (using the distance between Earth and the sun—the "astronomical unit"—as a base line). In the nineteenth century the spectroscope and the photographic plate were added to the astronomers' kit of tools. The spectroscope gave clues to the chemical makeup of astral bodies; the photographic emulsion made it possible to "collect" light from feeble stars by means of time exposures. It immediately became possible to photograph more stars than the eye could ever see. Photographic emulsions all but replaced the human eye; great telescopes became great cameras.

Galileo had begun with Solar System astronomy, but by the beginning of our century this field had been passed in importance by true cosmic astronomy—the study of the distant stars and nebulae. In the first half of our own century cosmological astronomy has been revolutionized. The universe has turned out to be much vaster and much more complex than anybody imagined before 1900 (see Chapter 3).

Since World War II the radio telescope has come into use. This instrument is as much a new departure in our time as Galileo's visual telescope was in his. It has opened a new window on the universe, giving us not only new discoveries but new mysteries. However, both optical and radio telescopes are now approaching their observational limits.

The limitations of optical and radio astronomy have nothing to do with the instruments that have been devised. All astronomical telescopes and their accessories are capable of much better performance than the atmosphere permits. It is the atmosphere that imposes limits and limitations.

The atmosphere is thick, turbulent, and even dirty. For our practical Earthbound purposes we seldom find it that way (except in smog-ridden big cities). One of our most common superlative expressions is "clear as the air"; but this air, this "most excellent canopy" of Shakespeare's, is just that—a canopy. The atmosphere is actually *opaque* to most of the light and other forms of electromagnetic wave energy arriving from cosmic bodies. Like other canopies, it is also a barrier to "rain"—in this case the rain of primary cosmic-ray particles and interplanetary dust that would pelt the Earth in its absence.

An occasional *meteoroid* gets through, flashes in the upper atmosphere as a glowing *meteor*, and perhaps lands as a *meteorite*. With special photographic emulsions, cloud chambers or other instruments we can detect indirect evidence of the existence of *primary cosmic-ray* particles in space.* Nevertheless, our canopy is mostly "solid." We can see the stars and we detect the radio noise of space, only because the canopy has two windows. They are not very clear windows.

---

* This evidence is in the showers of secondary particles generated by the impact of the primaries on gas atoms in the atmosphere's higher layers.

One of these windows admits the electromagnetic wavelengths we see with our eyes as *light*. The other window admits a set of much longer electromagnetic waves that we detect by means of radio receivers. We know that other kinds of electromagnetic radiation exist. These are commonly classed as forms of "invisible light"— infrared rays, ultraviolet rays, X-rays, and gamma rays. (All of these forms can be produced by man-made devices.) Along with visible light and radio waves they form one continuous electromagnetic *spectrum*, from the longest waves (radio) to the shortest (hard gamma). But the atmosphere is opaque to the long and very short waves. Yet, as theory and experiment have shown, the largest hottest stars must emit most of their energy in these invisible forms.

What are we missing? What are we not seeing with our Earthbound instruments? One remedy to the narrowness of the atmosphere's radio and light windows would be to get our instruments off the Earth, out from under the atmosphere.

Another compelling reason to put instruments out in space is the turbulence or "boiling" of the atmosphere. Really good closeup views of Mars and the other planets are impossible most of the time, since high magnification enlarges the boiling along with the desired image. High resolution (that is, fine image detail) is difficult to realize through a shimmering atmosphere. The atmosphere also boils for the radio astronomers and is a constant source of radio-noise interference. Furthermore, the atmosphere is plagued with water vapor, dust, clouds, precipitation, smoke, haze, and smog, all of which block the light from the cosmos and reflect or scatter man's own lights into the instruments.

In spite of all these difficulties physics and astrophysics had already generated many insights into what could not be directly seen, even before space rockets were ready to fly. Much had been learned or deduced about the magnetic, electrical, and particle fields of the sun and of their interaction with the Earth's various fields and its upper atmosphere. Tantalizing hints had been gained about the distribution of meteoroids and other small solid matter in the Solar System, about the true shape, mass distribution, and gravitational field of the Earth, and about many allied matters. Earth science was encroaching on space science, and vice versa.

As it turned out, the beginning of space rocketry was sponsored not by those who wanted to know more about the distant stars and galaxies but by scientists who were exploring the phenomena of the Earth—in alliance with scientists interested in the sun. The objective of the very first rocket probings of "near space" was the exploration of the Earth's upper atmosphere. Indeed, the first orbital launchings were scheduled for an international cooperative study of the Earth, called the International Geophysical Year of 1957–1958.

International Geophysical Year

The International Geophysical Year (or IGY) was a coordinated study of the whole Earth and the sun by scientists of 64 countries. Special communications arrangements were made to link observatories and laboratories for simultaneous, world-wide observations of a number of important phenomena. First among these phenomena was the eruption, at any time, of a solar flare, and also the appearance of a new sunspot. Expeditions were sent to the polar regions, the deserts, the glaciers, and many ocean islands to establish semipermanent observing stations. Oceanographic ships plied the seas on prescheduled courses. Rockets and aircraft were used in unprecedentedly large numbers for many kinds of observations.

Although the entire IGY was planned and conducted by the scientists involved, many of their governments pledged logistic support, especially for such enterprises as building observing stations in the polar regions and keeping them supplied. Governments also provided or financed the use of research ships, aircraft, and rockets.

During the planning for the IGY American scientists had suggested to the international committee that nations having a well-developed rocket technology should launch small packages of instruments into orbits around the Earth. Several nations were planning to contribute vertical rocket probes, but the advantages of satellites were obvious. A scientist using a rocket probe has some of the same difficulties as a fish would have if it wanted to take a look at the air environment: just a quick glimpse during a brief leap out of the water. Orbiting satellites could stay aloft indefinitely to perform many observing tasks for periods long enough to have a high statistical significance.

In July 1955 the governments of the United States and the Soviet

Union both announced that they would contribute small orbiting satellites as part of their support for the IGY scientific effort.

The Early Satellites

The first four IGY satellites—Sputnik 1, Sputnik 2, Explorer 1,
and Vanguard 1—were relatively simple test models for testing their
launching systems and the general design concepts for satellites.

THE RUSSIAN SPUTNIKS

Sputnik 1 carried only one instrument, a thermometer to measure
its own internal temperature.   Yet the whole satellite was an effective
instrument in itself, as will be seen from the following:

Sputnik had certain thermal characteristics—a definite way of absorbing or discarding heat energy; this was a matter of design and
choice of materials.   Sputnik's thermometer was an electrical type
(probably a thermistor) and was wired into the circuitry of Sputnik's
radio transmitter, so that changes in temperature would show up as
changes in the radio signals.

Sputnik was a highly polished sphere designed to reflect most of
the solar energy striking it so that it would not overheat.   The sphere
was filled with nitrogen gas under pressure, to distribute solar heat
evenly throughout the satellite.   Aso, the nitrogen stored some of
the heat that Sputnik absorbed in the daylight portion of its orbit;
this kept the internal temperature from falling too low when Sputnik
was in the night portion of its orbit.   (This temperature regulation
was important for the radio batteries, among other things.)

The satellite's nitrogen atmosphere also served as a micrometeoroid
detector.   If a meteoroid particle had punctured the metal shell, nitrogen gas would have escaped through the hole.   The internal pressure
would have fallen and the satellite's internal temperature would have
changed.   The change in temperature would "announce" the first
meteoroid collision.

Sputnik's transmitter was a double unit with outputs on two radio
frequencies.   The particular choice of these frequencies made Sputnik
useful for studies of the ionosphere, the electrically charged layers
of the upper atmosphere, at altitudes averaging between 60 and 200
miles.   The ionosphere has the well-known useful property of "reflect-

ing" radio signals around the curvature of the Earth (technically by a process of refraction, not reflection). Without the ionosphere, long-distance radio communications would not be possible, since radio waves, like light waves, are propagated in straight lines and cannot follow the curved surface of a planet.

Sputnik's radio frequencies were chosen so that one was always higher than the average *critical frequency* of the ionosphere expected for the early part of the IGY. Above this critical frequency the ionosphere becomes effectively transparent to radio waves and will not reflect them. Depending on the condition of the sun's surface, the critical frequency would sometimes fall below Sputnik's lower frequency. By comparing and analyzing the properties of the two signals as received (or as *not* received!) at the ground, scientists could deduce a great deal about the condition and properties of the ionosphere, and their relation to conditions on the sun.

Sputnik 2, the miniature space ship that carried the first space passenger—Laika, the space dog—tested life-support systems embodying the principles later used to maintain men in space flights. In its tiny cabin the dog was served by automatic systems for oxygen, feeding, water, and waste-disposal. Like the cosmonauts and astronauts to follow, Laika had her heartbeat and respiration rate monitored by pickups, painlessly attached, that radioed this medical information to the ground. Laika also enjoyed two-way radio contact with her masters on Earth.

Sputnik 2 carried a few scientific instruments as well. It had one instrument section that was actually a replica of Sputnik 1, complete to polished metal sphere, plus a cosmic ray counter. For the first time scientists were able to have the results of *sustained* measurements of primary cosmic rays in space rather than only brief counts from a rocket probe. Because of the heavy power drain on the electrical storage batteries demanded by Laika's life-support system, Sputnik 2 was able to transmit data for only one week; Sputnik 1 had broadcast for 23 days.

THE FIRST AMERICAN SATELLITES

Sputniks 1 and 2 were followed by the first American satellite, Explorer 1.* The Explorer instruments included thermistor thermom-

---

* The original American IGY satellite program, called Project Vanguard, was

eters, micrometeoroid detectors, and a radiation counter, all connected to a "beeping" two-channel radio transmitter. The governing principles for these instruments were quite simple, and Explorer 1, like most early satellites, is a remarkable example of how much can be achieved with an economy of means, if a scientific experiment is well thought out.

The micrometeoroid detectors consisted of a number of small plastic "cards," each supporting a network of fine wires. Each wire network had a definite total electrical resistance, which depended on the total length of wire in the network. If a meteoroid particle punctured the card, it would break one or more segments of wire, causing a change in the total resistance. Such a resistance change was registered as a change in the beeping tone of the radio. Deep inside the Explorer cylinder was a single microphone, also used as a micrometeoroid detector: the microphone would literally hear the impacts of the space dust and broadcast the resulting noise on the radio channels.

The radiation counters were Geiger-Mueller tubes that passed an impulse of electric current each time they encountered a certain level of X-ray-type radiation. Explorer's particular tubes were designed to store their impulses and release one signal for every 16 actual counts, since fairly high radiation levels were expected.

One of the Explorer's radio channels carried a "high-power" signal of 60 milliwatts (0.06 watt), quite a bit weaker than the full watt of power used by Sputnik, but still quite enough for sensitive modern receivers. The "low-power" channel delivered 10 milliwatts (0.01 watt). This small power drain conserved battery life, enabling Explorer 1 to broadcast data for almost four months.

By the time Explorer 1 was launched the far-flung American tracking networks originally planned for Project Vanguard were highly developed. The tracking stations—arranged in a north-south line through North and South America—used high-speed camera telescopes,

---

still in its rocket-development stage when Sputnik 1 was launched by the Soviet Union in the fall of 1957. However, the United States had a variety of military rocket types that could be used for satellite launchings. Because of public desire for a launching to match the Russian feats, the U.S. Department of Defense reversed an earlier policy and permitted an Army research group to attempt a satellite launching. Explorer 1 was thus a modified Vanguard satellite, fitted onto a military rocket, which launched it into orbit on January 31, 1958, four months after Sputnik 1.

radar, and radio-telescope tracking techniques. Amateur tracking teams, both visual and radio, were also in readiness and had practiced on the Sputniks. It was now possible to receive data reliably from many points on the Earth's surface, which had not been the case with the Sputniks. This was important because it led to the first real discovery in space.

Explorer 1 revealed the existence of the now famous Van Allen Belts, regions of trapped nuclear particles held by the Earth's magnetic field and surrounding the planet at distances out to 40,000 miles (see Chapter 3). This discovery resulted from what appeared at first to be a malfunction in the satellite's radiation counters. However, analysis of the data received at stations widely scattered over North and South America brought out what was really happening to the counters.

Over certain locations on Earth, and at certain altitudes in Explorer's slightly eccentric orbit, the radiation counters would abruptly register "zero count." This would occur even after the count had been steadily rising. It seemed odd that there could be sharply defined regions of space empty of radiation or particles. Naturally, it was suspected that the counter mechanism was breaking down. However, analysis of the tracking data showed that the "breakdowns" had a surprising regularity; they seemed to depend on the satellite's position at the time of zero count.

The Explorer project scientists theorized then that *excessive* numbers of particles could perhaps effectively jam a counter, that is, cause "zero" to be registered instead of the true high count. The group then proved this theory by testing a duplicate Explorer instrument section in a field of intense nuclear radiation from an atomic laboratory source. The duplicate instruments behaved just like the ones in the orbiting satellite—they registered "zero." Now the explanation could be developed: the satellite was encountering fields of particles much more concentrated than had been expected or provided for.

The group was then able to work out the explanation for this unexpectedly high particle density: energetic particles from space were being captured by the Earth's magnetic field, with each particle being constrained to spiral endlessly along one of the Earth's lines of magnetic force. This results in a concentration of particles near the Earth (see Figure 3.12).

The scientists were able to confirm the explanation with readings from Explorer 3, an almost identical satellite launched two months after Explorer 1, but carrying radiation counters of higher counting capacity. The existence of the trapped particle belts had been predicted as early as 1956 by Dr. S. Fred Singer, then of the University of Maryland, in one of his theoretical studies.

Explorer 1 was followed, six weeks after its launching, by Vanguard 1 (March 17, 1958). The Vanguard launching was the first complete test of the three-stage Vanguard rocket system. Vanguard 1 was (and is) an 8-inch metal sphere weighing 3.2 pounds. It carries internal and external thermometers and originally had two power supplies for its two radio transmitters. One of the Vanguard transmitters operated from chemical batteries and transmitted data for several weeks. The other transmitter operated from solar cells on the skin of the Vanguard sphere and transmitted automatically (when the satellite was in sunlight) for six years; the signal was still audible in the spring of 1964. The satellite itself, which was injected into a very high orbit, may stay there for 1000 years.

Vanguard 1 was the first satellite ever to use solar power. More important, however, is the fact that tracking data from Vanguard 1 led to the second major discovery from space: the "pear-shaped" component of the Earth's general shape (see later).

PERSPECTIVE ON EARLY SPACE DISCOVERIES

The discovery of the Van Allen Belts points up the vital relationship between theoretical and experimental science. Dr. S. Fred Singer had earlier been able to form a hypothesis concerning belts of trapped particles around the Earth.* Without the Explorer satellites, this intellectual achievement might have remained a hypothesis forever. On the other hand, the data from the satellites could not have been validly interpreted without a sound theoretical foundation to work from. This mutual dependence between theoretical and experimental work applies in all of science, of course.

It is not only the problem of the atmosphere that prompts scientists to design space experiments. Theoretical science has advanced to the point at which space experiments are vitally necessary for confirming theories or for making further theoretical progress.

For example, satellites can detect and measure scientifically important irregularities in the shape of the Earth because the precise shape

---

* An even earlier suggestion of the possible existence of trapped-particle zones had been made in 1910 by a Norwegian physicist, Carl Störmer.

of a satellite's orbit will vary with any slight change the satellite experiences in the influence of the Earth's gravity. This influence depends mainly on two variables: (1) the actual strength of the Earth's gravity field at any point under the satellite and (2) the distance between the satellite and the Earth at any point in the satellite's orbit.

Where the Earth bulges—as in the equatorial regions—the Earth has (in effect) come nearer the satellite. Thus the gravitational pull is greater and the satellite must move in a little closer. The resulting change in the orbit is very small but accurately measurable, especially by averaging the effects over many separate orbitings of the same satellite. This is how the extremely small "pear" component of the Earth's shape was derived; it could not have been found by any known surface-based technique, since the "pear" shape is a departure from sphericity of only a few feet.

Furthermore, the strength of the Earth's gravitational field is not uniform over the whole Earth. This strength, or *acceleration*, of gravity as measured by laboratory techniques in Washington, D.C., will differ slightly from that measured in, say, Munich, Germany, or Canberra, Australia, because the strength of gravity depends on *mass*, the true "amount" of substance. Where the light, *crustal* layers of the Earth are thin, as in the ocean beds, the acceleration of gravity is stronger because the denser, relatively heavier rocks of the Earth's inner *mantle* layer are closer to the surface in such regions. A moving satellite will therefore "feel" a slightly stronger pull of gravity while over the oceans and a slightly weaker pull while over continents or mountains, which are relatively lightweight rock. The satellite will also respond to *minor* density or gravity variations within a continent or within an ocean bed.

To sum up, both the precise shape of the Earth and the variations in its gravitational field from one place to another can be measured by repeatedly tracking an orbiting satellite. In this way a satellite is not only a carrier of instruments but can be an important geophysical instrument in itself.

The U.S. National Aeronautics and Space Administration

Encouraged by the success of the early space experiments, the United States chartered its National Aeronautics and Space Administration

(NASA) in 1958 to develop and operate a many-faceted, long-term *civilian* space program. NASA is responsible both for purely scientific space activites and for many applications of space devices (communications satellites, weather satellites, etc.). NASA's activities thus embrace a wide variety of manned and unmanned programs. NASA also supports ground-based laboratory research related to space science and space engineering. NASA was set up to operate nonmilitary space programs, but all of its findings are, of course, available for the national defense.

2.2 THE U.S. APPLICATIONS SATELLITES

Although scientific research must precede the development of economically useful devices in space (just as on Earth), the NASA space program rapidly developed two classes of practical *applications* satellites: for meteorology and communications. The military services developed two classes of their own: for surveillance and navigation.

Weather Satellites

The spectacular *Tiros* series of weather satellites has been successful in all nine of its launchings, the first of which was on April 1, 1960. "Tiros" stands for Television and Infrared Observation Satellite. Television photographs of the Earth's cloud cover and storm systems received from these satellites frequently appear in newspapers and magazines.

Tiros satellites have detected the telltale whirlpool shape of newly developing hurricanes before ground observations could indicate that a hurricane was being born.

Weather satellites supplement the national and world-wide networks of ground weather stations, including the high-altitude balloon (radiosonde) weather stations.

An important function of the Tiros satellites is observing vast areas of the Earth where weather stations do not exist or are too thinly scattered: the polar regions, the oceans, the great deserts, and the high mountain ranges. In addition, improved weather predictions can be made on the basis of cloud formations viewed from above.

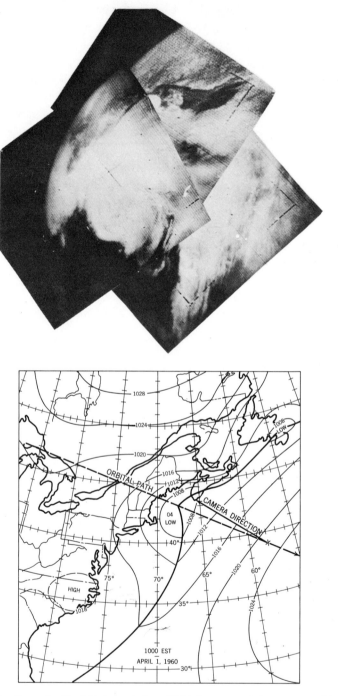

Figure 2.1. Composite Cloud Photograph From TIROS Satellite and Corresponding Weather Map. (Courtesy of National Aeronautics and Space Administration.)

Finally, viewing from below is frequently impossible when the weather is bad and always impossible when the skies are dark.

Besides photography, Tiros satellites carry out *heat-balance* measurements by means of their infrared detectors. Scientists are interested in whether the Earth, on its night side, radiates off into space the same amount of heat as it receives from the sun on its day side. This has been assumed in climatological theory, but now the satellites are checking the assumption. A weather satellite is the only practical means of checking such an assumption.

Early in its career the Tiros 1 performed the first international weather service from a satellite: it photographed a great storm building up in the Indian Ocean, which could be expected to strike western Australia within a few days. Because few ships ply the southern Indian Ocean, no surface weather reports were available from this region.

The normal outriders of such a storm—high cirrus clouds, high-altitude wind changes, etc.—had not yet reached the Australian coast. When this new storm was spotted on the Tiros pictures at NASA monitoring stations, the details were sent by cablegram to the Australian authorities. Airmailed copies of the photos reached Australia a day or two later.

Although nothing could be done to prevent the storm or to decrease its fury, Australia at least had a few days' extra warning time in which to prepare for it. The Australian weather service had received, for the first time, detailed information on an important storm approaching the country from its blind side—facing the great empty Indian Ocean.

On September 11, 1961, the Tiros satellites (two were then operating) had seven hurricanes and typhoons under surveillance on the same day. Information from the Tiros pictures was relayed to all forecasting centers concerned, in the United States and in Asia. Obviously, repeated sets of Tiros pictures are useful for tracking moving storms such as hurricanes.

A Tiros is spin-stabilized to keep it from tumbling at random, which would render its cameras useless. It is also equipped with a sensing coil for the Earth's magnetism, which helps to keep the lens-bearing bottom plate pointed toward the Earth (see Figure 1.2).

Remarkable as their achievements have been, the Tiros satellites are considered simple test models, and the Tiros system will be replaced

eventually by larger, more complex satellites of the *Nimbus* class.*
The first Nimbus test satellite was launched in the summer of 1964.

However, the U.S. Weather Bureau will operate several new "Operational Tiros" satellites while NASA goes on to complete the development of Nimbus.

Tiros 8, launched December 21, 1963, carried a useful improvement—a tape recorder system that need not erase on each readout. Concurrently, NASA has developed a special low-cost (30,000 dollars) receiving and command apparatus for Tiros that can be purchased by any weather service in the world. It is now possible for any nation having one of these receivers to command the Tiros to make immediate transmission of locally useful pictures. There is no need to go through the U.S. Weather Bureau and NASA or to wait for pictures to be sent from the United States. Tiros is now potentially an international service. The Nimbus series also has this "local use" feature, as has Tiros 9, launched January 21, 1965.

Communications Satellites

PROJECT SCORE

The earliest communications satellite was the U.S. Advanced Research Project Agency's Project Score, orbited in December 1958. In this experiment an entire 8000-pound second stage (Agena) of an Atlas booster was used as a satellite. It carried a system of tape recorders and radio transmitters and receivers. Score picked up messages from ground stations, recorded them, and retransmitted them afterward on command from other ground stations. Its first transmission was a greeting to the world and peace message from President Dwight D. Eisenhower, whose voice was the first ever heard from space.

---

* The Nimbus series will be launched into polar orbits to include the entire surface of the earth in their coverage. Nimbus satellites, having more power-generating capacity in their solar panels, will be able to utilize large-sized television camera lenses and image tubes. This will permit finer resolution, that is, better picture detail. Some Nimbus satellites will carry rainfall radar to detect whether and where cloud systems are producing precipitation. Under consideration for Nimbus are possible infrared television cameras for night observation of cloud patterns; the 1964 Nimbus tested such a "night camera."

ECHO

The Score system involved a time delay between recording by one ground station and playback by another. In August 1960 NASA orbited Echo 1, a hollow sphere 100 feet in diameter, made of thin plastic film coated with an even thinner layer of aluminum. The aluminum surface provided a reflector for radio waves. In the initial tests voice signals were bounced off the orbiting Echo between a Bell Telephone Laboratories station in New Jersey and a NASA-University of California station in California.

Echo permitted the use of ultra-high-frequency radio waves (which the ionosphere cannot reflect) over very long distances. This has important advantages because, for any radio channel, *message-handling capacity* increases with frequency.

The hollow Echo satellite was folded into a package about one foot in diameter in the nose fairing of its launching rocket. In space the fairing fell away, and crystals inside the Echo fabric sublimated (evaporated) into a gas. This gas inflated the fabric to its 100-foot size and spherical shape.

A second and larger Echo satellite (135 feet in diameter) was launched in January 1964 into a near-polar orbit. Echo 2 is the reflector for direct communications experiments between the United States and the Soviet Union.

These U.S.-Soviet experiments are being carried on under an agreement signed in July 1963. This agreement covers communications experiments, weather satellite experiments, and magnetic field studies. Since 1957 the United States has made cooperative agreements for various space activities with a total of 65 countries.

COURIER

On October 4, 1960, the U.S. Army launched the first *active, real-time* communications satellite, Courier 1B. This satellite picked up signals sent from one ground station, amplified them several thousand times, and transmitted them directly to a second ground station *with no time delay* (hence "real time"). Courier was used in tests of teletype, computer data, and voice signals for 17 days. Like Echo and all communications satellites launched since then, Courier used ultra-high-frequency (extremely short) waves that have great information-carrying capacity but which the ionosphere cannot reflect.

TELSTAR

The first television-relay satellite, Telstar 1, was designed and built by the American Telephone and Telegraph Corporation and launched by NASA in July 1962. This satellite first transmitted live television pictures and sound between the United States and Europe. Telstar 1 operated for seven months. Telstar 2 was launched in May 1963 and was still transmitting at the time of this writing.

RELAY

Relay 1, launched in December 1962, was a voice-data-teletype active satellite with a theoretical television capability. It was used for international communications experiments. The need for international voice, telegraph, and data-signal exchange is growing rapidly year by year. Total transatlantic message traffic is expected to double in volume well before 1970. It turns out that satellites can be cheaper than new transoceanic cables and they have a higher message-handling capacity than cables.

In January 1964 Relay 2 was launched as part of a continuing experimental series. This satellite has an actual television capability. All Relays and Telstars are powered by solar cells for continuous operation beyond the lifetime of chemical batteries.

SYNCOM

In a Syncom system three satellites are boosted into equatorial orbit some 22,300 miles from the surface of the Earth. At this altitude orbital speed is such that the satellite makes one complete orbital revolution in 24 hours—the same time it takes the Earth to make one full turn on its axis. Accordingly, a Syncom satellite appears to hover over one spot on the Earth's surface, if its orbit is in the plane of the Equator.

In a fully operational system three Syncoms would be equally spaced around their common orbit (that is, 120 degrees apart around the 360-degree circle). Messages could then be relayed anywhere on Earth by passing them from the ground to the nearest Syncom, which would simultaneously retransmit the messages to a second Syncom that would beam the signal back to the ground (see Figures 1.2 and 6.5).

The advantages of the Syncom system, in comparison to Relay and Telstar systems, are the small number of satellites required to cover the whole Earth and the ability to function without expensive movable tracking antennas on the ground. As yet no complete Syncom system has been launched. However, single Syncom satellites have been successful.*

Navigation and Surveillance Satellites

In addition to weather and communications satellites, the United States has used two other classes of applications satellite: for navigation and for surveillance..

Navigation satellites operate according to simple principles: a U.S. Navy *Transit* satellite sends out a continuous beacon signal that can be picked up by a ship using a fairly simple receiver and a radar-type movable antenna. By simple (and automatic) analysis of the signal the moment can be clocked when the passing satellite was at its closest to the ship. The bearing (direction) and distance between ship and satellite can also be determined by well-developed techniques. Since a satellite's orbit is closely predictable for some time in advance, the ship's navigator can simply consult a published *ephemeris* (table of predicted satellite positions) to determine the exact location of the satellite at the moment of closest approach. From this location and the signal data the ship's own location can be derived quickly and accurately. Since 1960 the U.S. Navy has launched a number of navigation satellites in its Transit series (see Figure 8.2) and the system is in regular operational use.

Two main types of surveillance vehicle are under development by the U.S. Air Force: the Samos class and the Midas class. *Samos* satellites use photography and television to record events on the Earth's surface. Examination of the recovered film or received television images can reveal the location of airfields, rocket launchers, and other military installations. *Midas* satellites use a variety of

---

*Syncom 1 and 2 were not aimed into precisely equatorial orbits, and the satellites, accordingly, do not hover but drift north and south about the equator of the Earth. However, Syncom 3 is in equatorial orbit and hovers over the Pacific Ocean at the intersection of the equator and the International Date Line. Syncom 3 was in operation in time to relay television coverage of the 1964 Olympic Games from Japan to America and Europe.

other tools, including radar and infrared sensing. Infrared sensors permit Midas to detect the launching of an enemy missile attack because of the release of heat from the missile exhausts. Since intercontinental missiles (ICBM's) require only 20 to 30 minutes to reach their targets, such early detection would provide short but militarily valuable warning time.*

2.3   THE UNMANNED U.S. SCIENTIFIC SATELLITES

The Explorer Series

GENERAL STUDIES

The Explorers are mostly geophysical satellites and probes used to study the Earth's "home" environment at distances ranging from 100 miles (i.e., within the atmosphere) out to 190,000 miles. This region, within the orbit of the moon, is called *cislunar* space.

The various Explorers have been instrumented for radiation fields, magnetic fields, solar plasma (charged particle emissions from the sun), cosmic rays, micrometeorids, solar radiation, gamma rays, temperatures, ionospheric studies, and air density.

A large number of "firsts" in space science and exploration have been realized by the Explorer satellites. Explorer 1 indicated the existence of the Van Allen Belts; Explorer 3 confirmed it. Explorer 4 measured an *artificial* particle belt created in the Earth's magnetic field by two small atomic bombs exploded at heights near 200 miles over the South Atlantic Ocean in 1958.†

Explorer 6 (1959) detected a "ring current" surrounding the Earth at a distance of several thousand miles. Nineteenth-century scientists had suspected the existence of this ring current, but they had no way to check the hypothesis. Explorer 6 also produced the first complete television pictures of the Earth's cloud cover before Tiros 1 was launched.

Explorer 10 (1961) detected the "solar wind," a continuous emission

---

* The Soviet Union registered continual official objection to the use of surveillance satellites by the United States until the fall of 1963, when it ceased making public protests. In the spring of 1964 the Soviet Union announced that it, too, was experimenting with surveillance satellites.

† This was Project Argus, a deliberate attempt to create a trapped-particle belt of known origin, which incidentally produced the first "man-made" Aurora displays—both "northern lights" and "southern lights."

of high-temperature charged particles from the sun. Such a field of energetic particles is now called a *plasma* and is regarded as the fourth state of matter (after solid, liquid, and gaseous states). Explorer 10 also showed a "cavity" in the solar wind and other interactions with the magnetic field of the Earth (see Chapter 3). It was able to make these discoveries because its apogee, or point farthest from the Earth, was 186,000 miles.

Explorer 17 (1963) discovered a belt of neutral (not ionized) helium gas surrounding the Earth at altitudes between 150 and 600 miles. Earlier Explorers and other satellites had detected *ionized* helium atoms at various altitudes up to 6000 miles.

Explorer 18 (1963), also known as the Interplanetary Monitoring Platform (IMP), discovered a "shock wave" effect in the solar wind on the sunward side of the Earth's geomagnetic cavity. This shock wave is analogous to the familiar shock wave produced in the air by an aircraft flying faster than the speed of sound.

Other Explorers have carried out a large number and variety of tasks. Some have investigated the density and characteristics of the ionosphere—these necessarily had low orbits. The series as a whole has shared the task of mapping interplanetary and solar magnetic fields, particle fields, and gamma-ray radiaton in cislunar space.

"Pegasus," a giant (23,000-pound) Explorer for meteoroid studies, was launched February 16, 1965, by a Saturn I rocket. Once in orbit, Pegasus extended a pair of "wing" sections having a 95-foot total span. These wings support 2,000 square feet of detector-panel surface, for micrometeoroid impact measurement. The satellite was designed for a working lifetime of 18 months and is often visible to the unaided eye. Its findings will aid the U.S. manned lunar project (see later). The orbiting of Pegasus marks the eighth successful test for the Saturn I booster, and the third successful test for the Saturn's hydrogen-fueled upper stage, with no failures in either test series. This launching was a landmark in the development of space technology.

The Explorer series seems to be open-ended, and no doubt many other Explorer experiments will be planned as space science develops.

INTERNATIONAL EXPLORERS

So far the Explorer series has included three launchings for international projects, with payloads designed and built in other countries. The first was the British satellite UK-1, also known as *Ariel 1,*

Figure 2.2.   Model of EXPLORER 18 (Interplanetary Monitoring Platform).   (Courtesy of National Aeronautics and Space Administration.)

launched by NASA in 1962. Ariel carried six British experiments to study the interactions between Earth's ionosphere and cosmic rays from outer space.

Also launched in 1962 was *Alouette,* a Canadian payload designed to study the ionosphere "from the top" and also known as *Topside Sounder*. This satellite is still active. Alouette emits bursts of radio signals that start on one frequency and end on another, sweeping across the radio spectrum in between. The characteristics of the ionosphere (at a given time and place in the orbit) can be determined by the nature of the received signal, according to which frequencies in the sweep are heard on Earth.

The third international satellite is *UK-2*, also an ionosphere tool, launched early in 1964.

Further international launchings are scheduled or planned for the Explorer series. The Italian *San Marco* project, scheduled to launch five satellites simultaneously into equatorial orbit in 1965, will use a Scout launching rocket supplied by NASA and will also make use of the tracking and telemetering stations used for the Explorers. The San Marco satellites will be launched from a floating launch pad, built by the Italians, which will be towed to an Indian ocean site on the equator.

A Japanese satellite project, now in the design and laboratory test stage, will probably also become part of the Explorer-International series.

NASA is cooperating in various ways with the European Launcher Development Organization and the European Space Research Organization, international endeavors through which European nations will develop a cooperative space program for scientific research and for applications satellite development.

NASA is also represented on the international Committee for Space Research, or COSPAR, a nongovernmental committee of scientists set up for the exchange of new scientific information and the determination of research needs. Finally, NASA cooperates with the various scientific agencies of the United Nations and of separate countries.

The Observatory Satellites

Three special classes of heavy, complex Observatory satellites are part of the long-term NASA program. These are the Orbiting Solar Observatories, the Orbiting Astronomical Observatories, and the Orbiting Geophysical Observatories.

ORBITING SOLAR OBSERVATORIES (OSO)

OSO 1 was launched in 1962 into an Earth orbit. Although this satellite was always near the Earth, its purpose was to watch the sun from above the atmosphere. Whenever it was on the sunlit side of the Earth, it telemetered data on solar flares, solar particle eruptions, and the sun's output of X-rays, gamma rays, and ultraviolet radiation.

OSO 1 was automatically stabilized by rocketlike gas jets that kept its instruments aimed at the sun to within a small fraction of a degree. Two of these instruments were actually telescopes for monitoring small-scale and fine-detail solar phenomena. OSO 1 transmitted data for seven months.

OSO 2, launched February 3, 1965, has instrument systems able to *scan* the solar image, searching out details rather than merely keeping steady aim on the whole sun. At least one OSO will be launched each year through a complete 11-year solar activity cycle.

Project Apollo, the American manned lunar project, is using data from the OSO series in its development work. Indications from OSO 1 are that solar flares are not so serious a threat to lunar astronauts as had once been feared; the increase in the flux of dangerous particles in the solar wind resulting from a solar flare is not so great as to create difficulties with shielding of the spacecraft. However, these indications will be checked by means of data from other OSO's launched between now and the time the first Apollo lunar expedition departs—about 1970.

The OSO satellites will be part of the scientific contribution of the United States to the International Quiet Sun Years (IQSY) of 1963–1967, a cooperative program that is a sequel to the International Geophysical Year of 1957–1958. The mid-1960's will be a period marked by relatively mild solar activity; the next peak will occur in 1968–1969.

ORBITING ASTRONOMICAL OBSERVATORIES (OAO)

The OAO astronomical series will carry large telescopes outside the Earth's atmosphere. These telescopes will operate both in the visible light region and in the ultraviolet, depending on the particular spacecraft. Ultraviolet "seeing" offers several advantages. One advantage is that most of the energy of the larger, hotter, brighter stars is emitted in the ultraviolet and other short invisible wavelengths (X-ray or gamma); the visible light we see from major stars is only a small percentage of the energy output. Also the short waves of ultraviolet offer possibilities of better resolution than any visible wavelength could afford.

Telescope mirror "lenses" up to 36 inches in diameter are being fashioned of beryllium metal for the OAO series. Beryllium, one of the light metals, has a very high strength-to-weight ratio along with other technical advantages over glass or aluminum for an orbiting telescope.

ORBITING GEOPHYSICAL OBSERVATORIES (OGO)

The new geophysical series, OGO, will be used for study of the Earth and its immediate environment in the manner of the Explorer series. However, where most of the Explorer satellites have been rather small and light (a few tens or hundreds of pounds), the OGO satellites will be large, heavy, and will carry many different kinds of experiments.

The OGO series will have several subclasses, among them POGO (Polar Orbiting Geophysical Satellite) and EGO or EOGO (Eccentric Orbit Geophysical Satellite). The latter subclass will have orbits with very high apogee (out to several thousands miles) and very low perigee (down to 100 miles) to afford repeated measurements of atmosphere structure, particle distribution, magnetic fields, etc., as these factors vary with height. OGO 1, launched in 1964, has done the equivalent work of several separate Explorer or IMP satellites.

Biological Satellites

A series of at least six biological satellites, called *Biosatellite,* will be orbited beginning in 1965. Each of these 1175-pound spacecraft will include a 250-pound recovery capsule and will orbit for 3 to 30 days. Their purpose will be to study the effects on living matter of weightlessness and radiation in space, including changes in biological rhythms (such as waking and sleeping and cell division time) when these conditions are no longer tied to the rotation of the Earth, to a sun-determined time of day, or to season. The biosatellites will carry a variety of living organisms, from microbes and plant specimens to insects and chimpanzees. The chimpanzee experiments will be valuable for determining the relation between weightlessness and calcium loss from bones, loss of muscle tone, and other medical matters of importance to long manned space flights.

2.4 THE UNMANNED EXPLORATION OF DEEP SPACE

Lunar and Deep-Space Probes

The launching and instrumentation of lunar and planetary probes present special problems. First, the payload must be accelerated to Earth-escape velocity (in excess of 25,000 miles per hour; see Chapter 4) to be sent on its mission. Second, especially sensitive instruments must be designed to monitor the particle, magnetic, and other fields of interplanetary space, which are extremely weak. Third, the transmission of data from the payload back to Earth is very difficult because the strength of radio signals falls off very rapidly with distance. This means that the radio equipment and antennas must be heavier and more complex than for Earth-orbiting satellites. Fourth, additional control circuits and rocketry must often be incorporated in the payload for mid-course corrections along the flight path. Fifth, the over-all weight of the payload must be kept small enough, in spite of all the other difficulties, to permit the launching rocket to generate the escape velocity that is the first requirement.

Nevertheless, both the United States and the Soviet Union began launching deep-space and lunar probes very early in this epoch of space flight.

U.S. PIONEERS AND SOVIET LUNIKS

The first attempts to send instrument payloads to the moon were made by the United States in 1958. These payloads were Atlas-Able 1, Pioneer 1, Pioneer 2, and Pioneer 3. Although all had rocketry malfunctions, two of these probes performed valuable scientific tasks.

Pioneers 1 and 3. The Pioneer 1 probe reached an altitude of 70,700 miles and took observations of micrometeoroids, magnetic fields, temperatures, and solar radiations. Pioneer 3 flew out to 63,600 miles and located the outer portions of the Van Allen Belt region.

These two payloads were the first man-made objects on record as having penetrated so far into space and of course were the first to provide data from such distances. The data came in double sets—from the outbound leg of the flight and from the return leg—so that a check could be had. Although neither payload reached the moon, both were scientifically rewarding. They were the forerunners of later Explorer satellites deliberately placed in cislunar orbits to map the complex near-space environment of the Earth.

Lunik 1. In January 1959 the Soviet Union launched Lunik 1, which missed the moon by 4660 miles. After it passed the moon this probe was renamed Mechta and then listed as an interplanetary probe. It made measurements of radiation in space, the gas components of interplanetary matter, and the magnetic fields in cislunar space.

Pioneer 4. In March 1959 NASA launched Pioneer 4, which like Lunik-Mechta missed the moon and went into orbit around the sun. (In both cases launching velocity was slightly excessive at the start, so that Lunik and Pioneer arrived at the moon's orbital region ahead of the moon itself. Neither Lunik nor Pioneer 4 carried rocketry for mid-course speed adjustments; see Chapter 4.) Pioneer 4 recorded useful data on radiation in space from a distance of 450,000 miles and was tracked by its radio signal to 567,000 miles. This was the record for the time.

Lunik 2. In September 1959 the Soviet Union succeeded in impacting the moon with Lunik 2. This probe's instruments detected no lunar magnetic field or trapped radiation, although they did send back faint, fleeting evidence of a lunar ionosphere. Scientists point out that any lunar magnetic field that might exist could have been weaker than the threshold sensitivity of Lunik's magnetometer. Lunik made a crash or "hard" landing, so that all readings were cut off at the moment of impact.

Lunik 3. Lunik 3, launched on October 4, 1959, was sent around the moon to take photographs of the moon's hidden side. The photos were taken from a distance of 43,000 miles, though at one point Lunik 3 was ten times closer. (The longer distance was used for a number of technical reasons, including speed too great for clear photography at the nearer distance.) The photographs are not very clear, but they show recognizable features from a portion of the moon's near side that had been included in the coverage. The photos seem to reveal a surface structure on the hidden side different from the crater-pocked structure of the familiar side. The far side apparently has a *linear* mountain range similar to mountain ranges on Earth (the near side is characterized by ring-shaped ridges at the rims of craters). There are sound scientific reasons for accepting possible differences in the surface structures of the two sides of the moon. However, because the far side of the moon was "full"—bathed in flat, direct sunlight—contrast and detail are lacking in the Lunik photographs (astronomers seldom bother to photograph the full moon from Earth because of this too-ample, washed-out lighting). The interpretation of the Lunik photographs is therefore still disputed.

Lunik's photographs were made on film which was automatically processed on board the spacecraft. The developed pictures were then scanned by a special television system, and the picture information was telemetered back to Earth.

Pioneer 5. The next American probe, Pioneer 5, was a deep-space probe rather than a lunar probe. This probe was placed in solar orbit between the orbits of Earth and Venus. Its instruments measured high energy radiation, the total radiation flux (from the sun and outer space), magnetic fields, micrometeoroid distribution, and temperatures.

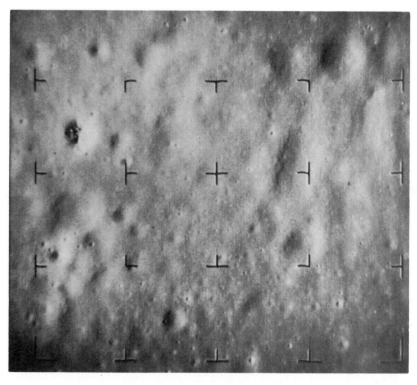

Figure 2.3. Ranger 7 television image of moon's surface from altitude of 3 miles, 2.3 seconds before probe's impact on moon. Crater at upper left (300 feet in diameter) shows angular rock mass in its center. (Courtesy of Jet Propulsion Laboratory.)

Pioneer 5 was tracked to a distance of 22,500,000 miles, setting a record for long-distance radio transmission (see Figure 1.5).

Ranger 7. The best pictures so far obtained of the surface of the moon were sent back by the completely successful U.S. probe Ranger 7 on July 30, 1964. Reception of these pictures was a landmark event in the histories both of space flight and of planetary astronomy. Image resolution at least 2000 times better than is possible for photographs made with Earthbound telescopes was obtained for the last few pictures in the series. Craters with diameters as small as 3 feet were plainly visible, and the best resolution obtained was 1½ feet. One photograph showed what appeared to be a jagged rock mass in the center of a secondary crater (see Figure 2.3, upper left-hand corner). The final picture was taken when the spacecraft was about 1000 feet above the lunar surface and covers an area of 60 by 100 feet. Ranger 7 carried six television cameras which used a variety of lens systems and two different exposure times to cover a wide range of lighting conditions on the moon. Two of the cameras used a scanning standard of 1150 lines (to be compared with the commercial television standard of 525 lines). All pictures were made in the last 13 minutes of flight. Preliminary analysis of these pictures indicates that the moon's surface is generally hard and firm, with any dust layer no deeper than a few inches to one foot.

U.S. AND SOVIET FAILURES

Since the early days of the Pioneers and Luniks the United States and the Soviet Union have both had a number of failures or partial successes with lunar and interplanetary probes. Two additional Pioneer launchings were attempted by the United States in 1960, with rocketry failures both times; Pioneer 6 had been intended to go into permanent orbit around the moon. The Soviet Union has experienced more than a dozen failures in attempts to launch Venus probes, possible lunar probes, and Mars probes.

In the United States, NASA began a new lunar series, as a support for the manned Project Apollo. This series is named Ranger; it has also been plagued with difficulties, although Ranger 6 was a brilliant success as an exercise in rocketry, and Ranger 7 was a total success that seems to have vindicated the entire program.

Many people find these failures mystifying or upsetting, especially in view of the long list of American successes with many launchings and the persistent legend of invariable Russian successes. However, we tend to forget that the art of deep-space rocketry is quite new. In the early years of automobiling and aviation nobody expected automobiles or airplanes to perform as well as rockets and their payloads usually have performed in these early years of their epoch.

In February 1961, almost a year after the American Pioneer 5, the Soviet Union attempted a Venus-probe launching. Its name was simply "Venus Probe." This probe did approach somewhat nearer to the orbit of Venus than did Pioneer 5, but did not come very close to the planet itself. Any question of what information it could have provided about Venus was sadly closed by a permanent loss of radio contact, when the Soviet probe was 4,700,000 miles from Earth.

This Soviet Venus probe, however, was the first important example of a launching from a "parking orbit" (see Chapter 4). The United States has also used the parking-orbit technique for all Rangers, the Mariner Venus and Mars probes, and a variety of high-satellite orbits (see later).

Rangers 1 and 2, launched in August and November 1961, went into initial parking orbits but were unable to achieve deep-space orbits. Ranger 3 (1962), like Pioneer 4 and Lunik-Mechta, had slightly excessive speed; instead of impacting on the moon, it passed the moon at a distance of 22,900 miles, then went into solar orbit. Ranger 4 (1962) impacted on the moon, but a retrorocket malfunction caused it to land on the moon's far side. Ranger 5 (1962) had control-timer difficulties in October 1962 and missed the moon by 400 miles.

It has been NASA (and Soviet) policy to sterilize any probe that has a chance of landing on the moon or on a planet. This is to prevent contamination of the surfaces of these bodies with biological material from Earth. Such contamination would be a confusing element in later studies of any possible original life on these bodies.

Because of the mishaps with Rangers 4 and 5, the high-temperature sterilization procedures, which may have impaired some electronic components, were modified in the case of Ranger 6.

In spite of this precaution, a malfunction did again occur: a switching circuit which was to supply full power to either or both of Ranger's two independent television systems broke down in flight. Ranger 6 struck the moon on target, but the high-power television transmitters did not react to commands to turn themselves on and no pictures were received.

Ranger 6 was, however, a perfect excercise in deep-space rocketry. Its over-all flight plan called for two mid-course corrections on the way to the moon (see Chapter 4). The accuracy of the initial aiming was so good that only one correction had to be made.

For Ranger 7 all vulnerable circuit elements had apparently been located, and this probe was sensationally successful, sending back hundreds of pictures with a resolution of detail more than 1000 times better than the best pictures that could be obtained by use of Earth-based equipment. These pictures indicate that the moon has a hard surface capable of bearing the weight of a manned spacecraft.

FUTURE LUNAR PROBES

All lunar probes launched for the remainder of this decade will have a double purpose. These probes will further the ultimate goal of sending a manned expedition to the moon under Project Apollo, and they will also gather scientific information about the moon for its own sake. They will aid the manned program by providing information on the nature of the moon's surface (by means of television, photography, and direct examination and analysis by soft-landed robot probes) and will provide detailed mapping information for the choice of landing sites.

Lunar probes are arranged in the following classes:

Ranger. At least two fully operational flights of Ranger lunar-impact spacecraft are scheduled for 1965. These probes will carry television cameras for detailed high-resolution, close-up pictures of the topography and surface texture of the moon's near side.

Surveyor. Gentle "soft" landings of instrument packages on the moon are the mission of the Surveyor series (see Figure 6.7). This series will have its first four test flights in 1965, followed by 13 fully operational flights in the period 1966–1968. At least one of these Surveyor craft will be a roving vehicle, capable of moving about on the moon's surface while being controlled from Earth.

As the name implies, the Surveyor series will survey various areas on the moon as possible sites for manned landings. Each Surveyor will transmit to Earth a variety of data, including high-resolution pictures of the terrain and surface texture. Stereoscopic (three-

Figure 2.4.   Ranger Spacecraft.   (Courtesy of National Aeronautics and Space Administration.

dimensional) and color television systems are under study for the Surveyor program.

Various Surveyor craft will take samples of lunar rock and "soil" and analyze them for physical characteristics and chemical composition.   Several different approaches are being developed for this mission. Automated chemical laboratory procedures are one approach; spectroscopic analysis is another. Solar radiation measurements, lunar seismic disturbances, and micrometeoroid impact frequency are also concerns of the Surveyor program.   Solar-cell power will be used to give all Surveyors long operating life.

Orbiter.   Ten flights of special spacecraft into permanent close orbits about the moon itself are scheduled for 1966–1968.   Besides television mapping tasks for Project Apollo, the Orbiters will have scientific purposes of their own.   Among these will be the determination of the moon's exact shape and measurements of its gravitational field.

INTERPLANETARY PROBES

Mariner—to Venus. Perhaps the most advanced—as well as brilliantly successful—deep-space probe launched to date has been the U.S. Mariner 2, the Venus probe of 1962. The magnitude of the Mariner achievement was hailed around the world, but its real significance has been grasped by only a handful of people.

What Mariner did is quite simple *in principle*. It went to the vicinity of the planet Venus, it took a look at the planet, and it radioed what it saw back to Earth.

The 447-pound Mariner spacecraft was a complete space laboratory carrying six classes of instruments (see Figure 4.25). Its observation program was designed by scientists of six universities and an Army scientific laboratory. Each single instrument provided results that would have been scientifically valuable by themselves. The instruments, and the complete spacecraft, are described in Chapter 4.

Mariner 2 was launched on August 26, 1962, and flew past Venus on December 14, 1962, at a distance of 21,648 miles. Mariner provided several main items of information about Venus, most of which would not have been obtainable through any kind of telescope technique from Earth, especially as all of Venus is covered by a thick cloud layer. Here are Mariner's major findings:

1. Venus is probably a lifeless desert: Mariner found temperatures approaching 800°F, hot enough to melt lead. No form of life as we know it on Earth can exist at such temperatures. Cloud temperatures were 200°F at the base of the cloud layer, nearest the planet's surface. Cloud temperatures were —30°F at the middle level and —60°F at the top level. Mariner's temperature instruments detected a spot in the cloud cover that was 20° cooler than the surrounding cloud area. This may be due to the influence of some prominent surface feature, such as a high mountain range.*

Mariner did not detect any carbon dioxide gas (CO_2) above the Venus clouds, although CO_2 (an essential to life on Earth) seems to be present at lower levels.

---

* Earth-based radar studies of Venus had earlier detected what might be such a surface feature.

2. Venus has no strong magnetic field and no trapped particle belts. Mariner found the magnetic fields near Venus no stronger than those in interplanetary space (see below).

This lack of a magnetic field may have implications concerning the internal structure of the planet. The Earth's magnetic field is now believed to arise from a "dynamo" action due to the movements of electrically conductive material in the Earth's heavy inner core. Although Venus is the approximate size of the Earth and almost as heavy, the lack of a magnetic field may indicate the lack of such a core.

3. The solar wind is a predominant feature of interplanetary space. The matter constituting the solar wind is very tenuous, however. Mariner's count showed averages of 10 to 20 particles per cubic inch. But Mariner found these solar particles everywhere, moving outward from the direction of the sun at speeds between 240 and 450 miles per second.

4. Weak magnetic fields are everywhere in space. Mariner found a continuous field with a strength ranging between 5 to 10 gamma (one gamma is equal to about 1/30,000 of the strength of the Earth's field at the magnetic equator).

5. Cosmic rays are fairly uniform in quantity and intensity throughout the space between the Earth and Venus. Scientists had expected that the distribution would be uneven, and this constancy of the strength of cosmic rays is not fully understood. Additional space-flight experiments will be needed for clarification.

6. Micrometeoroids are apparently rather rare, except in the immediate vicinity of the Earth. Mariner registered only two micrometeoroid impacts in 1700 hours of recorded data. A comparison with information from near-Earth satellites shows that meteoroid material is 10,000 times more abundant near the Earth than in distance space. This is in accord with accepted theory: the Earth's gravitational field tends to concentrate space dust.

7. Tracking data from Mariner's flight have helped refine the *astronomical unit*, the prime yardstick of astronomy (see Chapter 3). The tracking results have also helped determine the exact locations of tracking stations on the Earth. These findings will be important for future interplanetary flight, manned or unmanned. Tracking observations of Mariner's movements also helped refine measurements

of the masses of Venus and the moon. This is because gravitational effects of Earth, the moon, Venus, the sun, and the planet Jupiter all influenced the Mariner flight path.

The Mariner experiment set a new record for long-distance space communications: 53.9 million miles. Since Mariner's transmitter had a power of only three watts (less than half the power of a typical 7½-watt "night light" bulb), this demonstrated that reliable communications can be carried on at interplanetary distances.

Future Interplanetary and Deep-Space Flights

MARS PROBES

From 1964 onward a number of Mariner-type vehicles will be sent to the vicinity of the planet Mars,* first to perform a fly-by mission like the Venus mission of 1962, then to put a probe into orbit around Mars (for television, magnetism, and other experiments), and finally to land automated probes on the surface of Mars to conduct, among other things, biological experiments.

The biological experiments will involve examining Martian soil for evidences of life. Several automatic devices have already been developed for capturing samples of Martian microbial life, if any exists, and identifying it as such.

The question whether life exists on Mars or some other body in the solar system is important to the science of biology; it affects the general question of the origin of life on Earth. Is life unique to this planet, at least in this solar system? Is there only a narrow environmental range in which life can develop? Whichever way these

---

* Mariner 4 was launched toward Mars by NASA on November 28, 1964, for a fly-by mission. The probe carries a slow-scan television camera to be used during the period of close approach to the planet. An "occultation" experiment is also scheduled, in which characteristics of the Martian atmosphere will be measured by their effect on Mariner's radio signal as the spacecraft passes "behind" the planet as seen from Earth. This probe carries instruments for a number of other observations of both deep-space conditions and Martian-vicinity conditions (possible trapped-particle belts, etc.). Mariner 4 is the first probe to provide data from any part of the solar system beyond the orbit of Earth. Launched earlier during the same month-long launching window (for Mars) were Mariner 3 and the Soviet Zond 2, both of which had electrical system troubles and are considered "dead." However, all three probes will reach the vicinity of Mars during July 1965.

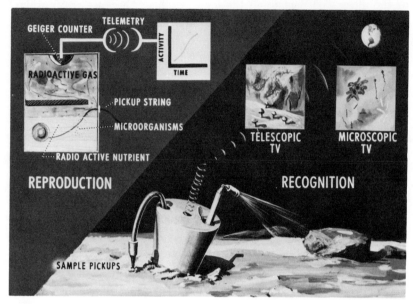

Figure 2.5. Possible Sampling Methods for Extraterrestrial Biological Specimens. (Courtesy of National Aeronautics and Space Administration.)

questions may be answered, our understanding of the origin, development, and nature of living organisms will be profoundly affected. This, of course, is why great care is taken to sterilize lunar and planetary probes so that life-associated chemical compounds or microbial corpses from Earth will not confuse the issues. This subject is discussed further in Chapter 5.

NEW PIONEERS

Between 1965 and 1967 a number of new-model Pioneer probes will be used to obtain detailed measurements of fields and particles in space and to determine the effects of solar radiation on the space environment. This particular Pioneer series will provide space-environment data for Project Apollo. Each spacecraft will carry four to seven basic experiments. The Pioneers now under development will weigh 140 pounds (including 30 pounds of instruments) and will have a design life of six months—ample for missions up to 60 million miles from Earth.

2.5 MANNED SPACE PROGRAMS

The thought of placing man into space has always been the most appealing aspect of space exploration to its imaginative and original planners. Besides the adventurous appeal of manned space travel, man is still a very desirable explorer in space—notwithstanding the great success of robot exploration described so far. Accordingly, there has always been a desire on the part of some space exploration experts to design manned space expeditions and to loft them as soon as possible. The task is tremendously difficult, and its first success marked a unique experience in the history of mankind. This first success was achieved in the Soviet program (see later). The U.S. manned program is focused on a manned round-trip voyage to the moon, and is being carried on in three phases: *Project Mercury* (one-man, near-Earth flight, *Project Gemini* (two-man, near-Earth), and *Project Apollo* (three-man, near-Earth and lunar).

U.S. Project Mercury

There is no room in this chapter to describe the unbelievable complexity of Project Mercury, which had a life of 4⅔ years from its official approval in 1958 to its completion with the 34-hour flight of Astronaut Gordon Cooper.

In its four-year life Project Mercury completed 25 flights, of which six were manned. These six flights were accomplished with complete pilot safety. Moreover, in spite of all problems, no changes had to be made in the original Project Mercury design and planning concepts.

During the development of the 3000-pound Mercury spacecraft many unmanned orbital and nonorbital qualification flights were made to test all systems from launching to landing. Two chimpanzees were also used in flight tests before manned flight was attempted. In a final test before the first manned flight an electromechanical "simulated man" was the passenger; this robot consumed water and oxygen, emitted heat, "breathed" and "perspired" like a real man.

Because the ability of man to function effectively in space could not be known until manned flight had actually taken place, Mercury spacecraft were designed to operate automatically. All automatic systems were backed up by secondary automatic systems, and all were

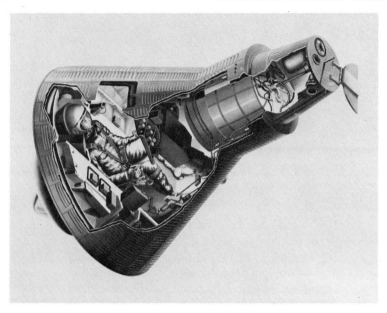

Figure 2.6. Interior Arrangement of Mercury Spacecraft. (Courtesy of National Aeronautics and Space Administration.)

subject to ground control. In addition, there was provision for complete control of the spacecraft by the astronaut.

To hundreds of millions of people Project Mercury provided the excitement of a great human advancement and the thrill of success. The success was really in the scientific and engineering achievements of manned flights. Project Mercury demonstrated that man could function in the space environment, both as pilot and observer. It also demonstrated that the known design principles of life-support systems were sound and that nothing new need be invented to permit man to make longer journeys in space—such as to the moon. The most prominent events of Project Mercury are summarized in Table 2.1. In addition, the following items are noteworthy:

All manned landings were in preselected ocean "target" areas. In each instance the astronaut landed in his spacecraft. In most cases the astronaut did not leave his craft until it had been hoisted to the deck of the recovery ship.

The suborbital flights of Astronauts Shepard and Grissom featured a ballistic trajectory like that of a cannon shell. However, the astro-

Table 2.1.   Summary of U.S. Project Mercury Flights

Astronaut and Date of Flight	Orbits Completed (number)	Flight Time (hr/min)	Altitude (statute miles) max.	Altitude (statute miles) min.	Maximal Speed (miles/hr)	Remarks
Alan B. Shepard, Jr. May 5, 1961	none (ballistic, suborbital trajectory)	0/15	116	—	5,180	Astronaut in free fall for 5 minutes. All objectives achieved.
Virgil I. Grissom June 21, 1961	none (ballistic, suborbital trajectory)	0/15	118	—	5,200	Astronaut rescued after spacecraft opened prematurely and sank on landing in ocean. Astronaut in free fall for 5 minutes.
John H. Glenn, Jr. February 20, 1962	3	4/55	163	100	17,550	Astronaut enjoyed flight, was weightless (in free fall) for more than 4 hours. All objectives achieved.
M. Scott Carpenter May 24, 1962	3	4/56	167	100	17,545	Same as Glenn's flight; additionally, "drifted" for 77 minutes (no controls used); first experiment with behavior of liquids in free fall. All objectives achieved.
Walter M. Schirra, Jr. October 3, 1962	6	9/13	176	100	17,540	Double number of orbits; all objectives of mission achieved; drifted for 136 minutes; conducted photographic experiments; covered a distance of more than 150,000 miles and landed within 4 miles of target in Pacific Ocean.
L. Gordon Cooper May 15, 1963	22	34/20	166	100	17,546	Longest duration flight by United States; astronaut launched and observed a small, flashing-light satellite from orbit; drifted for 8 orbits; photographed astronomic and atmospheric phenomena; all objectives of mission achieved.

nauts operated their manual controls throughout most of each flight, testing the systems for changing the ship's attitude in space.

At the end of Astronaut Grissom's flight an automatic door operated by means of explosive bolts opened prematurely, letting sea water into the spacecraft. Astronaut Grissom left the spacecraft and swam for four minutes, until a helicopter picked him up. The spacecraft sank and was lost.

During the first manned *orbital* flight, with Astronaut John H. Glenn aboard the spacecraft, an erroneous telemetry signal indicated that the craft's heat shield (for re-entry protection) was loose. Astronaut Glenn modified his re-entry procedure so as to retain the possibly loose shield. He landed safely, on schedule, and later examination of the spacecraft showed the heat shield to be intact.

Astronaut Glenn had reported sighting mysterious glowing objects, which he nicknamed "fireflies," apparently in orbit with him and frequently passing his window. The "fireflies" were explained on the next flight of Project Mercury, that of Astronaut M. Scott Carpenter. They were apparently ice crystals, frozen from water vapor produced by the spacecraft's attitude-control jets. Carpenter found he could produce fireflies at will by pounding the inside walls of his spacecraft with his hand to knock crystals off the outer skin.

Astronaut Walter M. Schirra carried a two and a half pound camera-and-accessories system to photograph the Earth below and its cloud patterns (in color and in black and white). His fuel conservation procedures were so good that he landed with 78 per cent of his control-jet fuel still in the tanks. He reported that both he and the spacecraft could have gone on well beyond eight orbits. Schirra's spacecraft carried a special external panel holding samples of different materials for heat shields and spacecraft structure to test their characteristics in the great heat generated by re-entry friction.

In the final manned Mercury flight Astronaut L. Gordon Cooper launched the first orbiting Earth satellite from a satellite already in Earth orbit. This was a small sphere bearing a set of flashing lights, which went into slightly lower (and faster) orbit than Cooper's own orbit. He was able to see this flashing beacon from time to time as it overtook him or passed below and ahead of him. Cooper also observed a flashing-light experiment set up on the ground near a South African town. Both experiments showed that a man in orbit could see and identify a known light source on the ground or in orbit. The ability to locate and identify lights will be important for experiments in joining, or "docking," two separately launched spacecraft while in orbit. Such experiments will be carried on in the U.S. Manned Project Gemini (discussed later in this chapter). Cooper also took photographs (see Figure 2.7).

Astronaut Cooper reported some dizziness on stepping out of his spacecraft at the end of his 34-hour flight. The physician in attendance detected that the astronaut also had a fast pulse. Careful medical observation showed this to be a temporary effect, probably resulting from weightlessness. It was similar to the dizziness and racing pulse

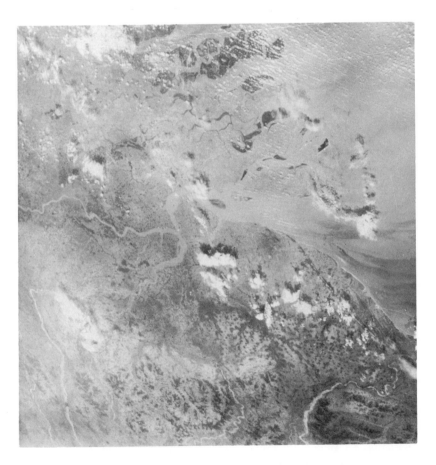

Figure 2.7. Photograph of Indian Landscape from Orbiting Mercury Spacecraft. (Courtesy of National Aeronautics and Space Administration.)

that long-bedridden hospital patients sometimes experience when they are first allowed to get up. Soviet astronauts have reported similar experiences.

Project Mercury demonstrated that man can perform well in space, with no serious aftereffects or risks to his health, for missions up to 34 hours. The project also showed that basic American design concepts for spacecraft and life-support systems were sound and could be used for more elaborate manned space projects. Finally, the project showed that man could be very useful in space flights, as either pilot or observer. The experience gained from Project Mercury is being applied to more extensive U.S. manned space projects now in development—Project Gemini and Project Apollo.

Soviet Projects

Up to the time of this writing the Soviet Union has had seven manned orbital launchings:

Vostok 1 (April 12, 1961). The world's first manned space flight. Cosmonaut Yuri Gagarin performed a single-orbit flight, with the spacecraft recovered on land in Siberia. The cosmonaut was ejected from the cabin and landed by parachute after re-entry into the lower atmosphere.

Vostok 2 (August 6, 1961). Cosmonaut Gherman S. Titov performed a 17-orbit flight, lasting 26 hours. Progress was continuously reported to the public over Moscow radio—a departure from the usual Soviet rule of secrecy. Cosmonaut Titov also used a parachute for landing, as did all Russian cosmonauts in the Vostok series.

Vostok 3 (August 11, 1962). This flight lasted 64 orbits, with cosmonaut Major Andrian G. Nikolayev performing a number of experiments, including floating free in his cabin for long periods. A television camera aboard this spacecraft showed the public some of the cosmonaut's activities, including knitting. Nikolayev also communicated directly with a partner in space, launched the next day.

Vostok 4 (August 12, 1962). Vostok 4 was launched from the same pad as Vostok 3 the day before, indicating excellent launching procedures and pad maintenance. On his initial orbit Cosmonaut Lieutenant Colonel Pavel R. Popovitch and his spacecraft flew within 3.1 miles of Nikolayev in Vostok 3. Many non-Russian experts speculated that an experiment in orbit-matching and docking was in progress. However, the orbits were not quite identical in size and not in the same plane, and Popovitch was not launched during the exact time "window" that would have permitted true tandem flight with Nikolayev. Neither spacecraft made any maneuver to bring itself closer to the other, so that the early impression that an orbit-matching, spacecraft-docking experiment was underway was erroneous. Both spacecraft landed within a few minutes (but several hundred miles) of each other on August 15, 1962.

Vostok 5 (June 14, 1963). Cosmonaut Captain Valerian Bykovsky's flight of 82 orbits lasted five days, setting a record.

Vostok 6 (June 16, 1963). Cosmonaut Valentina Tereshkova, the first woman in space. Miss Tereshkova flew for 49 orbits, landing on June 19 three hours before Vostok 5. Again, rumors of an orbit-matching experiment were erroneous. Vostok 6 was launched into a higher orbit than Vostok 5 and in the wrong time phasing, so that the orbital planes of the two spacecraft were 30 degrees apart at the equator.

Voskhod 1 (October 12, 1964). The first spacecraft to carry more than one person flew for 24 hours, 11 minutes, and completed 16 orbits. All objectives were apparently achieved. The occupants were Cosmonaut Colonel Vladimir M. Komarov, pilot and spacecraft commander, Lieutenant Boris B. Yegorov, a physician, and Konstantin P. Feoktisov, an engineer, who acted as scientific observer. This flight demonstrated the practicability of allowing passengers who are not pilots to fly on multimanned space missions. The three men landed in their space cabin, unlike earlier cosmonauts. The Voskhod weighed about 6 tons; at this writing it is not known whether it represents a new design or is a modification of the 5-ton Vostok spacecraft. However, it provided a comfortable "shirt sleeves" environment in which the men did not need to wear space suits.

All reliable indications are that the Russians were successful every time they attempted a manned space shot, just as Project Mercury was. Rumors of failures and losses of Russian cosmonauts are apparently well refuted by the evidence of the American tracking and monitoring networks. Doubters of Soviet success ought to remember that Russian launchings are usually "witnessed" by American radar and monitored by an extremely well-developed American tracking network.

U.S. Project Gemini

The early orbital flights of man were all inspiring achievements and all will stand forever as milestones in human history. Yet "manned space travel" implies a destination. To use an analogy with early sailing, there is a difference between demonstrating ability to build a boat and circle a bay in it, and accomplishing an actual voyage to the first remote destination on the other side of the ocean. In space travel, the nearest possible destination is the moon.

To land a man on the moon requires the development and practice of certain maneuvers in extended orbital missions. The most important of these is *docking*, or *rendezvous*—the bringing of two or more independently launched spacecraft to the same point in space and uniting or joining them. This will be one of the essential techniques to be mastered before Project Apollo and its astronauts can proceed to the moon. Orbit-matching and docking will also be important for the establishment and maintenance of large orbiting space stations.

Translunar missions—such as a manned expedition to Mars—will also need the docking technique. It would probably be easier to assemble the necessary large spacecraft and great fuel supply in a parking orbit rather than to try to launch a planetary manned ship from the surface of the Earth as a single heavy unit. Project Gemini, using two-man spacecraft and various unmanned spacecraft, will perfect this technique.

The four major objectives of Project Gemini are (1) to expose men to orbital operations for periods of several weeks in order to test man's tolerance of the space environment; (2) to undertake extended scientific investigations by men in space; (3) to develop and perfect docking maneuvers; and (4) to develop and perfect new reentry and landing procedures. In achieving these objectives, Project Gemini will accumulate between 2000 and 3000 hours of manned orbital flight time.

The two astronauts in each Gemini spacecraft will control their craft manually, spell each other on watches, or, at times, work together, and they may even don spacesuits to leave the spacecraft and work outside the ship—while tethered to it by a safety line. The first manned Gemini flights are scheduled for early 1965.

U.S. Project Apollo

Project Apollo is obviously the culmination of the first phase in manned space exploration. For the first time now the goal of a manned space mission is to reach a given destination—an actual journey will be undertaken; space *exploration* now becomes space *travel*. Because the moon is our nearest neighbor in the sky, the first real journey man can thus undertake into space necessarily involves a long trip. In terms of distances—approximately 250,000 miles each way—the round trip represents only the aggregate of some 100 round trips across this country (by air); however, the complexity of the early orbital flights in Project Mercury will be extended manyfold (see Figure 8.6).

The program is now well underway and the first manned lunar landings are scheduled for 1968–1970. The mission and the spacecraft, the maneuvers, and the launch vehicle for Project Apollo are described in some detail in Chapter 9. Ballistic and orbital flight tests of some spacecraft prototypes have been successfully carried out since 1963 (see Figure 1.4). Other preparations are proceeding now, and crew training will progress continuously.

Various teams of Project Apollo astronauts are scheduled to accumulate at least 2000 hours of flight experience in Earth orbits before a lunar flight will be attempted. This will require a moderate number of flights, possibly up to 30 days' duration, in the time period 1966–1968. During this period Project Apollo astronauts will practice docking and other techniques needed for the lunar expedition but will also conduct various scientific experiments valuable in their own right.

Project Apollo will send up its first manned lunar expedition only when a number of conditions have been met. First, the Apollo spacecraft and Saturn V launch vehicle must all have proved themselves in a sufficient number of orbital and sublunar flights. Unmanned probes in the Ranger, Orbiter, and Surveyor series must have sent back to Earth a sufficient amount of preliminary data for choosing the landing sites, etc. Spacecraft docking techniques must have been perfectly mastered. The Orbiting Solar Observatories and other satellites must report that all is well and all will probably continue to go well in the space environment. The long and repeated Gemini and Apollo Earth-orbital flights must demonstrate that man can withstand prolonged stresses of weightlessness, confined quarters, and the hostile space environment. Then, and only then, a manned Apollo capsule will be dispatched to its ultimate destination.

Project Apollo is a deliberate, carefully planned, step-by-step approach to all the problems involved, a measured march toward its goal that anticipates delays and setbacks and tries to take them into account. The United States is actually going to the moon at its own pace, making the attempt for the sake of all values involved. These include scientific and technological values as well as values related to an awareness that the United States must remain in the forefront of technological advance.

The point of Project Apollo is that mankind is ready for this kind of enterprise, that this is a logical step in the continuing development of technology, and that the effort and sacrifice required are probably necessary for the continued vigor of Western civilization.

These thoughts were expressed in dignified simplicity by the late President John F. Kennedy:*

"Those who came before us made certain that this country rode the first waves of the industrial revolution, the first waves of modern invention, and the first wave of nuclear power, and this generation does not intend to founder in the backwash of the coming age of space.

"We mean to be a part of it. We mean to lead it, for the eyes of the world now look into space, to the moon and to the planets beyond, and we have vowed that we shall not see it governed by a hostile flag of conquest, but by a banner of freedom and peace.

"We have vowed that we shall not see space filled with weapons of mass destruction, but with instruments of knowledge and understanding.

"We set sail on this new sea because there is new knowledge to be gained, and new rights to be won, and they must be won and used for the progress of all people. For space science, like nuclear science and all technology, has no conscience of its own . . . .

"We choose to go to the moon in this decade and do the other things, not because they are easy, but because they are hard, because that goal will serve to organize and measure the best of our energies and skills, because that challenge is one that we are willing to accept, one we are unwilling to postpone, and one which we intend to win, and the others, too."

* In a speech at Rice University on September 12, 1962.

CHAPTER 3

The Nature of Space

Myron G. H. Ligda
Stanford Research Institute

Contents

The Nature of Space

3.1 INTRODUCTION

Although for uncounted centuries man has gazed toward the heavens with wonder and speculation, only in recent years has he been doing so with firm confidence of his ability eventually to travel in space beyond the limits of the Earth's atmosphere. As a result of this confidence, the science of astronomy is receiving close study from many who never concerned themselves with it before. Technology and science have combined to provide new tools and techniques for obtaining information essential to space travel, and new findings are reported almost daily. These are based on observations made with ever more sensitive radio telescopes, artificial satellites, and inter-planetary probes.

In this chapter man's current understanding of the nature of the universe and the physics of space is outlined. By way of providing a perspective for the subject of space travel, the first section of the chapter summarizes the astronomical characteristics of the Universe and "deep" space (i.e., beyond the limits of the Solar System). It is extremely doubtful that any person living today will travel into deep space, although it is possible that unmanned spaceships will probe beyond the limits of the Solar System.

The other major section of the chapter describes the physics of space within the Solar System and some of the environmental conditions that must be taken into consideration for successful space travel. Man—and a woman—have already orbited the Earth outside all but a trace of the atmosphere and plans are well advanced for the first journey to the moon. It is within the Earth-moon, or cislunar, region that man must learn how to survive before he can undertake the much more difficult trips to the planets. If the Earth had no moon, it is doubtful that this generation would see anything more than Earth-orbiting.

3.2 ASTRONOMY

The Solar System

Our own planet Earth is the third one of nine counting outward from the sun. In order, the names are Mercury, Venus, Earth, Mars, Jupiter, Saturn, Uranus, Neptune, and Pluto. As viewed from, say, the North Star, the planets all circle or *revolve* around the sun, which itself *rotates* on its axis, in a counterclockwise direction. The principal characteristics of the planets are summarized in Table 3.1.

It will be noted that the more distant a planet is from the sun, the longer is its year or time for one circle around the sun. An approximate formula by which the length of a planet's year may be determined if its distance from the sun is known may be expressed by

$$\text{period} = \sqrt{(\text{distance})^3};$$

the distance is expressed in terms of the *astronomical unit,* or mean distance between the Earth and sun, and the period is expressed in terms of Earth years. The same relationship holds true for the moon and artificial satellites circling the Earth; the more distant a satellite

Table 3.1   Planets of the Solar System

Name	Diameter (miles)	Mean Distance from Sun (miles)	Length of Year (in Earth years)	Number of Natural Satellites
Mercury	3,100	36 million	0.241 (88 days)	0
Venus	7,600	67 million	0.62 (225 days)	0
Earth	7,900	93 million	1.0	1
Mars	4,200	142 million	1.9	2
Jupiter	88,800	484 million	11.9	12
Saturn	75,100	887 million	29.5	9
Uranus	31,000	1,787 million	84	5
Neptune	33,000	2,797 million	165	2
Pluto	Doubtful, roughly 5,000	3,765 million	248	Unknown

is from its primary, the more time it takes to circle around it. The moon takes about four weeks to circle the Earth completely but an artificial satellite a few hundred miles above the surface takes only about an hour.

Between the orbits of Mars and Jupiter is a zone occupied by a number of small solid bodies called *asteroids*. More than 1500 of them are known, and there may be as many as 50 times more. It was once hypothesized that they comprised the remnants of a primordial planet that exploded or somehow failed to coalesce during the evolution of the solar system, but since the total mass of the known asteroids—and they must represent the largest that exist—would not make a body the size of our moon, the "spoiled planet" theory is discounted today.

The remaining members of the *Solar System* (excepting the sun and moons of the various planets), as the entire assembly is called, are the *comets*. The Solar System is presently believed to possess many thousands, perhaps millions of these rather mysterious objects. Some comets travel in definitely elliptical orbits and are observed periodically; others are apparently observed only once. The tails of comets develop as they approach the sun; they also get brighter during approach. These and other characteristics suggest that they are partly composed of gas that glows under the stimulus of solar radiation and partly of solid matter shining by reflected light. As comets recede from the sun toward more distant portions of their orbit they grow dimmer more rapidly than their rate of recession from the Earth and sun would suggest. Virtually all comets recede beyond telescopic detection as they approach the *aphelion* or most distant portion of their orbits from the sun. They often appear rather suddenly and sometimes in quite unexpected places in the sky. This factor makes them a favorite object for amateur astronomers who are often the first to report them. When a new comet is reported, an orbit is computed for it as soon as observations made on three different nights are available. The orbital elements sometimes identify it as a previously observed comet, but if it appears to be a new one it is named after its discoverer. A rather large number of the so-called *short-period* comets have aphelions very close to Jupiter's orbit. This had led to the hypothesis that Jupiter and perhaps the other major planets Saturn, Uranus, and Neptune have comet "families" somehow acquired by capture.

Some comets are the largest or most extensive objects in the Solar System, even including the sun, although they vary greatly in size. The tail of one, the great comet of 1843, was measured at 200 million miles in length, or a greater distance than lies between the sun and Mars.

From year to year and decade to decade the number of comets observed varies widely. Unfortunately, the first half of the twentieth century and so far the second half have been relatively poor for their occurrence compared with intervals in the eighteenth and nineteenth centuries.

The orbits of all the planets and the great majority of comets are within about 15 degrees of being coplanar. The sun's axis of rotation is also perpendicular to the general plane. The sun rotates on its axis in the same direction as all the planets revolve about it. These facts suggest that the sun and its family of planets and comets had a common origin and that the sun did not capture the planets one by one or in groups some time back in astronomical history. If the latter were the case, it would seem likely that the planets would have orbits greatly inclined to each other and that these orbits would be much more eccentric.

The Galaxy

Our sun with its family of planets and their satellites, asteroids, and comets is but one of myriad stars in an assemblage called a *galaxy*. *Our* Galaxy, in turn, is but one of known millions of other such stellar concentrations that may be observed in the Universe.

From counts of the number of stars of our own Galaxy in different directions from our sun and observations of the shape of other relatively nearby galaxies of stars, the shape and appearance of our own Galaxy and the relative position of our solar system within it has been deduced. Two "views" of our Galaxy, one from edge-on and one from "above" or its pole are shown in Figure 3.1. It will be seen that, edge-on, the Galaxy has a lens-shaped appearance, and, as viewed from above, it has a spiral structure like a pinwheel. Our sun, which is quite an average star with respect to size, temperature, and probable age lies close to the plane of the Galaxy but away from the central concentration, or *Milky Way*, as it is popularly called. Although to the naked eye the Milky Way, as seen on summer nights, appears as a continuous cloud of light, even a very low-powered telescope or good pair of binoculars reveals it to be composed of a vast number of individual stars. If the sun were close to its center, the Galaxy would be observed as a belt of stars across the sky during

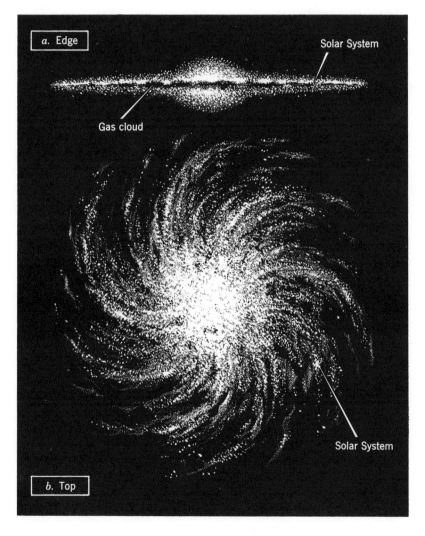

Figure 3.1. Probable Shape of the Galaxy.

all seasons of the year instead of appearing only during the summer months. Sharing the general revolution of stars around the center of the Galaxy, the sun and its family has a speed around the central star concentration of about 170 miles per second.

Extragalactic Stellar Systems

Long-exposure photographs made through powerful telescopes across the vast reaches of space reveal the presence of millions of other swarms of stars or galaxies, presumably quite similar in size and structure to our own. The nearest such galaxy to us, called the "Great Nebula in Andromeda" (located in the *constellation**of Andromeda), is visible to the naked eye as a rather indistinct star. Its telescopic appearance, however, indicates it to be a galaxy; it is shown in Figure 3.2.

To apply convenient terrestrial or earthly units of distance such as miles or kilometers to interstellar and intergalactic distances would involve the use of awkwardly large numbers; astronomers have there-fore defined more practical units for their work. One of these, the *astronomical unit* (sometimes AU) or mean distance between the Earth and sun (93 million miles), has already been introduced earlier in this chapter. Two others which are commonly employed by astron-omers and astrophysicists are the *light year*, or the distance light can travel in a year, and the *parsec*, which is the distance at which the astronomical unit subtends an angle (or has a parallax) of one second of arc ($\frac{1}{3600}$ of a degree). The relationships between these various units are presented in Table 3.2.

Some feeling for the vastness of these distances may be obtained by the realization that it takes light only about eight minutes to reach the Earth from the sun.

By spectrographic analysis of light it is possible to determine whether its source is moving toward or away from the observer. The speed of approach or recession may also be determined spec-trographically. By this technique it has been observed that all other

---

* A constellation is an arbitrary grouping of stars as seen from the Earth, according to imaginary figures, or parts of figures, which they appear to outline across the sky (Southern Cross, Scorpio, Big Dipper, etc.). Constellations are convenient for indicating general regions of the sky of objects of interest, al-though they have no physical or scientific significance.

Figure 3.2. The Great Nebula in Andromeda, nearest galaxy to our own, which probably looks similar when viewed from Andromeda. (Courtesy of the Mount Wilson and Palomar Observatories.)

stellar galaxies are apparently moving away from our own with a speed that is inversely proportional to their brightness. If the reasonable assumption is made that the brightness of a galaxy is inversely proportional to its distance from us, the conclusion may be reached

Table 3.2   Astronomical Measures of Distance

	Miles	Astronomical Unit	Light Year
Astronomical unit	93×10^6	1	1.58×10^{-5}
Light year	6×10^{12}	63,400	1
Parsec	2×10^{13}	206,265	3.26

that the entire visible universe is expanding at an explosive rate.* It might be termed "hyperexplosive," for the most distant observable galaxies are apparently receding at a speed about one seventh of that of light itself. Some astronomers question this interpretation of the observation by offering the alternative hypothesis that, in traveling across vast distances of space, the speed of light may somehow be reduced to give the illusion of rapid recession of the source. If the "exploding universe" interpretation is accepted, it may be computed that the visible Universe started its expansion from some localized region about 5 billion (5×10^9) years ago. Curiously, this estimate of the "age" of the Universe agrees reasonably well with approximations of the age of the Earth itself as estimated from proportions of radioactive elements and their decay products in ancient rocks. That two such dissimilar and admittedly coarse estimates should agree well on the possible time of "creation" is indeed remarkable and deserving of further attention.

That region of space that lies between the galaxies is evidently the emptiest in the Universe. This is supported by the observation that galaxies so distant that the light from them can take a billion years to reach the Earth can be detected only because there is virtually nothing to scatter or absorb the energy along the way. It is estimated that the concentration of matter in intergalactic space cannot exceed about *10 atoms of hydrogen gas per cubic inch;* this exceeds the highest vacuum that can be achieved in our best physical laboratories by a factor of several thousand. Although it was at first believed that no stars occupied the region between galaxies, in recent years as a result of deliberate search for such objects a few have been identified. Whether these are "escapees" from our own Galaxy or "stragglers" from others—or whether they perhaps were formed in intergalactic space—is presently unknown.

The Local Group

Somewhat outside the Milky Way concentration, in fact extending to and including the nearest galaxy, the Great Nebula in Andromeda

---

*In illustration, consider a balloon covered with polka dots. As the balloon is inflated each dot moves away from each of its neighbors with a speed that is proportional to the distance between them. This is a two-dimensional analogy of the expansion of the three-dimensional Universe.

(which is about the size of our own), are to be observed a number of isolated star concentrations which, together with our own Galaxy, astronomers term the *local group*. Included are the star system of the Magellanic clouds, rather shapeless and relatively small galaxies visible only in the Southern Hemisphere, and some unnamed spiral nebulae totaling about 16 systems which are physically associated by gravitational attraction. The gravitational center of the whole complex lies somewhere between the Great Nebula in Andromeda and the Galaxy.

Features of the Galaxy

DIMENSIONS

Our own Galaxy (hereafter designated by Galaxy) is far more than a simple patterned agglomeration of stars. As noted previously, the stars are mostly concentrated in a lens-shaped volume. This concentration defines what is termed the "galactic plane." The distance across this plane from one side of the Galaxy to the other or the galactic diameter is estimated to be about 30,000 parsecs. The great majority of stars making up the Galaxy lie within a thousand parsecs or so of the galactic plane. Thus the Galaxy is roughly 15 times as wide as it is thick.

OPEN STAR CLUSTERS

Within the Galaxy are numerous local concentrations of stars termed "star clusters" or "star clouds." Star clusters are of two main types: *open* clusters and *globular* clusters. The former are loose, irregular assemblages; typical examples are easily visible clusters of the Pleiades and the Hyades in the constellation of Coma Bernices. Figure 3.3 shows an open cluster in the constellation of Cancer. Hundreds of such open clusters have been catalogued, the great majority within the Milky Way. Some open clusters contain only a few dozen stars; others may have several thousand with a wide range of brightness, or *magnitude*. The fact that a group of stars is truly a physical cluster and not a chance distribution of a number of stars at greatly differing distances along the same line of sight from the Earth is established by their proper motion through space; all members of a true physical (as contrasted to optical, or apparent) cluster will have about the same velocity through space.

Figure 3.3. Open Star Cluster in the Constellation Cancer. (Courtesy of Mount Wilson and Palomar Observatories.)

GLOBULAR STAR CLUSTERS

Globular star clusters are interesting objects, both for observation and for study. Only about 100 are known, and it is quite likely that that is about all there is in the Galaxy. A typical globular cluster is shown in Figure 3.4, and it will be noted that, in contrast to the open clusters already described, globular clusters are more symmetrical and may contain up to an estimated million or more stars concentrated in a sphere-shaped swarm. The central region or nucleus of most globular clusters is so crowded with stars that individual members often cannot be distinguished in the photographs. In contrast to the region of the Galaxy of our Solar System, in which the average distance between stars is several light years, stars in the nucleus of a globular cluster may be only a few light hours or days apart. If our solar system were in such a region, the night sky would be brilliant with dozens of stars showing perceptible disks to the unaided eye, each giving more light than the full moon. Many stars would also be visible in full daylight.

A very interesting feature of globular clusters is their distribution in space with respect to the Galaxy. As shown in Figure 3.5, they are observed to be fairly uniformly distributed throughout a roughly spherical or ellipsoidal volume, which is symmetrical about the galactic plane, in contrast to being concentrated in or near the galactic plane, as are the open clusters. Any theories of the origin of the Galaxy must take due account of the distribution and causes of the globular clusters. As individual systems, they pose interesting problems of formation and of the ultimate fate of the Galaxy. Some globular clusters are quite "open," or have very low central concentrations of stars as compared with others; does such a condition indicate

Figure 3.4. A Globular Star Cluster in the Constellation Hercules. (Courtesy of Mount Wilson and Palomar Observatories.)

Figure 3.5.   Galactic Distribution of Globular Clusters.

that the cluster is newly formed or of great age? Mutual attraction between various members would seemingly serve to increase the concentration of a cluster, but some astronomers hypothesize that open clusters may be very old, having lost stars by a process similar to evaporation.

GALACTIC NEBULAE

Lying close to or actually in the plane of our Galaxy are great clouds of unagglomerated dust and gas, high concentrations of which have been observed (see Figure 3.1). Some of these clouds are closely associated with and sometimes produced by nearby stars; others are relatively isolated in interstellar space. As a whole they are termed "galactic nebulae"* and three types are identified:

1. *Planetary Nebulae.* These nebulae are roughly circular in shape and have very distinct edges, causing them to resemble the telescopic

---

* Galactic nebulae and extragalactic nebulae are not to be confused. The former consist of clouds of dust or gas, the latter of star systems far beyond the limits of the Galaxy. The term "nebulae" (from latin *mist* or *cloud*) was applied to both astronomical objects before astronomers had established the existence of other stellar galaxies beyond our own.

images of planets in the Solar System. However, the nebulae are clearly not solid bodies like the planets (see Figure 3.6). The spectra of planetary nebulae are of the bright emission-line type, which is characteristic of a glowing gas. The shape and juxtaposition of these nebulae to stars strongly suggests that they may be shells of gas produced by star explosions, the luminescence being stimulated by ultraviolet radiation from a star within the shell. Spectroscopic analysis often shows the nebulae to be increasing in size, supporting the explosion theory.

An interesting feature of the planetary nebulae is that the advent or formation of several have been observed in recent time, one in 1901 and another in 1918. Both were faint and have since disappeared,

Figure 3.6. A Planetary Nebula in the Constellation Vulpecula. This is a "cloud" of glowing gas. (Photograph from the Mount Wilson and Palomar Observatories.)

Figure 3.7. The Ring Nebula in the Constellation Lyra, as photographed by the 200-inch telescope on Mount Palomar (compare with the planetary nebulae in Figure 3.6). (Photograph from the Mount Wilson and Palomar Observatories.)

the expanding gases having evidently blown away from the original stars and cooled beyond visibility. An intriguing aspect of planetary nebula is that one may appear at any hour among the stars in the neighborhood of the sun and make a most spectacular sight for many years.

Some planetary nebulae are of interesting appearance; for example the Ring Nebula" in the constellation of Lyra (see Figure 3.7) looks like a tiny smoke ring among the stars, even through a telescope of modest power. Actually, it is a spherical shell of glowing gas and is not torus-shaped; more light comes from the greater depth of gas at the edges of the shell, giving it the appearance of a ring.

2. *Diffuse Nebulae.* These nebulae have diffuse, ill-defined edges and are quite shapeless and irregular in appearance similar to a wind-

torn cloud (see Figure 3.8). They are thought to be clouds of dust illuminated by starlight. This hypothesis is supported by spectroscopic analysis which indicated that the light coming from them has the same characteristics as starlight, that is, a continuous spectrum with a number of dark absorption lines in it, produced by clouds of absorbing gas. If the nebulae consisted of incandescent solid particles such as might be produced by the collision of particles of iron, silicon, or carbon in space, their spectra would be continuous with no dark lines.

Figure 3.8. The Great Diffuse Nebula in the Constellation Orion. This object is clearly visible to the naked eye as a moderately bright slightly diffuse star. (Photograph from the Mount Wilson and Palomar Observatories.)

The diffuse nebulae can nearly always be associated with one or more stars in their neighborhood that are probably responsible for their illumination. However, their irregular shape and general appearance suggest that nothing more than chance brings the stars and nebulae together. That is to say, it is not believed that diffuse nebulae and the stars that illuminate them have an evolutionary association.

3. *Dark Nebulae.* These nebulae, as their name suggests, do not give off visible light and are identified only by their obscuration of more distant stars. The assumption that more distant stars are being obscured is based on the low probability that large, straight, starless "tubes" containing only our Solar System at one end exist in the Galaxy (no extragalactic nebulae are to be seen in dark nebulae either).

The dark nebulae (Figure 3.9) have posed interesting problems

Figure 3.9. Horsehead Nebula of Orion. A dark nebula ("The Horsehead") in the constellation of Orion is sharply outlined against a bright field of diffuse nebulosity. (Photograph from the Mount Wilson and Palomar Observatories.)

of composition, density, and nature for many years and there still exists considerable uncertainty about some of their features. Because their presence is revealed only by their obscuring power, the powerful tool of spectroscopic analysis by which the chemical nature of a glowing gas and the radial velocity of luminescent sources may be determined is rendered useless. Such nebulae are sufficiently tenuous that stars may be faintly seen through them; some inference concerning their concentration or density may be drawn by comparing the number and brightness of the stars that are visible with stars in fields of comparable but unobscured regions of the sky. (The comparability of the fields of various stars is based partly on assumptions of symmetry of galactic shape and partly on the uniform distribution of stars over reasonably small areas of the sky.) By such techniques conclusions have been drawn that the dark nebulae must in general be extremely tenuous, probably containing not more and sometimes considerably less than about a ton of finely divided solid matter or gas in a volume of the nebulae equal to that of the Earth.

This amount of matter per unit volume is a "harder" or higher vacuum that can be produced in the laboratory. Dark nebulae are able to obscure bright areas because they are so vast. Several are known to be several parsecs in extent, or much larger than our whole solar system. It has been hypothesized that these nebulae may be stars in the process of formation; that is, the dust and gases of such clouds could be in the process of compression by virtue of the pressure of starlight (and other wavelengths of electromagnetic radiation) shining on them from all sides. The reasoning may be illustrated by considering only two particles of dust or atoms of gas some distance apart between two stars—the particles and stars all lying in the same line. Each star would exert stronger, repelling radiation pressure on the particle nearest to it, so that each star would push or accelerate the particle nearest to it toward the other particle. As the two particles drift toward each other, their mutual attraction by the force of gravity (assisted by electrostatic force, perhaps) would increase and function to bring them close together or into actual contact. The same compressive action operating on particle pairs or systems throughout the nebulae working on all sides could thus, conceivably, in time produce one or several stars in the same region. It is hypothesized that the solar system evolved from such a dust cloud.

The Characteristics of Stars

TYPE AND MAGNITUDE

The stars of the Galaxy, estimated to be perhaps 30 billion in number, vary greatly in size, brightness, surface temperature, color, probable age, and other respects. With reference to size, some stars are known that are about the size of the Earth. Others, notably the red giant Antares in the constellation of Scorpio, if placed in the position of the sun would extend beyond the orbit of Mars; that is, it has a diameter of more than 284 million miles. It is interesting to note that the mean density of Antares is so low— 1/10,000 of sea level atmospheric pressure on Earth—that it would make a good vacuum for electric light bulbs.

Astronomers type stars according to certain characteristics. At one end of the classification are those of very high surface temperature, the blue stars, at the other are the relatively cool stars, the red giants. Many interesting studies have been made to determine relationships between a star's type and some of its properties. In some cases readily anticipated relationships have been found, as, for example, between probable age and type. However, some relationships are quite surprising. For example, an apparent relationship exists between star type and its average velocity toward (or away from) the solar system. It would appear that the hotter stars are moving more slowly toward (or away from) us than the cooler stars.

As yet to be integrated into the star types are the so-called *radio stars*, which emit strong radiation at radio wavelengths. Their place in the theory of stellar evolution is still not clear.

The brightness, or *magnitude*, of a star is of considerable interest and importance in many astronomical studies. Clearly, some stars are visually brighter than others in the sky, but this is usually because they are closer to the solar system than others. A star's brightness, as seen or photographed from Earth, is called its *apparent* or *photographic* magnitude. To determine the *true* relative brightness or *absolute magnitude* of stars, it is necessary to establish their apparent magnitude at the standard (and arbitrary) distance of 10 parsecs. If the distance, or more directly the parallax, of a star is known and its apparent magnitude is measured, the absolute magnitude M is a simple calculation:

$$M = m + 5 + 5 \log P,$$

where $P =$ the parallax of the star in seconds of arc,

  $m =$ the apparent magnitude.

As this formula indicates, if a star is more than 10 parsecs distant $P < \frac{1}{10}$), its absolute magnitude will be a smaller number than its apparent magnitude and can even be a negative number. By agreement astronomers have defined the "unit" of magnitude as 2.512; that is, a star of the first magnitude is 2.512 times as bright as a star of the second magnitude, $(2.512 \times 2.512 =)$ 6.32 times as bright as a star of the third magnitude, and so on. This seemingly awkward factor or unit works out, however, to make a first-magnitude star just 100 times (2.512^5) as bright as a sixth-magnitude star, which is about the magnitude of the faintest stars visible to the unaided eye on a clear dark night. The brightest stars in the sky are about of the first magnitude. This, of course, excepts our *own* star, the sun, which has an *apparent* magnitude of -26.7. Its *absolute* magnitude, however, is only $+4.7$, and if removed to a distance of 10 parsecs it would be a very inconspicuous star in the sky.

VARIABLE STARS

Careful observation of the brightness or luminosity of stars over a period of weeks and months reveals that a large number of them exhibit periodic variations in magnitude. The physical processes involved are unknown. It may be that such stars are continuously going through a cycle of expansion and collapse; during expansion, which would be a virtual explosion, the outer shell of gas would cool in rising from the star because of reduction of pressure and increasing distance from the hotter, more central regions. During collapse these processes would be reversed and the shell would grow hotter. The variation of luminosity and other pertinent characteristics with time of a number of variable stars is consistent with this explanation, but it does not serve for all. The study of variable stars is a highly interesting branch of astronomy and one which would be greatly assisted if our sun were also a variable star—assuming that life on Earth would be possible under the circumstances.

One very important class of variable stars is termed "Cepheid" variables. It has been deduced that the absolute magnitude of stars of this kind is directly proportional to the frequency of their light variations; that is, a Cepheid variable, which reaches maximum brightness every six days has a lower absolute magnitude than one that reaches maximal brightness every ten days. This fact is extremely useful, for it enables astronomers to determine the distance of star systems, such as open clusters, in which Cepheids can be identified. For example, if a Cepheid in a distant system is one tenth as luminous as one with the same period whose distance is already known, the fainter Cepheid must be about ten times more distant, assuming that all Cepheids with the same period have the same absolute magnitude.

BINARY STAR SYSTEMS

Many pairs of stars appear to be very close together in the night sky merely because they lie in nearly the same direction as viewed from the Earth; these are termed *optical pairs*. However, more than 25,000 star pairs, triplets, and higher number groups are known to be physically associated systems in that gravity links them together, that is, the stars are close enough together to be orbiting around each other. These multiple-star systems occur in a wide variety of star sizes, colors, and luminosities. In some systems one of the members may give no detectable light; in others the companions may be of equal luminosity. Some binary and trinary systems have been discovered by spectroscopic observation; that is, although the members may be so close together that telescopes show them only to be a single point of light, spectroscopic analysis shows a periodic movement of one light source toward and another away from the earth. These systems are termed *spectroscopic binaries*.

In a binary star system in which the two members are of equal mass they will orbit in a common plane about a point that represents the center of gravity of the system midway between their centers. If the masses are unequal, the center of gravity about which the members orbit will be closest to the more massive member but the orbits will still be coplanar.

If, by chance, the solar system including our earth also lies in or close to the orbital plane of a binary star system, we may observe what is called an *eclipsing binary* star system. Such systems are most readily observed when both members of the system are about the same size and one member is much less luminous than the other. The time-luminosity curve of such systems is distinctive: the luminosity as observed from earth will be constant for a period of hours, days, or weeks; then for a few hours or so it will decrease sharply and as suddenly return to its original value. This is readily explained. If the stars take a few weeks to circle about the center of mass, their light will radiate earthward without interruption during this

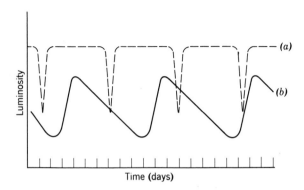

Figure 3.10. Time-Luminosity Curves: (a) eclipsing binary; (b) cepheid variable star.

interval. Then, for a few hours—like the moon eclipsing the sun—the darker member will partly or completely block the light of the bright member and a deep valley will appear in the time-luminosity curve.

The time-luminosity curve of eclipsing binary systems is entirely different from that of Cepheid variables, which is more sinusoidal or "sawtooth" in character. The variation in luminosity of a typical eclipsing variable and a Cepheid variable is illustrated in Figure 3.10.

NOVAE

From time to time throughout the Universe a star will suddenly "explode." This event is detected by a sudden tremendous increase in brightness of the star, following which it slowly decreases in brightness over a period of a decade or so, sometimes returning to the brightness it possessed before the event, sometimes growing even fainter. It was once hypothesized that the events resulting in novae were produced by a collision of stars; however, they are known to occur so frequently (more than 100 per year have been observed) and the probability of the collisions of stars is believed to be so small, that it is now theorized that the explanation must reside in the physical nature or structure of some stars.

SUPERNOVAE

A distinct class of exploding stars is termed "supernovae." These stars are about 10,000 times rarer than ordinary novae; apparently only a few, at most, occur in the Galaxy in each millennium. A supernova was recently (1964) reported near the bottom star nearest the handle in the bowl of the Big Dipper constellation. It is in another galaxy. Supernovae are distinguished by their extreme brilliance; historical accounts tell of their visibility in full daylight. This means a luminosity equal to or exceeding the planet Venus at its brightest. Supernovae may be considered perhaps the most dramatic events in the Universe. Their cause may only be speculated on, but it probably involves a sudden and wholesale conversion of mass to energy which is then released in the form of radiation not unlike a nuclear explosion. Some idea of their brightness is conveyed by the fact that when supernovae are observed in other distant galaxies their luminosity may exceed that of the galaxy itself, which is the total light of the millions of stars of which it is composed.

3.3   THE PHYSICS OF SPACE

Introduction

Having outlined the general structure and constituent members of the Solar System, Galaxy, and Universe, attention may now be focused on the nature of space in the region of influence of the sun. Quite obviously, knowledge of the physical conditions in this region is essential to the success of space travel. However, procurement of this knowledge is fraught with difficulties because of the tremendous effort required to send probes into space—which limits the number that can be sent—and the lack of basic knowledge needed to design suitable experiments. The discovery of the Van Allen Belts (which are described later) illustrates this point. A charged particle counter was carried into space by one of the early Explorer satellites. This counter was designed to measure what were theorized to be reasonable levels of radiation at some distance from the Earth. The actual radiation levels encountered by the satellite were so high that the counter went "off scale" and a different instrument had to be designed and injected into space to determine the conditions. In exploring space we are in the position of a man who is preparing to venture outside an air-conditioned house for the first time in his life to make a long journey that nobody has ever made before. We live, very descriptively, on an air-conditioned planet. Out atmosphere not only maintains temperatures within livable bounds but also affords us protection from harmful radiation from the sun and cosmos and from being continually bombarded by tiny but nonetheless injurious meteors.

Although seemingly quite empty, Solar-System space is pervaded with matter, radiation, and force fields of several kinds. By virtue of the proximity of the sun, planets, and comets, these phenomena are undoubtedly present to a greater degree within the solar system than in interstellar space. By the same token, these phenomena are present to a higher degree in interstellar than in intergalactic space.

In the remainder of this chapter these various phenomena are discussed—their nature, distribution or variation within the solar system, and their general influence on space travel.

Matter in Space

Matter can exist in three different forms or phases in space: solid, liquid, and gas. Because the liquid phase of any element or substance is attained only within a relatively narrow pressure and temperature range, matter in the liquid form is probably quite rare in space. As in the Earth's atmosphere (which we may consider as a special and important region of space), where liquid H_2O molecules are observed in clouds and raindrops, other planets may have partly liquid atmospheres, although the liquid may not necessarily be water. Beyond the limits of the planetary atmospheres it is probable that matter in the liquid state does not exist more than temporarily.

Gas

Matter in the gaseous phase pervades all of space, albeit the range of concentration or density is enormous. Molecules and atoms of gas are attracted by gravity toward massive bodies such as the sun and planets; accordingly, these bodies have higher concentrations of gas, or *atmospheres*, surrounding them. Gravitational force serves to compress the lower layers by virtue of the mass of gas at higher levels. The density, therefore, decreases gradually with increasing distance from the main body, and it may be accurately stated that the atmospheres of the sun and all the planets actually merge with each other. In some cases the atmosphere of a planet may be so tenuous as to be utterly undetectable from the Earth, but every body in the Solar System doubtless has at least a few atoms of gas accompanying it on its orbit around the sun.

Detection and identification of gas in space beyond our own atmosphere is primarily accomplished by means of spectroscopic analysis. Relatively cool gas in space will absorb electromagnetic radiation passing through it at wavelengths depending on the nature of the gas. By this means we know that the sun has a gaseous atmosphere composed of nearly all the elements known on Earth. Detection and identification of gas in interplanetary and interstellar space is a more difficult matter, for the absorption of the space gas has to be distinguished from the absorption by the atmosphere of the luminary and also the Earth's atmosphere. Hydrogen is the most abundant gas in space, and in 1963 the first molecular fragment, hydroxyl (OH), was discovered after a very complex analysis of radio signals of 18-cm wavelength emitted by certain stars.

The Earth's lower atmosphere is a well-mixed combination of gases whose relative abundances are given in Table 3.3. Ozone, O_3, is the only gas (with the exception of water vapor) that is not uniformly distributed throughout the lower 100 kilometers of the atmosphere. Ozone is created by the action of the sun's ultraviolet radiation on oxygen and is fairly sharply concentrated in a layer about 20 kilometers above the Earth's surface. At very high levels the lightest gases, hydrogen and helium, become more abundant than they are in the lower atmosphere.

Table 3.3.   Gases of the Terrestrial Atmosphere

Gas	Molecular Weight	% by Volume
Nitrogen (molecular)	28	78
Oxygen (molecular)	32	21
Argon	40	0.9
Carbon dioxide	44	0.03
Neon	20	0.002
Helium	4	0.0005
CH_4, Kr, N_2O, H_2, O_3, Xe		0.0004
A very important constituent, water vapor, is variable in amount		
Water vapor, H_2O	18	1 to 0.1

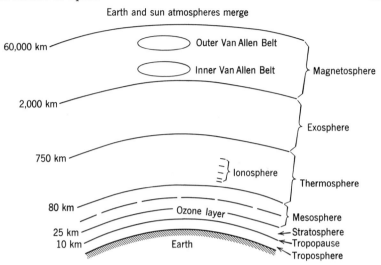

Figure 3.11.   Nomenclature of the Earth's Atmosphere.

For convenience of discussion and study the Earth's atmosphere is divided into a number of concentric shells somewhat like an onion. The exact limits of these shells are not well defined and are somewhat controversial among meteorologists; even their nomenclature is variable. On the other hand, the classifications are quite useful, even though they are arbitrary.

One version of the atmospheric model is shown in Figure 3.11, and it is emphasized that this is an *average* not an exact, picture of the atmosphere. Also, the figure is not drawn on a linear but rather on a quasilogarithmic scale in the vertical. It will be seen that six layers or shells are identified:

1. *The Troposphere.*   Most of what we call weather such as clouds, fog, rain, and snow, occur in this region.

2. *The Stratosphere.*   This is a cloud-free region immediately above the troposphere, where the temperature changes very little with height. Only occasional violent thunderstorms penetrate this region.

3. *The Mesosphere.*   This region is characterized by a warming of the atmosphere with increasing height in its lower portion, partly because of the absorption of solar ultraviolet radiation by ozone.

4. *The Thermosphere.* This region contains the ionized layers of the *ionosphere* which reflect radio waves and make long-range communications between stations close to the surface possible.

5. *The Exosphere.* In this region the atmosphere has become so tenuous that the normal gas laws fail and the molecules have to be considered as if they were miniature ballistic missiles. Put another way, the distances through which molecules travel before colliding with one another are very large and the times of these collision-free modes are large compared with the collision modes, or "events."

6. *The Magnetosphere.* In this region the Earth's magnetic field rather than its gravitational field is the most important influence on certain phenomena. This region contains the polar aurora and the radiation belts to be described later. The outer region of the magnetosphere may be identified as a zone of perhaps 100-km thickness, on the outside on which charged particles are entirely under the influence of the sun and on the lower side of which particles are primarily under the influence of the Earth's magnetic field.

The atmosphere has no well-defined upper limit as does the surface of the ocean. Instead, as one ascends, the atmosphere gradually becomes thinner and less dense, although at several altitudes visible boundaries are created by the presence of smoke and dust particles concentrated there by convective currents. Visual evidence of the presence of the atmosphere 1000 miles and more above the Earth exists in the polar aurora, which are the gasses of the upper atmosphere excited by energetic charged particles produced by eruption or disturbances on the sun.

The Earth's atmosphere is both a help and a hindrance to the departing and returning astronaut. In launch operations it is a hindrance because of the viscous drag it exerts on the vehicle, the possibility of turbulence which may buffet his vehicle at high levels and cause it to drift off course, and the radiation hazards it presents in the magnetosphere. The atmosphere does offer a slight assist in the buoyant force it places on the vehicle which makes it weigh a little less than if no atmosphere existed. When returning to Earth, the viscosity of the atmosphere is quite helpful in slowing down the spacecraft. However, the energy released in this braking process acts to heat the spacecraft, and careful design is essential to avoid injurious or fatal heating.

At least at the present time, very favorable tropospheric weather conditions must exist at the launch, landing, and other key points around the Earth to help ensure the success of space missions.

The Earth is by no means the only planet known to have a sensible atmosphere. On Mars white cloudlike markings are seen to move in relation to the surface features. Photographs of the planet taken in red and blue light occasionally show differences that can be explained only by the presence of a differentially absorbing gaseous atmosphere. Mercury has no detectable atmosphere, although shifting markings have been reported by a few astronomers. The high temperature of its sunlit side—sufficient to melt lead—would presumably quickly boil off any atmosphere. On its dark side temperatures are too low to maintain a gas (it is believed that Mercury continually keeps the same face toward the sun). There may be a slight atmosphere created by gases escaping from the interior of Mercury, such as volcanoes and fumeroles, and by momentary contributions to its atmosphere created by meteors vaporized on impact with its surface.

Venus, on the other hand, certainly has some sort of atmosphere, although its composition is still uncertain. Venus supports clouds that are dense enough to prevent our visual observation of its surface, and it is extremely rich in carbon dioxide. The Mariner II satellite, which completed a Venus fly-by in December 1962, confirmed earlier observations made from Earth that Venus has very little water vapor in her atmosphere.

Mars, as already mentioned, apparently has an atmosphere somewhat like the Earth's in that it supports some kind of clouds and haze; these are not so extensive as to deny us a good view of the surface features. Low surface temperatures at Mars' equator (—35 to 45°C) would suggest an atmosphere with a very low water-vapor content; oxygen also seems to be lacking in the Martian atmosphere. Attempts have been made to formulate a meteorology as well as a climatology for Mars based on movements of what apparently are dust clouds. The atmosphere of Mars is quite thin by terrestial standards; the low mass of the planet could not retain an atmosphere as substantial as that possessed by the Earth. The main constituent of the Martian atmosphere is not known, but it is probably at least 50% nitrogen, with argon, carbon dioxide, and a trace of oxygen (less than 0.1%) making up the bulk of the remainder.

The major planets, Jupiter, Saturn, Uranus, and Neptune, have low visible disk temperatures (although their interiors are hot). In the case of Jupiter spectroscopic analysis reveals the presence of ammonia and methane gas. The radiation temperatures of Saturn and Uranus are so low that only methane can be detected; the ammonia is presumably frozen and not detectable spectroscopically. On Neptune methane would be in liquid form.

No atmosphere of any sort has been detected on Pluto, and it is doubtful that the low surface temperatures could support one.

In the upper atmosphere of the Earth and, as revealed by Mariner II, in space between the Earth and Venus (at least) gases exist in the form of dissociated charged particles composed chiefly of electrons and protons called *plasma*. The particles composing this plasma constantly stream outward from the sun with a speed varying between 200 and 500 miles per second. Mariner II reported their concentration between 10 and 20 per cubic inch.

PARTICULATE, SOLID MATTER

Although at much lower concentration of particles per unit volume than the gases, interplanetary and interstellar space is pervaded throughout with tiny solid particles which, for lack of more specific knowledge concerning their composition, astronomers and astrophysicists call "dust." The presence of relatively dense clouds of this dust, termed Dark and Diffuse Nebulae, in interstellar space has already been discussed. Direct observational and physical evidence of the presence of dust in the solar system is readily available. The Earth in its revolution around the sun sweeps up estimated tons of this dust each day; this is in part evidenced by the numerous meteors observable on any clear night. In addition, there is a phenomenon called the *Zodiacal Light*. This is a very faint diffuse cone of light visible on exceptionally clear nights rising from the point on the horizon where the sun has set (or will rise). The axis of the cone coincides with the direction of the sun's track across the sky viewed from the latitude of the observer. The spectrum of this light is that of scattered sunlight, indicating that its source must consist primarily of dust particles.

More tangible evidence of the presence of dust in space was obtained many years ago above 100 kilometers by means of appropriately instrumented rockets. The Mariner II Venus probe encountered a few particles in interplanetary space, at concentrations of about 0.01 per cent of those observed near the Earth.

Deprived of the powerful tool of spectral analysis—for the particles scatter sun and starlight alike, irrespective of their composition—it is not possible to make statements concerning the precise nature of this dust. Some clue may be gleaned from the study of the composition of meteorites. The abundance of elements found in representative sample runs iron, 72 per cent, oxygen, 10 per cent, nickel, 6 per cent, silicon, 5 per cent, magnesium, 4 per cent, and traces (less than 1 per cent each of other elements) in the remainder. No new elements have been found in meteorites, although tiny diamonds have been reported. Considerable effort has been made to detect traces of organic matter in meteorites, which would constitute direct evidence of extraterrestrial life, but, because the chances of contamination by exposure to the terrestrial atmosphere and surface in which biological life abounds are so great before recovery, considerable uncertainty attends the results when they are apparently positive.

In the Earth's atmosphere dust and smoke particles are carried by the winds from the surface and pervade the troposphere. The temperature inversion at the tropopause suppresses the convective currents which would otherwise carry much dust into the stratosphere. Occasional violent thunderstorms and volcanic eruptions from time to time inject solid particles into this region. Very recent observation with *lidars*—a radarlike device employing light produced by lasers— suggests at least two dust layers high in the Earth's upper atmosphere near 90 and 140 kilometers.

CHARGED PARTICLES AND RADIATION BELTS

Charged or ionized particles, primarily ions of gas, are constantly streaming outward from the sun in all directions. Their flux is not perfectly constant, but solar flares and eruptions on the sun can temporary increase the streaming—sometimes termed the *solar wind*—by large amounts. Evidence exists that disturbances on the sun sometimes eject charged particles in a single direction, like the jet of water streaming from the nozzle of a spinning lawn sprinkler. The first indication that such a jet may form is usually the detection of sunspot activity sometimes accompanied by localized intensely bright regions which flash up rather suddenly. These flashes are called *flares,* light from which takes about 8 minutes to reach the Earth. Some 17 to 19 hours following this, auroral activity commences and world-wide disturbances in the Earth's magnetic field occur. These phenomena may last for several days; thereafter things return gradually to normal. The elapsed time between the observation of the flare and commencement of terrestrial geophysical activity suggests that some form of corpuscular radiation travels from sun to Earth at speeds up to 2500 kilometers per second.

Such corpuscles, being of very small mass and traveling at high speeds, are little influenced by the Earth's gravitational field. On the other hand, being electrically charged, they are strongly influenced—and presumably many are captured—by the Earth's magnetic field which extends well into cis-lunar space. The rotation of this magnetic field, produced by the rotation of the Earth itself, causes the particles to follow complex paths as they weave back and forth from pole to pole through the magnetosphere.

The magnitude of a given subatomic, atomic, or molecular particle's mass, charge, and velocity when it encounters the Earth's magnetic field will control its future trajectory. Massive, fast-moving particles of cosmic origin, are little deflected and may pass directly down to Earth producing what are termed *cosmic rays.* Electrons, having negative charge, are deflected toward one magnetic pole, protons toward the other.

In some way that is not yet comprehended these charged particles concentrate themselves into torroidal or doughnut-shaped shells, or *belts,* around the earth. A cross section of the arrangement of these belts is shown in Figure 3.12. It will be noted that the belts are asymmetric with respect to the Earth, being somewhat compressed on the side of the sun. This recently discovered fact is believed to be produced by the "pressure" of the solar wind, which might be thought of as "blowing" the belts as the wind might blow and distort a soap bubble still adhering to its pipe.

The lower two radiation belts are commonly identified with the name of their discoverer, Dr. James A. Van Allen of the University of Iowa, who suggested the experiment and designed the instruments carried in early Explorer satellites which found them (see Chapter 2). These belts present a potential hazard to space travel in the radiation damage which they can cause to living tissue as well as to the electronic equipment in the spacecraft. Either extra protection in the form of shielding in the space ships must be provided or the ships will have to be launched from and return to a site near the Earth's poles, where the belts are not present.

The outer radiation zone indicated in Figure 3.12 was first announced early in 1964 and has not yet been named. This zone, disclosed by the IMP (Interplanetary Monitoring Platform) satellite, is apparently a hyperboloid-shaped shell with the open side away from the sun. The limits of the zone on the open side extend out at least 120,000 miles or 15 Earth diameters and may even extend as far as the moon, the mean distance of which is 239,000 miles from the Earth. On the solar side of the Earth the zone is about 54,000 miles or 7 Earth diameters above the Earth. The zone may, perhaps, be thought of as a sort of "shock wave" created by the encounter of the solar wind with the particles moving in the magnetosphere. Radiation levels in this zone are not believed to be intense enough to present such hazards to space travel as the radiation levels which are known to exist in the Van Allen Belts.

Man has created more or less temporary radiation belts by detonation of nuclear bombs in the upper atmosphere. Such bombs produce large numbers of charged particles which move through the atmos-

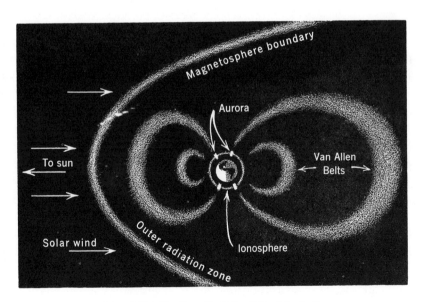

Figure 3.12. The Great Radiation Belts of the Earth.

phere just as do those of solar or cosmic origin. Artificial aurora are produced and radio communications are affected.

Force Fields

The phenomena of space are not limited to the various radiations and material to be found there. Extending throughout all space also are force fields of several different kinds which can impose accelerations of significant magnitude on spacecraft.

Gravitational Forces

Of primary concern in most problems of space travel is the force of gravity. This is a mysterious, natural attractive force which every body in the Universe has for every other. Any two bodies (or particles) attract each other with a force proportional to the product of their masses and inversely proportional to the square of the distances between them, or

$$F = G\,\frac{M_1 M_2}{d^2},$$

where M_1, M_2 = masses,

$\qquad G$ = force between unit masses at unit distance,

$\qquad d$ = distance between centers of gravity of the bodies.

It is this force that holds the planets in orbits around the sun, satellites, both natural and artificial, in orbits around their primaries, and raises the ocean tides.

The moon and spacecraft in orbit around the Earth may be considered to be in a state of free, continuous fall toward the Earth. The explanation of this statement is illustrated in Figure 3.13. Missiles are launched in a horizontal direction from a mountain top with different speeds. At lower speeds (trajectory A) the missile falls close to the base of the mountain; at higher speeds it reaches greater range (trajectory B). Given sufficient launching speed (orbit C), it may travel all the way around the Earth without hitting the surface. Of course, at very low levels the friction of the atmosphere will quickly slow the missile (or spacecraft), and when this happens the orbit has a curvature greater than the curvature of the surface of the Earth and the spacecraft will hit the surface. If the spacecraft is projected into orbit at a greater speed than that required just to circle the Earth, the resulting orbits will at first be elliptical with the center of the Earth at one focus (orbits D and E). Eventually, provided sufficient projective impulse is available, the spacecraft will have orbits which are parabolic or hyperbolic and will, after leaving the Earth, travel off into space indefinitely. When the Mariner II satellite was launched toward Venus, it was first put into a so-called "parking orbit" which was circular several hundred miles above the surface of the Earth. Calculations were then quickly made to determine the precise point in the orbit at which the spacecraft should be given a second impulse which, taking advantage of the orbital speed it already possessed, would start it traveling toward the orbit of Venus. This was accomplished and, after the space vehicle had been on its way for several months and its orbit—then around the sun—had been accurately determined, it was given a slight additional acceleration to correct its orbit so that it would rendezvous with Venus at the proper time. After about 110 days out of the Earth the satellite passed within 22,000 miles of the surface of Venus. It was going so fast at that time—13,000 miles per hour toward Venus, 86,000 miles per hour around the sun, and 39,000 miles per hour away from the Earth—that it was not captured by the gravitational field of Venus but continued on to orbit around the sun like a miniature planet or asteroid. Other aspects of orbits and trajectories are discussed in Chapter 4.

After being boosted into orbit, whether around the Earth, the moon, or the sun, with the spacecraft motors turned off, the ship and all the objects within it are in a weightless state, or similar to a state of free fall. This weightlessness presents some of the most intriguing

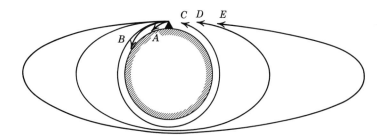

Figure 3.13.   Trajectories of Projectiles and of Satellite Orbits.

questions of space travel, some of which may take years to answer. The solutions to some of the problems of weightlessness have been relatively straightforward. Dry foods may be eaten from the hand, liquids obtained from collapsible tubes, and most tools (wrenches, pliers, screwdrivers, etc.) can be used while the astronaut is strapped in a seat or with minor redesigns to avoid external torque forces.

The prolonged orbital flights by the Russian and American astronauts have demonstrated that human beings can survive and even tolerate the weightless state for at least a few days with no *immediately* obvious ill effects. It remains to be determined whether short-period exposure to the weightless state has long-range effects, such as rendering certain parts of the body more prone to infection, or that extended periods of weightlessness have no immediate or long-range ill effects. Because the human frame is "engineered" to withstand continuously the force of gravity, subtle difficulties may arise in the extended weightless state such as troubles with digestion, blood circulation, deterioration of muscle tone, or even with bone structure. Only experience will reveal whether man can eat, excrete, reproduce, and work and think effectively for indefinite periods of weightlessness; if not, some substitute for gravity must be found. A sort of artificial gravity can be created in a space ship by spinning it, but whether this solution is an entirely satisfactory one remains to be seen. These and similar aspects are discussed further in Chapter 5.

RADIATION PRESSURE

A second force field which spacecraft experience is produced by electromagnetic and corpuscular radiation. The sun, the primary source of this radiation in the solar system, radiates most energetically in the visible region of the electromagnetic spectrum, so that a convenient designation of this force is "light pressure." Solar corpuscular radiation, or "solar wind," has already been described.

Although gravity is an attracting force, radiation pressure is a repellant force; that is, although bodies are attracted to the sun by gravity, they are, at the same time, repelled by the radiation it emits. Whereas gravitational attraction is proportional to the masses of the bodies involved, radiation pressure is proportional to the exposed *area* of a body and the intensity of the radiation. Both forces become weaker with increasing distance between the bodies involved.

For relatively large massive bodies such as spacecraft the attracting force of gravity of the sun greatly exceeds the repelling force of its electromagnetic and corpuscular radiation. However, on bodies which have a very large surface area and relatively low mass, such as extensive sheets of thin metal film, radiation pressure may be stronger than gravity. It has been suggested that space ships may be able to exploit the force of radiation pressure in traveling away from the sun by spreading huge "sails" of thin metal film to catch the sunlight. This would be practical in space, since the weightless and dragless state of the sails and the relatively weak pressure of radiation would enable the erection of vast surfaces with almost no supporting structure required.

MAGNETIC FIELDS

The magnetic fields of the Earth and sun (Mariner II revealed that Venus has little or no magnetic field) comprise the third type of force which will be of significance in space travel. Many features of the sun's and Earth's magnetic fields are still not understood, especially with respect to the phenomenology of solar flares. The Earth's magnetic field, which is shaped much like the Van Allen Belts shown in Figure 3.12, is demonstrably related to sunspot activity, but not all sunspots appear to influence it.

The manner in which magnetic fields may be exploited in space travel is not entirely clear. For astrogation the sun and stars would seem to be entirely adequate because they are fixed and always visible. The presence of the Earth's magnetic field has been employed in meteorological satellite systems to control the orientation of the axis about which such satellites are spun for stabilization—somewhat like a gyroscope: a coil of wire is inserted in the satellite and an electric current induced in it at desired times. The current creates a magnetic field around the coil of wire and this field interacts with the Earth's magnetic field, causing the spin axis of the satellite to shift to a new direction in space.

3.4 CONCLUSION

From the foregoing it should be quite clear that space is complex, that it is filled with actual and potential hazards, and that it presents a challenge of the first magnitude to mankind. To some extent that age of exploration of space may be likened to the earlier age of exploration of the world. Long before the availability of radio communications and navigational aids men of courage ventured into uncharted oceans, depending largely on their wits, skill, and nerve to survive and get back home again. The same thing is happening again today, for the first men to set foot on the moon will be as cut off from direct human aid in the case of difficulty as were Magellan, Amundsen, Columbus, and many other explorers who turned their backs on home to seek what lay beyond the horizon.

CHAPTER 4

Orbits and Trajectories:
Their Mechanics and Control

Daniel B. DeBra

Lockheed Missiles and Space Company*

* Presently at Stanford University.

Contents

Orbits and Trajectories:
Their Mechanics and Control

4.1 SCIENTIFIC DEVELOPMENT

Introduction

The history of orbital motion is perhaps the most interesting and enlightening example of the evolution of the scientific method we have. The phenomenon of seeing sun, stars, and our moon in motion is familiar enough so that a statement of the problem is meaningful even though the solution is not apparent. In retrospect, the many years of observation and inadequate theories seem a comical period, though if one really starts without knowledge or instruments the observation problem alone is formidable. The undisciplined lack of objectivity—basic to theories which placed the Earth at the center of the Universe—is an example of the unscientific beginning of the subject. Some of the principal personalities are colorful and their contributions in other fields warrant additional attention to their lives.

The Scientific Method

All of our physical laws are expressions that unify many observations into a single statement of behavior. For example, Hooke's law of elasticity states that elastic materials (e.g., springs) exert a force proportional to their deflection. The law holds for big springs, little springs, red ones, and black ones. The law is a statement of the fact that after observing many springs being pushed and pulled they all exhibited this property. In order to have observed this, measurements must have been made, and there is always some inaccuracy in making any measurement. So our laws are a statement of our experience and are valid only to the accuracy to which we were able to observe and under the conditions of the observation. For example, if we stretch a coil spring far enough, the turns open and eventually the spring appears as a straight piece of wire. It then takes a great deal more force to get additional extension than it did when the spring was still coiled. Therefore Hooke's law does not apply when the forces or extensions get too great. When a physical law is extrapolated, tests must be made again to ensure that the law will still hold with the accuracy of observation for the new conditions.

The scientific method then is basically one involving three steps:

1. The observation of the phenomenon.
2. The guessing of theories (trial laws).
3. The verification of the law by quantitatively comparing observed values with those predicted by the theory.

The last step must be continually repeated as accuracy of observation improves. If discrepancies are found, the whole process is repeated. When a new law is found, the old theory frequently is not completely discarded, but rather it is modified or improved.

The success of the scientific method depends a great deal on the objectivity of the observer. He must state his observations in as cold and factual a form as possible. He must avoid implications about what is observed and why it occurs or he may inject ideas that mask the truth and hinder the discovery of the laws involved.

Evolution of Celestial Mechanics

CELESTIAL OBSERVATIONS

The ancients looked at the sky and observed that all of the heavenly bodies moved overhead. They were not objective enough to recognize this as relative motion and stated that the heavens moved, a conclusion that helped to keep theories on the natural order of "fire over water" in good stead for centuries. The slow movement of the bodies in the solar system in relation to the stars finally paved the way for Copernicus (1473–1543) to propose that the planets moved about the sun. This proposition was not met with great favor, for it contradicted the dogma of the contemporary church which taught a geocentric universe.

Gradually, as the sun was accepted as the center of the solar system, more accurate measurements were needed to improve the theory of planetary motion. This was made possible by an egotistical nobleman, Tycho Brahe (1546–1601), whose interest, influence, and mechanical ability made it possible to design and build accurate instruments and to assemble the necessary data and complete the observations which were needed to deduce the orbital shapes and behavior.

THE THEORIES OF KEPLER

Johan Kepler (1571–1630), who worked with Tycho Brahe for many years, tried innumerable theories before he enunciated his famous laws of planetary motion. These laws are a monument to his industry, for the amount of calculation necessary to test each theory was prodigious. Kepler's determination is all the more impressive when it is realized that his work was accomplished in spite of monetary, political and personal misfortune. After six years of incessant calculation he published his first two laws in 1609.

> Kepler's first law: Planets move in ellipses with the sun at one focus.
>
> Kepler's second law: The radius vector (or line joining the sun and planet) sweeps out equal areas in equal times.

He continued his work and finally announced his third law in 1618.

> Kepler's third law: The square of the time it takes each planet to revolve around the sun is proportional to the cube of its mean distance from the sun.

In order to understand the implication of these laws and how they may be used in astronautics, it is essential to be familiar with the laws of motion that were being developed during the same era.

THE LAWS OF MOTION

During the time when Kepler was trying to fit theories to the observations made by Tycho Brahe, Galileo (1564–1642) was busy compiling a body of observations of the motions of bodies in our own terrestrial environment. It was not fully appreciated at that time that celestial and terrestrial motions are subject to the same laws. Kepler, on the one hand, was concerned with finding laws which described the nature of planetary orbits. He was not trying to state why the bodies moved that way. Galileo, on the other hand, was interested in the cause of motion. From his extensive research he observed a common quantity which we now call momentum. It is the product of mass and velocity. Although Galileo recognized certain properties of motion and apparently understood the basic behavioral

laws, it took the genius of Sir Isaac Newton (1642–1727) to see
the simplicity of motion and to express it all in his three basic
laws of motion.

Newton's first law: If no force acts on a body in motion, it con-
                      tinues to move uniformly in a straight line.

Newton's second law: If a force acts on a body, it produces a
                     change of motion proportional to the force
                     and in the same direction.

Newton's third law: When one body exerts a force on another,
                     the second body reacts with equal force on
                     the first.

For several hundred years following the statement of these laws
the accuracy with which we could make our observations and the
range of physical phenomena that we observed revealed only one
anomalous behavior which could not be described by these laws. This
was the precession of the perihelion of the planet Mercury. The
perihelion of a planet is the point at which it comes closest to the
sun. If the planet moved in a perfect ellipse, the perihelion would
remain fixed in space. The orbit of each planet is disturbed by
the gravity of other planets, and so their ellipses change very slowly.
These changes can be predicted from our knowledge of the other
planets, but in the case of Mercury there was a small but significant
discrepancy. The perihelion of Mercury moved more than could be
explained by Newton's laws of motion.

As the interest in atomic physics led to observation of particles
at higher and higher velocities, additional discrepancies appeared.
Newton's laws were inadequate, and it was Albert Einstein
(1879–1953) who provided the necessary modification with the theory
of relatively to extend our understanding into this new region. It
should be emphasized again that an inadequate theory is often
not thrown away when new regions of application are found for
which it does not apply, but rather it remains useful within the
now restricted region in which experimental verification exists.
This is perhaps the whole crux of the scientific method that our
physical laws are just empirical tools for understanding and predicting
behavior within the regions of experience from which they were deduced. To the accuracy needed in almost all astronautics, Newton's
laws suffice as the tools for describing motion.

THE LAW OF GRAVITY

Kepler stated how the planets moved. Newton's laws of motion gave the basis for understanding the way a body moved. It remained to state what forces existed that would be consistent with the motions Kepler observed. Newton supplied the answer when he verified by calculation that an inverse square law force was consistent with the elliptical path the planets had been observed to follow. He perceived that this force was the same as the gravity force that caused apples to fall from trees and so he stated the law of gravitation: bodies attract each other in proportion to the product of their masses and inversely proportional to the distance between them squared.

Newton had to overcome the prejudice that existed at the time against the notion that forces could act at a distance. He was also troubled by the difficulty in proving that a uniform spherical body acted as if all of its mass were concentrated at its center. He was not satisfied with proving the law explaining the elliptical motion of the planets; he waited many years until he had calculated the motion of the moon accurately and was able to show that the force of gravity, which can be measured on the Earth, was the right magnitude to explain lunar motion.

In teaching, one cannot afford the luxury of guiding each student over the sinuous paths of unsuccessful experimentation that eventually leads to the development of a correct physical law. The desirable aspect of teaching our physical laws by the description and development of their historical derivation is that it emphasizes the application and significance of scientific method. A more efficient teaching method of a phenomenon is to state a theory and explain the phenomenon with examples. Because this occasionally loses sight of the scientific method that was responsible for our understanding, supplemental historical reading is important.

4.2 ORBITAL MECHANICS

Introduction

The heavenly bodies have been observed by man for centuries. The motion of these bodies presented puzzles in understanding that were partly responsible for the evolution of scientific thinking and principles.   The long history of astronomy gives us a body of knowledge that applies directly to the understanding of orbital mechanics for space travel.

Orbital mechanics, governing the motion of all heavenly bodies and man-made spacecraft alike, determines the trajectories or orbits that a spacecraft must follow to reach its target; and it determines the velocities and directions that must be imparted to the spacecraft so that it can reliably follow that course.

This chapter describes in general the theoretical background for trajectory determination and for the maneuverability required to attain and change velocities and attitudes—in other words, *what* it is that must be functionally available.   Chapter 6 describes in general *how* position determinations, velocity, and attitude measurements can be made—in other words, the equipment available to achieve and maintain the desired course or trajectory.

Guidance, attitude control, and some definitions of concepts are briefly introduced here.   In the subsequent sections of this chapter orbital maneuvers and ascent requirements are discussed.   Finally, this material is illustrated by a description of the remarkable flight of the Mariner II, the first American Venus mission.

ORBITAL MOTION

An orbit or trajectory is the path a body follows.   The term orbit usually refers to the path a body follows when it is moving under

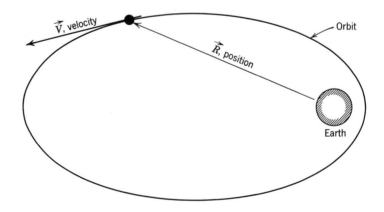

Figure 4.1.   Orbital Motion about Earth.

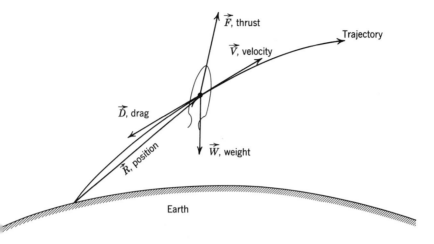

Figure 4.2.   Motion and Principal Forces on a Trajectory.

the influence of a set of natural forces. For example, the moon moves around the Earth in a path called its orbit (see Figure 4.1). When there are other forces acting, such as rocket thrust, aerodynamic drag, etc., the path is more often referred to as a trajectory (see Figure 4.2).   (The arrows above the symbols in the figures indicate vector quantities, which are explained on p. 125.)

The motion of a body is described by stating the position $\vec{R}$, (where it is) and the velocity $\vec{V}$ (how fast and in what direction it is going). Orbital motion is therefore described by the position and velocity of a body in an orbit, as shown in Figure 4.1.   The techniques used to analyze orbital motion and to relate the forces and the motion are called orbital mechanics.   Before discussing orbital mechanics it is necessary to define some terms, and it will help to discuss some of the functions of guidance.

GUIDANCE AND ATTITUDE CONTROL

A mission with a missile or a spacecraft is usually stated in very general terms, such as getting from one point to another or arriving at a location with a certain speed. These requirements must then be translated into the details of how this should be done. A trajectory must be chosen and a method of guiding the vehicle must be developed so that the trajectory can be followed.

The velocity changes that are needed in space flight affect only the translational motion of the vehicle. However, the propulsion system is usually fixed in the space vehicle, and in order to produce the velocity change required in the desired direction it is necessary to have the vehicle properly oriented. Translation and rotation are related only when forces relate them. In this case the force that changes the velocity comes from the rocket engine which is part of the vehicle. It therefore depends on the orientation of the vehicle and cannot be considered independently. Since this is generally true, guidance and attitude control work are always interrelated.

The automatic control systems which are used to orient the vehicle are illustrated in the last section of this chapter. Basically, once the desired orientation is given it is compared with the actual orientation of the spacecraft, which is determined by sensors. The difference is the error signal used to actuate the vehicle torquers, such as reaction jets; this signal is processed through a controller to ensure that the control is stable. The torques are applied to reduce the orientation error and to reduce the angular velocity as the spacecraft approaches its desired orientation. This is called attitude control. It is depicted schematically in Figure 4.3. The equipment used is described in Chapter 6.

Guidance is a similar control process of determining an error from the desired conditions and producing a maneuver which corrects the situation. First the spacecraft position and velocity are determined. This process is called navigation. It can be performed in many ways, for example, by radio, radar, visual tracking, or through the use of inertial instruments that sense accelerations, etc. Mariners have for years used celestial navigation to determine the location of their ships at sea. A similar process can be performed in space. When the position and velocity are known, they are compared with the normal or desired trajectory and a decision can be made as to what action must be taken (e.g., change in velocity) to achieve the mission. During ascent this process usually occurs continuously, but in space the decision may be to wait for days before performing a maneuver, if one is needed. The controller in the guidance control system is sometimes very complicated and requires a sophisticated computer. This can be placed on the ground or in the spacecraft. Sometimes the best trajectory is determined before a flight and the spacecraft merely compares its position and velocity against the stored values of the desired position and velocity to determine the error. The error

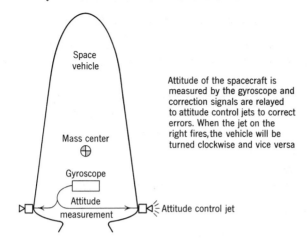

Attitude of the spacecraft is measured by the gyroscope and correction signals are relayed to attitude control jets to correct errors. When the jet on the right fires, the vehicle will be turned clockwise and vice versa

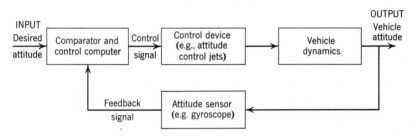

Figure 4.3.   Physical and Schematic Arrangement of Attitude Control.

is treated to determine the actuator commands which effect the proper maneuver.   One of these commands is to the attitude control system so that the propulsion system will act in the proper direction.   Another command is to the propulsion system to control the size or duration of the maneuver (velocity change).

Trajectory determinations, that is, specific analyses of orbital mechanics and maneuvers to remain on course, are described in subsequent sections of this chapter.   It is well to precede such discussion with a review of common quantities employed in such analyses; the definitions are therefore collected directly below.

DEFINITION OF CONCEPTS

Vectors.   When quantities have both direction and magnitude, it is convenient to call them *vector quantities* (or simply vectors) and to represent them by an arrow having the same direction and magnitude.

Position and velocity are vector quantities and are represented as such by placing a small arrow over the symbol (e.g., $\vec{V}$). It is not necessary to have skill with analysis of vectors to utilize them. The ideas they embody from our sensual experience are so natural that there is no reason why they should not be introduced conceptually.

Motion itself is called *kinematics*, whereas the relationship between motion and force is the study of *dynamics* or *kinetics*. Kinematics, like geometry, is the description of *position* and the manner in which position changes.

Velocity describes the rate at which *position* changes. In Figure 4.4 the position changes from the location at the head of the arrow $\vec{R_1}$ to the position indicated by $\vec{R_2}$ in the *time* $(t_2 - t_1)$. If the position changed uniformly, the average velocity would be in the direction of the arrow indicated by $\vec{V}(t_2 - t_1)$ and would have a magnitude great enough to cover the distance indicated by the length of the arrow in the time $(t_2 - t_1)$.

Acceleration, $\vec{A}$, is also a vector quantity and, as shown in Figure 4.4, it represents the average rate of change of the velocity vector. When the time difference $(t_2 - t_1)$ gets small, the average value of $\vec{V}$ is called simply the velocity and similarly, the average value of $\vec{A}$ is called the acceleration.

Force is not as easy a concept to visualize as position or velocity because we do not sense it visually. Our sensory awareness of force

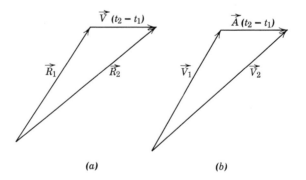

(a)   (b)

Figure 4.4. Kinematics: (a) velocity, the rate of position change; (b) acceleration, the rate of velocity change.

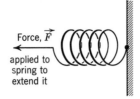

Force, $\vec{F}$ applied to spring to extend it

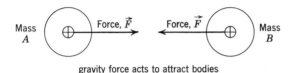

Mass A   Force, $\vec{F}$ Force, $\vec{F}$ Mass B

gravity force acts to attract bodies

Figure 4.5. Examples of Forces.

is through feel—we only see the effects of force, not the force itself. If we pull a spring, we apply a force to it, but we see only the elongation of the spring (Figure 4.5). Similarly we are aware of *gravity force* because we feel the weight of an object or we see the motion that results when an object falls. Because bodies attract each other wherever they are, the gravitational effect is like a field. When a mass is in the *gravity field* it experiences a gravity force. The laws of motion do not suggest causality but only state the relation that exists between force and acceleration.

Momentum is simply the velocity $\vec{V}$ of a particle multiplied by its mass m, or $\vec{M} = m\vec{V}$. Conceptually, it is important because it plays the key role in the statement of the laws of motion. The rate of change of momentum is proportional to force. When mass is constant, this law reduces to the statement that force is proportional to mass times acceleration, $\vec{F} = m\vec{A}$.

Motion is sometimes described about a center, or axis. When this occurs, it is frequently easier to represent some quantities in terms of the angular motion about the center. To represent a rotational quantity by a vector, the measuring of direction has to be redefined. Direction for rotational quantities is taken as the direction of the axis of rotation. The positive sense is defined by the right-hand

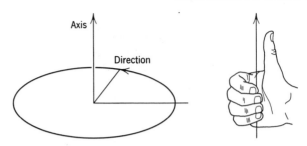

Figure 4.6.   Right-Hand Rule.

rule as shown in Figure 4.6.   The fingers of the right hand are pointed in the direction of rotation.   The resulting direction of the thumb is taken as positive.

In a closed orbit such as the motion of the moon about the Earth the motion can be described approximately as angular motion about the Earth.   The axis of rotation is perpendicular to the plane in which the moon revolves around the Earth.   *Angular momentum magnitude* is defined as the mass times the product of the radius and the component of velocity perpendicular to the radius (i.e., that part of the velocity which contributes to the motion around the center as opposed to the motion to and from the center).   Because angular momentum is a rotational quantity, it can be represented by a vector which has a direction given by the right-hand rule and a length equal to the angular momentum magnitude.   This is the orbital angular momentum vector (occasionally, but imprecisely, referred to as the orbital momentum vector).

The combining of two vectors to get a third which is perpendicular to them can be done by a type of vector multiplication called the *cross product*.   It is represented by a multiplication sign, $\times$.   By definition the cross product of $\vec{R}$ and $\vec{V}$ is $\vec{R} \times \vec{V}$ which has the magnitude

$$\left| \vec{R} \times \vec{V} \right| = RV \sin \beta.$$

As shown in Figure 4.7, a cross product has the direction given by the right-hand rule when the first vector is rotated into the second.   The direction of the axis of rotation is perpendicular to the position and

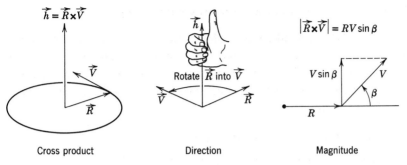

Figure 4.7. Cross Products of Vectors.

velocity vectors because they both lie in the plane of motion. There-fore, the angular momentum vector $\overrightarrow{h}$ can be represented as the cross product of $\overrightarrow{R}$ and $\overrightarrow{V}$ (for a unit mass).

$$\overrightarrow{h} = \overrightarrow{R} \times \overrightarrow{V}.$$

When a force acts about a center so that it causes a turning effect' the effect is called a moment or torque. As can be seen in Figure 4.8' the position vector and force form a plane and the turning effect can be represented by using the right-hand rule. Torque, $\overrightarrow{T}$, can there-fore also be represented by a cross product

$$\overrightarrow{T} = \overrightarrow{R} \times \overrightarrow{F}.$$

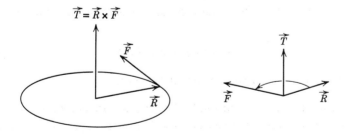

Figure 4.8. Torque as Cross Product of Position and Force.

Some Physical Concepts Used in Orbital Motion

The analytical solution for orbital motion can be quite complex. However, there are several physical concepts which are useful in many dynamic problems that allow us to discuss orbital motion qualitatively. These concepts are the conservation laws, which can be understood without proof.

Energy and Angular Momentum

When two bodies revolve around each other in orbits because of their mutual gravitational attraction, there is no energy dissipated as long as no other forces act. As one body moves away from the other, it slows down, but this loss of kinetic energy (KE) is stored as potential energy (PE) in the gravity fields; that is, the gravity force is conservative and the total energy, E, is constant:

$$E = \underbrace{\left(\frac{mV^2}{2}\right)}_{\text{KE}} + \underbrace{\left(-\frac{mk}{R}\right)}_{\text{PE}} = \text{constant,} \qquad (4.1)$$

where E = orbital energy,
$\quad V$ = orbital velocity,
$\quad m$ = mass of body in orbit,
$\quad R$ = orbital radius,
$\quad k$ = a constant of the gravitational field in which the body moves.

Similarly, in the absence of other forces the orbital angular momentum is constant because the gravity force acts through the center about which the body revolves and does not produce any moment or torque about it. The magnitude of the angular momentum, h, is constant:

$$h = mRV_\theta = \text{constant,} \qquad (4.2)$$

where V_θ = horizontal component of velocity.

This equation (see Figure 4.9a for graphic presentation) is sometimes called the law of areas because it also expresses the fact that equal areas are swept out by the radius vector in a given length of time, even though the length of the radius vector changes. Newton proved this to be true for any central force field; a graphic presentation is given in Figure 4.9b, in which equal areas are swept by the radius vector in equal times.

The energy and angular momentum specify the size and shape of an orbit. When the size and shape need to be changed, for example, when a spacecraft maneuvers, the changes in the energy and angular

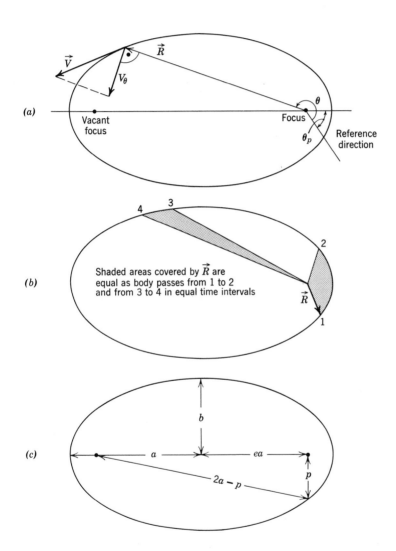

Figure 4.9. Orbital Motions and Areas; Parameters of Orbits: (a) vectors and coordinates describing orbital motion; (b) law of equal forces; (c) parameters defining orbits.

momentum are closely related to the radius and velocity and therefore make apparent the maneuvers that are possible.

ENERGY AND ANGULAR MOMENTUM CHANGES

The energy equation (Equation 4.1) contains a great deal of information about the size of an orbit. For example, V^2 is always a positive number and so is R. Therefore, unless the energy E is positive, it is not possible for R to become infinitely large (i.e., for k/R to become negligibly small). If a spacecraft is required to escape from the Earth, its speed must be at least great enough so that the kinetic energy term ($V^2/2$ in Equation 4.1) is at least as large as the potential energy magnitude (k/R). For a closed orbit the converse is true, that is, $V^2/2$ is smaller than k/R.

The size of an orbit can be given by any of the parameters shown in Figure 4.9c. The one most simply related to the orbital energy is the semimajor axis of the orbit, a. The relationship is

$$2a = \frac{-k}{E}. \qquad (4.3)$$

This relationship is shown in the graph of Figure 4.10. The curve slopes upward to the right, that is, the higher the speed, the larger the semimajor axis at a given radius, R.

The angular momentum, h, is also related to size. An increase in

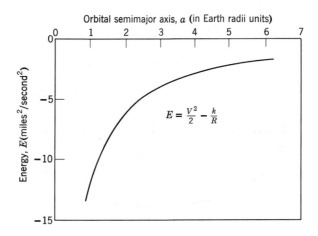

Figure 4.10. Orbital Semimajor Axis as a Function of Orbital Energy.

the component of velocity perpendicular to the radius increases the angular momentum. As we have just seen, an increase in speed increases the orbit size. The measure of size most simply related to the angular momentum is the semilatus rectum, p, which is also shown in Figure 4.9c. The relation between h and p is

$$p = \frac{h^2}{k}. \tag{4.4}$$

The size and shape of an ellipse are determined if a and p are given. Therefore the size and shape of an orbit is determined if E and h are given. Changes in E and h can now be directly related to how the orbit will change, and because E and h each clearly displays its dependence on velocity, this establishes a basis for understanding how a rocket can maneuver a spacecraft from one orbit to another.

A spacecraft cannot instantly change its position. By using rockets it changes its momentum and therefore its velocity. Sometimes the rocket burns for such a short time compared with an orbit period that it appears as if the velocity vector changes instantaneously, in which case it is referred to as an impulsive maneuver.

As an example, consider the problem of going from one circular orbit of 1000-mile altitude to a higher circular orbit, say, of 2000-mile altitude. Both the energy and momentum have to be increased to achieve the new orbit. An increase in velocity increases both quantities, so that each maneuver should increase velocity. We will calculate the amount later but note first that more than one maneuver will be required: after the first maneuver, that is, after the first velocity change, the spacecraft will be in a new elliptic orbit. Because it will continue around in this orbit, it will always pass through the point at which the maneuver was originated. It is therefore necessary to perform at least two maneuvers unless the final desired orbit intersects the initial one. For the same reason the final maneuver must necessarily be performed at a point on the final orbit.

The most efficient way of transferring between circular orbits in the same plane is referred to as a Hohmann transfer,* shown in Figure 4.11.

---

* After W. Hohmann, who discussed the problem in a complete and interesting monograph on the system design of a vehicle for planetary travel: *Die Erreichbarkeit der Himmelskörper*, R. Oldenburg, Munich, 1925.

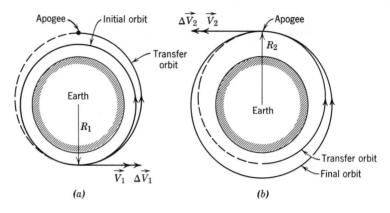

Figure 4.11. Hohmann Transfer: (a) first maneuver, $\Delta \vec{V}_1$, places spacecraft on transfer orbit along which it travels to the apogee; (b) second maneuver, $\Delta \vec{V}_2$, is performed at apogee to place spacecraft on final orbit.

The path of a spacecraft performing a Hohmann transfer is shown in Figure 4.22. It can be seen that each maneuver being tangent to the velocity vector and perpendicular to the radius effects the required changes in energy and momentum most efficiently at each radius.

SPECIFYING AN ORBIT

An orbit is completely specified when its size, shape, and orientation are given. Orientation means how the orbit is placed in space. In a plane the quantities E, h, and θ_p define an orbit. The orientation parameter, θ_p, is shown in Figure 4.9a. In space it is also necessary to specify the orientation of the plane, which requires two more variables. Any set of numbers which together specify all these quantities specifies the orbit. The numbers are called the orbit parameters or orbit elements.

Geometrical parameters have also been introduced: a and p determine orbital size and shape. Perhaps the most common parameter used to specify an orbit shape is the orbital eccentricity, e. It is related to a and p through the geometry of an ellipse and is given by

$$p = a(1 - e^2) \tag{4.5}$$

from the right triangle in Figure 4.9c.

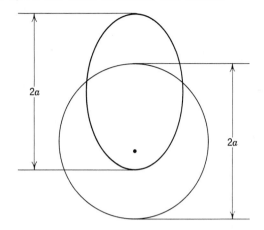

Figure 4.12.   Ellipses of Different Shape, but with Identical Semimajor Axis.

There are many more parameters that can be used, but the choice of which pair to use to specify size and shape is already large. For example, a,e, a,h, e,h, e,p, or p,E, serve equally well. However, a and E would not specify size and shape because they are not independent; that is, each can be determined from the other. Two orbits can have the same semimajor axis, a, and be different in shape, as shown in Figure 4.12.

We have talked mostly of elliptical orbits, but all of the foregoing remarks and equations apply to parabolic and hyperbolic escape orbits as well. All of the orbits that result from two bodies moving in each other's gravity field are of one of these three types. They are referred to as conics because all can be obtained by intersecting a plane and a cone.

The equation for a conic when expressed in polar coordinates (see Figure 4.9a) is

$$R = \frac{p}{1 + e \cos (\theta - \theta_p)}, \tag{4.6}$$

where p, e, θ_p are the parameters specifying, respectively, size, shape, and orientation. Equation 4.6 is referred to as the orbit equation.

GEOMETRY OF TWO ORBIT PLANES

A good way of getting familiar with the spherical geometry of orbit mechanics is to consider two orbits that do not lie in the same plane and draw them on a sphere. (A spherical blackboard is easily made with a flat-finish paint on an old globe.) On the sphere, motions are great circles because each orbit plane passes through the center of force (center of the spherical blackboard). At the point of intersection of the two great circles we can see very clearly the change in direction that is required of the velocity vector. This angle is sometimes hard to define because it requires knowing the direction of motion that the vehicles will have in approaching this intersection. The angle between the angular momentum vectors which are normal to each plane does not have this ambiguity. For this reason the use of a normal to define a plane is usually the most convenient. The direction of the line completely determines the orientation of any plane perpendicular to it.

In Figure 4.13 two planes are shown intersecting along the vector $\vec{R}$. It can be seen from the figure that the plane change due to changing the velocity $\vec{V}_1$ to $\vec{V}_2$ is the same as the change in the direction of $\vec{h}$ from $\vec{h}_1$ to $\vec{h}_2$.

When a torque (due to rocket thrust, for example) is applied to the orbital motion, the tip of the angular momentum vector moves in the direction of the applied torque. For example, to change an orbit plane, the direction of the velocity vector must be changed at the line of intersection of the two planes. Velocity is changed by changing the momentum of a spacecraft with a rocket. The

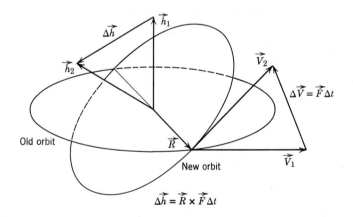

Figure 4.13. A Change of Orbit Plane.

longer the rocket thrust (i.e., force) acts, the more momentum change occurs. The thrust (or force) multiplied by the time through which it acts is called an impulse. The momentum change (for a unit mass) is therefore equal to the impulse or

$$\vec{F}\,\Delta t = \Delta\vec{V}$$

where the symbol Δ is used to indicate a change. The effect of the velocity change, $\Delta\vec{V}$, on the angular momentum vector is shown in Figure 4.13 and is given by the expression

$$\Delta\vec{h} = \vec{R} \times \Delta\vec{V}.$$

Orbital Maneuvers

Orbital maneuvers are necessary to achieve some missions. There are many kinds of missions and a few are discussed in detail. The size of the maneuvers might divide them into:

Major changes in the orbit to achieve an escape, or a rendezvous, to initiate a re-entry, to place a satellite over a certain part of the earth or to obtain a new orbit at higher altitudes. Depending on the mission, major changes may include changing the plane, the period, or the eccentricity of the orbit.

Orbit corrections, which are required to make up for errors in guidance equipment and for perturbations to the orbit due to aerodynamic drag, etc. Such corrections may be needed for station-keeping; for example, to prevent a satellite from leaving a pattern around the orbit, which may be needed to get continuous communications, or extremely accurate control over the period may be required so that a satellite will cross over the same ground station each day as the Earth rotates beneath the orbit.

Two examples will help to clarify these ideas.

EXAMPLES OF IMPULSE MANEUVERS

Two applications in which impulse maneuvers help in understanding the requirements of space guidance are (1) making fine adjustments to the orbital period so that a vehicle will continue to pass over a cerain point on the Earth, and (2) the maneuvers necessary to accomplish the rendezvous of two vehicles in space.

1. In the first example we employ Kepler's laws, according to which the period of an orbit is directly related to the energy of the orbit:

$$P^2 = 4\pi^2 k^2 (-2E)^{-3}, \qquad (4.7)$$

where P = the orbital period,

E = the orbital energy (Equation 4.1),

k = the constant of the gravitational field.

By increasing the speed the period can be increased (see Figure 4.14).

2. In the rendezvous problem it is necessary that the two vehicles have the same position and the same velocity. If they start in two arbitrary orbits that do not intersect, it will be seen that at least two maneuvers are necessary; the first changes the original orbit so as to create a new orbit which intersects with the final orbit and a second maneuver so that at some time the two vehicles will approach each other and have a common position. The final maneuver must make the two velocity vectors the same. Some of these maneuvers must change the orbit plane as well as its size and shape. In each case there is a certain velocity increment that has to be added and this must be controlled in both direction and magnitude. The special case of a Hohmann transfer will be calculated later.

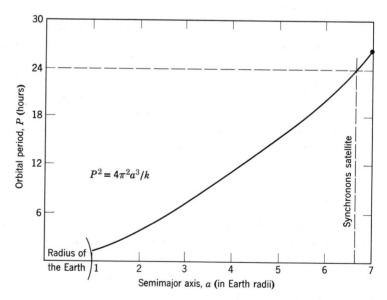

Figure 4.14. Orbital Period as a Function of Semimajor Axis.

Maneuver Requirements

The accuracy with which the period must be controlled depends on the mission of the satellite. When a satellite has to be synchronized with another satellite so that they will stay in the same relative position or synchronized with the Earth's rotation, even a very small error will allow the satellite to drift from its desired station. Given enough time the error can get large. Figure 4.15 shows the effect

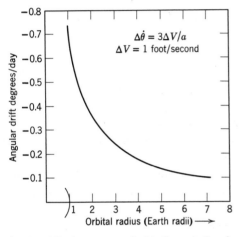

Angular drift due to error in injection velocity of one foot per second

Example: At an altitude of 1.0 Earth radius, a satellite drifts with respect to its nominal position by −0.3 degree per day (due to an error in injection velocity of one foot per second).

It would therefore drift by −1.8 degrees per day if the injection velocity error were 5 feet per second, and it would be −54 degrees away from its nominal position after one month.

The error in period would be 11.6 seconds (due to an error in injection velocity of 5 *feet* per second).

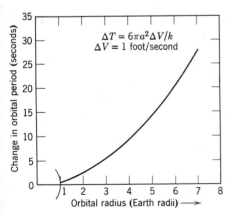

Change in orbital period due to error in injection velocity of one foot per second

Figure 4.15. Effect of Injection Velocity Error upon Satellite Position in a Nominally Circular Orbit.

of injection errors. This curve can also be used to determine the velocity maneuver required to correct a station drift.

When a mission life is long, the accuracy required of the ascent guidance equipment gets unreasonably hard to achieve. Furthermore, there are always disturbances due to drag, radiation pressure, and the gravity fields of other bodies which make it necessary to make corrections after a period of time. Therefore on missions in which long life maintenance of satellites in fixed stations is required some form of orbit adjustment is required.

In the rendezvous problem, in which a satellite must transfer to a new orbit with another spacecraft or with a planet, there is a restriction on when the transfer can start. When the desired orbit is achieved, the other spacecraft or planet must be there. The range of time during which the transfer can begin is called the *window* or *launch window*.

Consider a transfer of a spacecraft from an initial circular orbit. After a maneuver it starts on the transfer orbit with speed V_1. It arrives at the desired final radius with a transfer orbit speed of V_2. The radius of the initial orbit is R_1 and of the final orbit, R_2. The maneuvers do not effect the radii at the time they are performed, so that R_1 and R_2 are the radii of the transfer orbit at the time of the first and second maneuvers, respectively.

To solve for the maneuver requirements, each transfer orbit will have constant parameters (e.g., energy and momentum). The initial and final velocity on the transfer orbit are determined from the equations for the parameters and the initial and final position. The total maneuver capability required is the sum of differences produced in the velocity vector to go from the initial orbit to the first transfer orbit and from first transfer orbit to the second, if there is more than one transfer orbit, until the final orbit is achieved. For the Hohmann transfer the results are simple and make a good example.

In a circular orbit the attracting force due to gravity, k/R^2, is equal to the centripetal acceleration. Therefore

$$\frac{V^2}{R} = \frac{k}{R^2} \tag{4.8}$$

and the orbital speed is given by

$$V = \sqrt{k/R}. \tag{4.9}$$

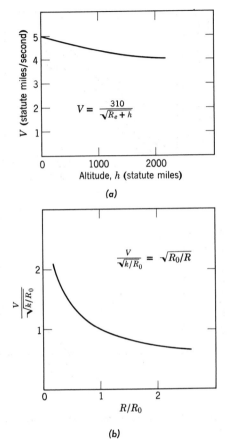

Figure 4.16. Circular Orbital Speed: (*a*) about the Earth; (*b*) normalized with respect to a reference radius, R_0.

This relationship is plotted in Figure 4.16 for orbits near the earth (*a*) and in a normalized form (*b*). The normalized curve can be used for any value of R_0. For example, if an orbit 1000 miles above the Earth is used as a reference, then R_0 is approximately 5000 miles and from curve (*a*) the corresponding speed k/R_0 is 4.4 miles per second. At a radius of 10,000 miles, $R/R_0 = 2$ and $V = (0.7)(4.4)$, or 3.1 miles per second. The other conditions are that the energy and angular momentum must be constant on the transfer orbit. These give the following equations which are also given in graphical form in Figure 4.17.

Energy:
$$\frac{V_1{}^2}{2} - \frac{k}{R_1} = \frac{V_2{}^2}{2} - \frac{k}{R_2}. \tag{4.10}$$

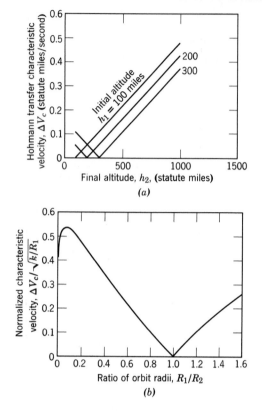

(a)

(b)

Figure 4.17. Characteristic Velocity Required for Hohmann Transfers. (a) near Earth transfers (b) normalized results.

Momentum: $V_1 R_1 = V_2 R_2,$ (4.11)

from which

$$V_1 = \sqrt{2k/R_1(1 + R_1/R_2)},$$ (4.12)

$$V_2 = \sqrt{2k/R_2(R_2/R_1 + 1)}.$$ (4.13)

The total maneuver requirement, called the characteristic velocity, ΔV_c, is the sum of ΔV_1 and ΔV_2, where

$$\Delta V_1 = V_1 - \sqrt{k/R_1}$$ (4.14)

and

$$\Delta V_2 = \sqrt{k/R_2} - V_2,$$ (4.15)

from which

$$\frac{\Delta V_c}{\sqrt{k/R_1}} = \left|[\sqrt{2/(1+r)} - 1]\right| + \left|\sqrt{r}\,[1 - \sqrt{2/(1+1/r)}]\right|, \quad (4.16)$$

where

$$\Delta V_c = |\Delta V_1| + |\Delta V_2|$$

and

$$r = \frac{R_1}{R_2}.$$

It is interesting to note that as the second radius gets large the ΔV^c required to go to a higher circular orbit is larger than the velocity required to escape the gravity field entirely.

For example, the worst case is for $R_2/R_1 \approx 15.6$. By starting from a circular orbit near the Earth with a radius $R_1 = 4100$ miles the characteristic velocity required to reach a circular orbit with radius $R_2 = 64{,}000$ miles is 2.59 miles per second. This is quite a bit higher than the characteristic velocity of 2.0 miles per second necessary to escape the Earth's field entirely. By definition, for escape, $V = 0$ when R becomes very large; therefore $E = 0$. The condition for this gives the escape speed

$$V_{\text{esc}}^2 = \frac{2k}{R}. \quad (4.17)$$

Note that the speed required is independent of the direction of the velocity and depends only on the radius.

Once the maneuver requirements have been determined, the propulsion system can be specified. The propulsion problems in meeting requirements for large velocity changes are discussed in Chapter **7**. Because the size of the rocket varies exponentially with the maneuver requirements, the importance of finding efficient trajectories is greater in space travel than on the Earth, where the costs of propelling a vehicle are modest by comparison.

Escape From a Planet

Our discussion has been restricted so far to the motion of two bodies with respect to each other, and the only additional forces considered were those of rocket thrust, introduced intentionally for maneu-

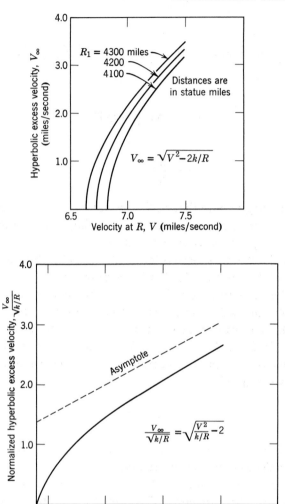

Figure 4.18. Hyperbolic Excess Velocity as a Function of Injection Velocity.

vering. However, other perturbations exist; for example, atmospheric drag and the gravitational attraction of other bodies. When two bodies are close to each other but far from another attracting body, the predominant force is their mutual attraction. For example, a situation can exist in which the disturbance of an Earth satellite orbit caused by the sun is of the same magnitude as the disturbance

caused by the Earth to the motion of the spacecraft when it is considered as a satellite of the sun. These equal-disturbance points are
on the surface of a "sphere of influence" of the Earth, which has a
radius of approximately one million miles.

When very much less than one million miles away from the Earth
(and not near the moon), the predominant effect on the spacecraft is
due to the attraction of the Earth; conversely, when the spacecraft is
far beyond the million-mile sphere, the sun's attraction produces the
predominant effect. A good estimate of the velocities necessary to
achieve a given orbit around the sun can be calculated by ignoring the
sun up to the sphere of influence and then ignoring the Earth's influence
beyond the influence sphere; at the sphere of influence the Earth's
potential energy is ignored and all the remaining energy is kinetic.
The speed the spacecraft has with respect to the Earth is called the
hyperbolic excess velocity, V_∞, and is the velocity that must be added to
the Earth's velocity around the sun to get the heliocentric spacecraft
velocity. As before, the energy is constant in escaping the Earth,
and therefore the hyperbolic excess velocity completely determines the
speed required at the position at which the escape maneuver was
initiated because it determines the orbital energy:

$$E = \frac{V_\infty^2}{2}. \qquad (4.18)$$

This relationship is plotted in Figure 4.18.

Ascent Requirements

An ascent is the portion of the trajectory from the ground to an
altitude and speed comparable to those of an orbiting satellite. Some
space vehicles are accelerated beyond orbital speed so that they escape
the Earth's field. Whether a vehicle is intended to escape or go into
orbit, it must be accelerated to enormous speeds by our standards on
Earth and rise above the atmosphere. Several rockets, each successively smaller, may be used in order to achieve this. In spite of
the huge force exerted by these rockets and the high acceleration that
results, it takes five minutes or more for the ascent phase of a mission.

Maneuvers, in orbit have been discussed previously. The changes
in velocity are frequently small and can be treated as resulting from

an impulse acting on the vehicle (the velocity change is assumed to occur instantly). This simplifying assumption makes it possible to solve many problems without being concerned with the nature of the propulsion system. In addition, the nongravitational forces that act on the vehicle while the propulsion system is operating are negligible. By contrast, the position and speed of a vehicle, the environmental forces, and the mass of the vehicle change drastically during the ascent phase of a mission, so that the analysis required is correspondingly more difficult. A few of the effects are discussed in general terms.

GRAVITY AND DRAG LOSSES

If a rocket is released with an upward thrust that is less than its weight, it will remain on its launching pad; that is, the rocket thrust for ascent must, of course, be greater than the vehicle weight in order to get started. Since a velocity is also to be imparted to the vehicle in *addition* to lift-off, it is found that ascent is more efficient if the fractions of the total thrust which serves only to counteract gravity is small: when a rocket is released in space, where gravitational effects are negligible, the propulsion system produces a certain velocity change which is called the characteristic velocity of the rocket. When the same rocket is used for ascent, the gravity forces prevent the rocket from achieving a speed equal to its characteristic velocity. The velocity reduction caused by the gravity field is called the gravity loss and is, of course, reduced by minimizing the time spent below circular speed. A second factor that effects gravity loss is the direction of the rocket thrust: a rocket released horizontally with a thrust less than its weight would fall to the ground, but it would accelerate horizontally. When it reached the ground it would have more energy than when it started because its total speed would be greater than if it had fallen without thrusting. Energy is added at a rate that depends on the thrust and the velocity:

$$\text{rate of energy addition} = \vec{F} \cdot \vec{V}$$

$$= FV \cos \theta,$$

where F = thrust,

   V = rocket velocity,

   θ = angle between the thrust and velocity.

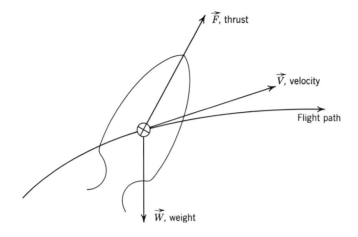

Figure 4.19.   Ascent of Vehicle.

As discussed earlier in considering orbital energy, the lower the vehicle altitude (smaller R) at constant energy, the larger its speed. Therefore a low trajectory will give the largest rate of increase in energy.

In addition to the gravity force which retards the ascent of a rocket, there is also an opposing drag force (wind resistance). The loss in speed that results from drag is called the drag loss. The higher

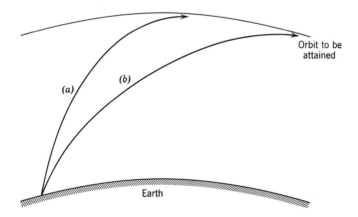

Figure 4.20.   Comparison of High and Low Trajectories: (a) high trajectory; (b) low trajectory, i.e., longer, faster path through the atmosphere.

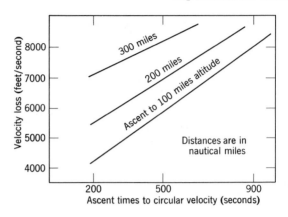

Figure 4.21. Combined Gravity and Drag Losses for Typical, Single-Burn Ascents to Circular Orbits.

the speed, the greater the drag force, and when the trajectory is low, the vehicle has a longer path through the atmosphere (see Figure 4.20).

A low fast trajectory therefore appears best from a gravity loss standpoint but worst for drag loss. The drag loss is less than the gravity loss, however, and in general the lowest trajectories are the most efficient. Many trajectories have been studied for a wide variety of rockets and the gravity and drag losses have been tabulated. A good estimate of the combined gravity and drag loss for orbital missions and beyond can be obtained from Figure 4.21. As an example, a satellite which must reach a speed of 26,000 feet per second at an altitude of 100 miles uses a rocket which burns for 500 seconds during ascent. This rocket must have a characteristic velocity of 26,000 + 5900 = 31,900 feet per second.

DUAL-BURN ASCENT

The excessive losses indicated for gaining high altitudes are usually somewhat offset by performing the ascent in two parts. The first part of the ascent is just like a lower-altitude ascent, except that the final velocity is great enough so that the vehicle can coast to a higher altitude, and then complete its ascent during a second phase of propulsion. In this manner a large fraction of the trajectory is traversed efficiently. When the trajectory has two distinct propul-

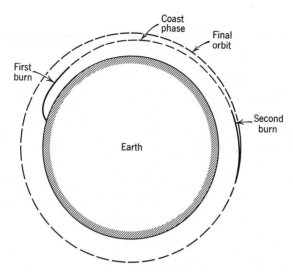

Figure 4.22.   Dual-Burn Ascent.

sion phases, it is frequently called a dual-burn ascent. As suggested in Figure 4.22, the coast and second burn are similar to the Hohmann transfer described under orbital maneuvers.

RESTRICTIONS ON THE ASCENT PATH

There are a number of restrictions which are limitations to the qualitative guides discussed under gravity and drag losses. Extremely low trajectories might be ruled out by drag losses, but there is another aerodynamic effect which places a lower bound on trajectories before this point is reached: the air flow heats the vehicle, and at its high speed heating can get so severe that the structure of the vehicle is weakened. Since the alternate provision of extra strength means extra weight for structural members (which are useless in space), the heating constraint usually determines the lower limit for an ascent trajectory.

Because sites are located near civilization it is not safe to launch a rocket in all directions. For example, at Cape Kennedy a western launch would require the rocket to fly over inhabited sections of Florida. The limitations in direction in which a rocket can be launched is called its launch restrictions. The launch restrictions at Cape Kennedy are shown in Figure 4.23.

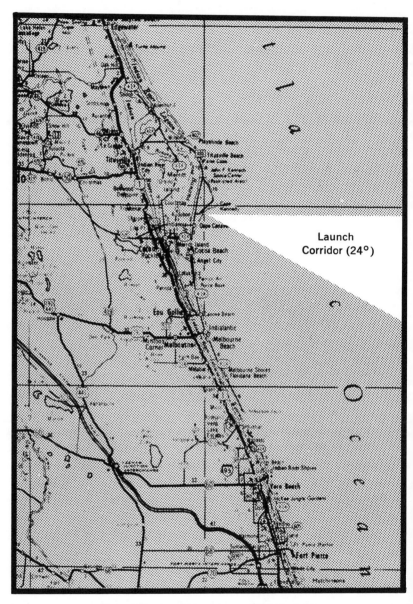

Figure 4.23.   Launch Restrictions at Cape Kennedy.

GUIDANCE AND OPTIMIZATION

After all the restrictions on a trajectory have been defined, it is possible to select a trajectory. The size of the payload is usually a critical item in most missions, so that the trajectory chosen is that which is most efficient; that is, the payload is maximized. This, however, is not the only criterion that can be utilized; when the accuracy with which the rocket ascends is of the most importance, the trajectory that is least sensitive to guidance errors (but still within the rocket's capabilities) may be chosen. The word optimal trajectory is meaningful only for the specific mission and vehicle for which it has been optimized.

Once an optimal trajectory has been established, a guidance system must be developed which is capable of steering the rocket along this optimal path. Sometimes the guidance system becomes so complicated that an engineering compromise must be made between the loss in foregoing an optimal trajectory and the gain in a lighter, more reliable guidance system.

The simplest guidance systems do not correct errors that accumulate during ascent. They are called open-loop systems because they do not feed information back (about how well the rocket is being guided) from which corrections could be made. More sophisticated systems obtain information about the position and velocity either from ground-based tracking systems or from self-contained equipment such as gyros and accelerometers. The nominal trajectory, that is, the desired path, is stored explicitly or implicitly in equations, and this information is compared with (subtracted from) the actual position and velocity. If they differ, a correction has to be made so that the final conditions at the end of ascent will be correct. Because most rockets deliver a constant thrust, the corrections are made by changing the direction of the thrust to correct the error (see Chapter 6).

4.3 A TRIP TO VENUS

This section is intended to illustrate, by example of the flight of Mariner II, some of the earlier discussions. To give a fuller understanding of the Mariner, some additional descriptive material is included. After some preliminary remarks about the mission, the spacecraft is described; then the trajectory and its propulsion for ascent and injection into an interplanetary orbit are discussed. Finally, the actual flight, including its midcourse maneuver to correct ascent errors, is described.

It would be nice to be able to design an interplanetary trip by starting with the mission, determining the payload of scientific sensors, and then simply designing the rocket boosters required to get it there, but that is not the engineering process. In view of the complicated interrelationship of the many systems components, the problem is worked from both ends. The early phases of a design more nearly answers the question: given certain rockets and a mission, can the job be done? If not, a process of cutting back on the scope of the mission and redesigning the payload is tried. If this is not successful, the mission may have to wait for newer and bigger rockets.

One of the many remarkable things about the Mariner II flight was that it was completely redesigned at the last minute and that the new design performed successfully. It was originally to have been launched from a two-stage booster composed of an Atlas and a Centaur. The Centaur was under development, but because of a change in schedule it was not ready in time to boost the Mariner II on its way. Within nine months the entire spacecraft was redesigned to fly instead with an Atlas-Agena booster (see Figure 4.24), a design task that normally requires several years! The allowable spacecraft weight had to be reduced from 1100 to 447 pounds. In this new weight were to be included its scientific payload of 41 pounds, the systems for power, guidance and control, propulsion, and communications, and all the subsystems necessary to perform the many complicated functions of a spacecraft!

The mission was to get the spacecraft to Venus so that it would pass the planet within 40,000 miles of its surface but no closer than 8000 miles. To accomplish this feat, the spacecraft had to perform a number of carefully planned maneuvers and to operate in the space environment for nearly four months, starting nearly 93 million miles from the sun and ending at a distance of about 67 million miles from there (although it traversed a much greater distance around the sun than the difference of 26 million miles). During this trip the intense radiation from the sun would increase twofold, which presented a heating problem for the equipment on board. Communications had to be maintained in spite of the vast distances to the Earth,

Figure 4.24. Launch of MARINER and AGENA Stage with ATLAS Booster. (Courtesy of Jet Propulsion Laboratory.)

which ranged up to 36 million miles. Signals could be stronger if more power were used for transmission, but the extra power would mean more weight in batteries and solar panels. The tight weight restriction resulting from the decreased booster power available therefore made communications designs difficult.

Description of the Mariner II

The Mariner II is shown in Figure 4.25. The spacecraft was divided into six segments, each of which contained a case of electronics and

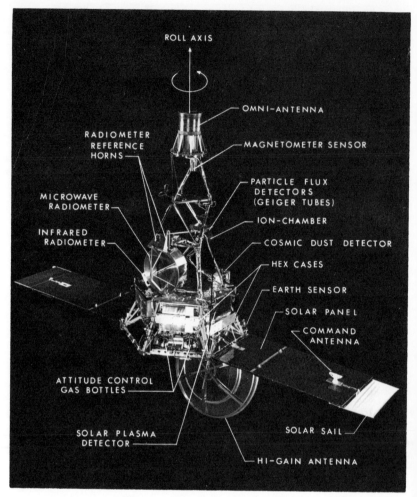

Figure 4.25. MARINER Spacecraft. (Courtesy of Jet Propulsion Laboratory.)

mechanical equipment. Two segments contained power-supply equipment including batteries to store electrical energy generated by the solar cells. Three segments were devoted to communications and interpreting equipment (see Chapter 6 for details of the equipment listed here). This included a 3-watt transmitter, the signal from which was used for tracking the spacecraft from the Earth, and the equipment used to switch on instrumentation in the vehicle or the scientific payload and prepare it for transmission to Earth. Commands from the Earth were also received and processed in these sections. The sixth section contained the three gyroscopes which were part of the attitude-control sensing system and the digital computer.

The orientation of the vehicle was sensed with an Earth sensor, sun sensor, and the gyroscopes. On the way to the sun the combined directions of the sun and Earth from the spacecraft defined the spacecraft orientation. The gyroscopes can sense the angular velocity of the vehicle, and by keeping track of how much the vehicle rotated they could give the orientation. But instruments are not perfect, and all gyroscopes are subject to some drift. They sense things that are not due to the vehicle angular velocity and hence allow the error in vehicle orientation to build up over a period of time. For this reason the earth and sun sensors are needed, but the gyros do a better job of short-term attitude sensing so the sensors and gyros are used together to sense the attitude and the angular velocity of the vehicle. (Details of such attitude-determination equipment are also described in Chapter 6.)

The Mariner II orientation was controlled, that is, kept pointing at the sun (while the antenna pointed toward earth) by using gas jets. Two spherical titanium containers were used to store nitrogen gas at a pressure of 3500 pounds per square inch (psi). Each "bottle" contained 4.3 pounds of gas which was connected to a pressure regulator which allowed only enough gas to pass so that the pressure at the gas jets was 15 psi. The gas jets were controlled by valves actuated by the control system. The jets operate on the same principle as the rocket motor, but they are purposely offset so that the force does not pass through the center of mass; as a result they produce a torque, that is, the control torque desired.

The Earth sensor performed a second job, that of pointing the high-gain antenna toward the Earth. The high-gain antenna was 4 feet in diameter and focused the meager energy being transmitted toward the Earth. When the midcourse maneuver was performed, or if the spacecraft lost control, the transmission was performed on the omnidirectional antenna (see also Chapter 6). Signals coming from the Earth, on the other hand, were received by command antennas on the solar panels.

A propulsion system for performing a midcourse maneuver to correct guidance errors was located in the center of the structure. It could burn for a very short period of time or for any length of time up to nearly a minute. It thereby had the capability of producing any velocity changes desired, ranging from 0.7 to 200 feet per second. The rocket thrust was small by booster standards, producing an acceleration of only about 0.1 that of gravity on the earth. During the midcourse maneuver the spacecraft would experience a change from the weightless condition to a condition equivalent to weighing about 45 pounds. The low thrust was desirable from three standpoints. (1) Once in space the solar panels were unfolded. This structure of the spacecraft need only be strong enough to tolerate the midcourse maneuver thrust. (2) If the rocket engine is slightly misaligned, the attitude control system must be able to control the torques. The smaller the torques that had to be controlled, the easier it was to design the control system to perform efficiently. (3) In performing the midcourse maneuver, the vehicle disturbance produced by shutting the engine off is generally smaller for longer burn times.

Much of the guidance system was located on Earth. The computer on board the Mariner II was not given many tasks requiring logic (see Chapter 6). It contained a highly accurate electronic frequency reference (oscillator) which was used as a clock by counting the number of oscillations: a certain number of oscillations corresponded to a given elapsed period of time. Mariner needed a clock so that it could execute at the precise time the commands sent from the ground and stored in its computer. The computer's function was to store instructions and sequence operations commanded from the ground. Some instructions were stored in the computer prior to launch and some commands were received and stored in flight. Navigation was performed by using data from the ground stations at Woomera, Australia, Johannesburg, South Africa, and at Goldstone, California in the United States. These stations are the three Deep Space Instrumentation Facilities which allow spacecraft to be tracked as the Earth rotates. Their huge parabolic antennas gather the incoming energy to make it discernible against the background of noise, and they focus commands precisely to the spacecraft. The data from these tracking facilities were used in a computer at the Jet Propulsion Laboratory in Pasadena to calculate the path followed by Mariner II. From trajectory calculations the best point for making a midcourse correction, its magnitude and its direction, could be determined. This information could then be relayed to the spacecraft.

The data from the tracking facilities were received in two forms: the direction of the tracking antenna when it was pointing directly at the spacecraft was available to indicate *location* of the Mariner, whereas its *velocity* was obtained from the Doppler shift in signals. As a vehicle sending out radio signals (waves) moves away from the antenna, the distance traveled by each successive transmitted wave is greater; each successive signal takes longer to travel from the transmitter to the receiver than the previous one. Therefore the time between receipt of successive waves is greater than the time between their transmission, or, stated another way, the frequency becomes lower. The reverse is true when the vehicle approaches the antenna. We frequently experience a Doppler shift in our daily lives; for example, when a train with its whistle blowing at a constant frequency approaches a crossing. To a listener at the crossing the whistle pitch becomes progressively lower as it passes. The Doppler measurement of Mariner II gave information about the radial speed of the spacecraft to a very high degree of accuracy. A stable frequency of transmission from the ground (accurate to one part in 10^8) shifted to a lower frequency when received at the spacecraft, from which it was retransmitted to earth, suffering a second Doppler shift, by the time it was received on the ground. The net result was a measuring accuracy of 0.00001 per cent, even when the spacecraft was in the vicinity of Venus!

The Atlas and the Agena boosters each had their own guidance systems; the Atlas used a radio tracking system which sent commands to its attitude control system to steer it on course. In the Agena gyros held the proper attitude, while an accelerometer sensed the rate of velocity change and a computer kept track of how much the Agena stage had increased in velocity. At a predetermined value the computer shut the Agena engine off. These phases will become clearer as the over-all trajectory is described. Some of the equipment also is described in Chapter 6.

Getting to Venus

Let us first consider the interplanetary part of the flight. In Figure 4.26 the orbit sizes of the actual flight are given. Although some important differences are introduced by the eccentricity and inclinations of the orbits of Venus and Earth, a good estimate of the velocity

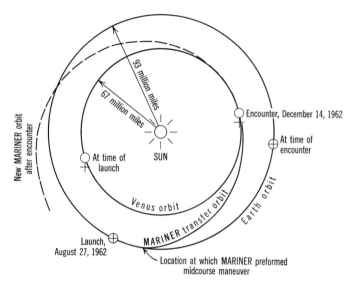

Figure 4.26. Earth, Venus, and MARINER Heliocentric Orbits.

required can be obtained by considering a Hohmann transfer. After the velocity change needed to leave the Earth's orbit is computed, the end conditions of the transfer orbit can be used to study the hyperbolas of escape from Earth and arrival at Venus.

According to equation 14, the first maneuver (velocity change) will be negative because the radius of the Venus orbit is smaller than the orbit radius of the Earth. In order to calculate the velocity change from Equation 14, it is necessary to calculate R_1/R_2 (the ratio of the Earth's orbital radius, 93×10^6 miles, to the radius of the Venus orbit, 67×10^6 miles),

$$\frac{R_1}{R_2} = 1.39,$$

and to compute the value of $\sqrt{k_{\mathrm{sun}}/R_1}$, the speed of Earth in its orbit. It takes the Earth one year to go around a circle of radius 93×10^6 miles. The speed is therefore

$$\frac{(2\pi)(93 \times 10^6)}{(365)(24)(3600)} = 18.5 \text{ mi/sec}$$

$$= \sqrt{k_{\mathrm{sun}}/R_1}. \qquad (4.19)$$

With these values the maneuver (i.e., velocity change required) is

$$\Delta V_1 = 18.5(\sqrt{2/2.39} - 1)$$
$$= -1.57 \text{ mi/sec} \qquad (4.20)$$

(which is smaller than the actual value used, i.e., approximately 2.2 miles per second).

The speed at which the spacecraft would approach Venus, if the orbits were coplanar and circular and if the trip was made by a Hohmann transfer, is calculated in the same way. It is

$$\Delta V_2 = 22(-0.08)$$
$$= -1.76 \text{ mi/sec.} \qquad (4.21)$$

The actual transfer orbit near Venus and Earth crossed the orbits of the planets instead of being tangent to them, so that the actual relative velocity was higher. Precise calculations become very complicated because the simple energy and momentum relations do not hold when there are more than two bodies and when the actual trajectory must join two orbits which are not in the same plane. It is also desirable to get there fast.

In order to leave the Earth's orbit and fall inward toward the sun, it was necessary to have the spacecraft's velocity reduced from that of the Earth. Therefore in escaping from the Earth it must have a residual velocity of 1.57 miles per second which is directed away from the earth, that is, backward along the Earth's orbit around the sun. Considering the energy equation, this means that the spacecraft must depart from near the Earth with a speed of V given by

$$\frac{V^2}{2} = \frac{V_\infty^2}{2} + \frac{k}{R}. \qquad (4.22)$$

Instead of calculating k/R as before, the most familiar parameter is gravity rather than the near-Earth orbital period. Gravity is related to k by the equation

$$g = \frac{k}{R^2}, \qquad (4.23)$$

from which

$$\frac{k}{R} = gR \qquad (4.24)$$

At the surface of the Earth, then,

$$\frac{k}{R} = \frac{32.2}{5280} (3960)$$

$$= 24.1 \ (\text{mi/sec})^2. \tag{4.25}$$

From Eq. 4.22 the necessary speed is then 7.13 miles per second (when $V_\infty = 1.57$ mile per second for departure from the surface of the Earth). The speed is somewhat less for the more realistic altitudes of about 100 miles (see Figure 4.18).

If V_∞ were zero, the velocity to escape is 6.95 miles per second, only 0.18 mile per second less. In other words, an increase of only 0.18 mile per second over that necessary just to escape near the Earth, causes an increase of 1.57 miles per second in the speed at escape. This is because the thrust which causes the increase is acting at 7 miles per second and therefore produces tremendous power which causes a big increase in the energy during the time the rocket burns. If the last part of the rocket burn—which produced the extra velocity of 0.18 mile per second—was delayed until escape was achieved, it could change the motion only with respect to the sun by 0.18 mile per second. For this reason the main rocket maneuvers are performed as close to the Earth as possible. Usually only corrective maneuvers to make up for guidance errors are performed in deep space.

Although no maneuvers were performed near Venus, the speed near Venus can be estimated. The value of k for Venus can be obtained from a table. It is approximately 78,000 miles^3/second^2. When the spacecraft is 40,000 miles from the surface of Venus ($R = 44,000$ miles) and the approach speed is 1.76 miles per second, the speed would be 2.58 miles per second whereas at 8000 miles in altitude ($R = 12,000$ miles) the speed would be 4.01 miles per second.

The Flight

Three Mariner spacecrafts and two booster systems were ready for launch at a time when Venus was in appropriate position. The best trajectories were computed for each day over a wide range of dates on either side of the particular launch date (the launch window) for which the trajectories to Venus required the least propulsion; the Atlas/Agena boost system had enough power to send Mariner to Venus if it were launched during a "window" of 51 days. Considering that three to four weeks are required to prepare the pad after a launch and a similar time to get an Atlas Agena off the launching pad at Cape Kennedy, this barely allowed for two launches if the first was a failure. This was fortunate because the first flight *was* unsuccessful. A problem in the guidance system required that the rockets be destroyed for range safety.

The second successful launch occurred on August 27, 1962. The rockets needed to send the tiny spacecraft on its way weighed more than a quarter of a million pounds and stood nearly 100 feet high. But there was little performance to spare.

The first stage (the Atlas; see Figures 4.24 and 4.27) boosted the vehicle up through the atmosphere to an altitude of approximately 100 miles. Then the Agena's rocket was ignited, and it burned long enough to put the Mariner in an orbit around the Earth. This orbit was the first transfer orbit. It is sometimes called a parking orbit when its main purpose is to provide the time necessary for tracking to determine accurately what the next maneuver should be. In the case

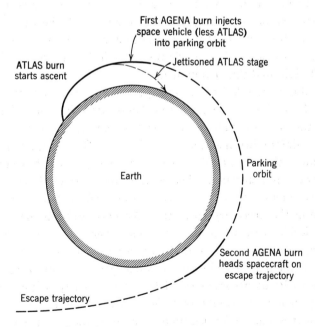

Figure 4.27.   Schematic of Propulsion Phases.

of the Mariner the purpose of the orbit was to transfer the vehicle to that location from which best to perform the escape maneuver. The vehicle coasted about a fourth of the way around its orbit and from a point over the South Atlantic the Agena rocket was ignited again and propelled the Mariner on its way to Venus with the proper velocity.

To avoid possible interferences with the attitude control and payload sensors of the spacecraft, the Agena was separated and given a small impulse to place it in a new orbit which would miss Venus.

During the ascent a long sequence of preparing Mariner for space had begun when the outer shell (the nose cone, which protects the spacecraft) had been ejected. Next, the spacecraft unfolded its solar panels and started a search mode to acquire its proper orientation. The sun is such a dominant feature of the sky, it is easiest to orient one axis of a vehicle toward it first. After allowing the gyros to stop all tumbling, the vehicle was oriented so that the solar panels faced the sun, from which orientation they could start to recharge the battery. Any angle around the sun line is the same for the panels. This gives an axis about which to rotate while searching for the Earth. Later, when the Earth was dimmer (farther away), the Earth sensor was preset to the known angle between the sun and Earth directions, so that it would acquire the Earth in one vehicle rotation. Any time this orientation was lost, the spacecraft automatically initiated this search mode.

According to the desired trajectory, Mariner would arrive at Venus in 109 days after launch. A few hours after launch the tracking system was able to evaluate how well the guidance systems had performed. Before Mariner had even left the Earth's gravity field it was known that it would pass on the wrong side of Venus by a quarter of a million miles. The Mariner rocket would have to correct this error along the way. Since it was well within its capability to perform the necessary correction, the only problem that remained was to decide when to perform the maneuver. The closer to Venus, the more accurately the desired correction could be determined, but the size of the maneuver increases as the spacecraft approaches Venus. Because sufficient accuracy could be achieved early in the flight and an early maneuver would provide higher reliability of succeeding, the maneuver was performed nine days after launch. The commands for orienting the rocket resulted in a 9-degree roll about the sun line

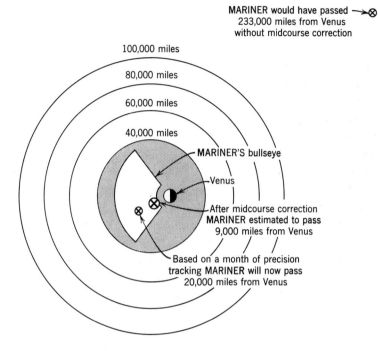

Figure 4.28. Targeting of MARINER. (Courtesy of Jet Propulsion Laboratory.)

and a 140-degree pitch about the solar panels. The rocket fired and
produced a 66 foot per second change in the velocity. The new trajectory would allow the spacecraft to pass Venus on its sunny side.
Errors in the correction itself finally resulted in a distance of closest
approach of about 22,000 miles altitude instead of the nominal design
distance of 10,000 miles (see Figure 4.28). However the design range
was 8000 to 40,000 miles, so that the achieved approach of 22,000
miles was well within the specifications for the mission.

Problems in Flight and Results

The possibility of difficulties always faces an undertaking as complex as the Mariner trip to Venus, and that flight was not without
its anxious moments.

Just prior to the mid-course maneuver the Earth-sensor signal was
weaker than it should have been. Some detective work finally con-

vinced the engineers that Mariner *was* looking at the Earth and not at the moon or some other false target and the maneuver proceeded.

On the twelfth day the vehicle lost its orientation but later recovered, apparently having been hit by a meteorite. Those who adhere to kicking as the best means of getting a dime back out of a broken coffee machine were not surprised to find the Earth sensor working properly again after the encounter!

Temperature problems also plagued the spacecraft. The estimates on how to paint a deep-space vehicle were slightly off, and as Mariner got closer to the sun it got hotter. Some temperature instrumentation went off scale and many instruments were subject to temperatures well above their design point. A partial failure of the solar array was compensated by the increased radiation near Venus.

None of these difficulties proved serious enough to prevent a successful completion of the mission. Many controversies were solved and new problems posed by the results. In addition to the close look afforded the scientific sensors aboard the spacecraft, orbit motion is well enough understood that the accurate tracking will enable the scientists to determine the astronomical unit to greater precision than ever before. The relative size of the orbits of the planets with respect to each other is well known, but these distances are not accurately known in terms of any units that can be measured in the laboratory. The tracking data tie the astronomical unit to the speed of light and hence to laboratory units. In addition, the mass of Venus was determined more accurately than ever before from the tracking data. The theories of orbit motion are therefore not only a means of computing trajectories but also a valuable research tool for measuring properties of the planets, the moon, and the sun.

References

1. Arthur Berry, *A Short History of Astronomy from the Earliest Times through the Nineteenth Century*. New York: Dover, 1961 (reprinted from John Murray 1898).
2. Sir Oliver Lodge, *Pioneers of Science*. New York: Dover, 1960 (reprinted from Macmillan and Co., Ltd. 1893 corrected 1926).
3. Staff, Jet Propulsion Laboratory, *Mariner Mission to Venus*. New York: McGraw-Hill, 1963.
4. Y. Ryabor, *An Elementary Survey of Celestial Mechanics*. New York: Dover, 1961 (reprinted from Foreign Language Publishing House, Moscow, 1959, under the title *Celestial Mechanics*).

CHAPTER 5

Life in Space

Poul Anderson
Author and Lecturer

Contents

Life in Space

The title of this chapter can be read in two different ways. Does "life in space" mean "human survival in the interplanetary environment" or does it mean "extraterrestrial biology"? Although either of these subjects is enormous and many books have been written about them, I shall try to cover both. This is not so illogical as it seems. We may link them by two homely questions: "How can we get there alive and what might we find when we do get there?"

Of course, in so brief a survey we cannot do more than glance at a few of the problems and possibilities. But these are tremendously exciting; one might well say romantic. The challenges to be met and the rewards of discovery and adventure to be won, are like nothing since the days of Columbus. Now he was willing to undergo a long apprenticeship as a seaman and years of homeless poverty while he tried to raise funds, all in the service of his dream. Today's student will surely be as willing to do the hard work of fitting himself for the interplanetary age if only he can be shown what a wonderful Homeric life it offers him.

5.1 HUMAN SURVIVAL

Let us begin, then, with the issue of human survival in space, and let us admit at the outset that it is still inadequately understood, partly because of its complexity. Man is the result of a billion or more years of evolution on this one planet. Only now, as he exposes himself to alien conditions, does he begin to see how exquisitely adapted he is to every facet of the terrestrial environment. Granted he can endure unnatural stresses for a short time, just as he can survive small doses of poison. But what are the limits? For that matter, what are the stresses?

Another reason why there is little accurate knowledge is, to put it bluntly, that less research has been done than should have been done. Engineers working on space projects often say to their physiologist teammates, in effect, "Well, tell us what the specifications are, what you need to keep a man alive, and we will build it into the capsule." The physiologist replies, "We don't know. It will take time—and a good deal more money and staff than my department is now allotted—to find out. If you go sending men on long missions before we have carried our studies further, you may very well kill them."

In spite of this, some excellent work is being done. And, as the knowledge of the necessity sinks in, engineers, physiologists, and psychologists are beginning to cooperate more fully.

To survey a few of the obvious problems—doubtless less obvious ones will turn up as astronautics progresses—let us imagine a manned expedition to the moon or Mars, name some unearthly conditions we know the men will encounter, and see what they may do to the men and what can be done about them.

Acceleration

In getting off Earth the ship has to start at high acceleration. We must not confuse this with the high speed it will eventually reach. Speed in itself never hurt anybody. A man in a supersonic airplane feels no different, if the ride is smooth, from a man on the ground. But acceleration, the change of velocity in direction or magnitude, acts like gravity and produces a force. The man in the airplane notices the tug of this force during takeoff and landing or during an alteration of course.

Acceleration is commonly measured in "gravities," that is, in multiples of the acceleration caused by Earth's pull at sea level: 32.2 feet per second per second. Thus under 5 gravities (abbreviated 5 g) a man experiences a weight five times as much as normal. His heart must work correspondingly harder to pump blood, at the same time as the demands on his voluntary muscles have increased fivefold. Every molecule in him is dragged downward—again, five times as much as normally. The delicate balance of the body is thrown out of kilter. Fluids begin to seep through the cell walls. The nervous system is affected.

Cats and monkeys put in centrifuges went into pseudo-epileptic seizures as they approached 5 g, lost consciousness when this acceleration was prolonged, and showed punch-drunk behavior for some time afterward. Noise and shaking affected them similarly, and it is therefore essential to damp out vibrations in a space vessel. No long-range

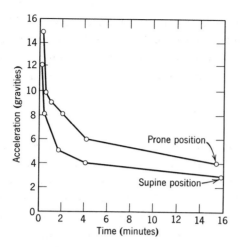

Figure 5.1. Limits of Human Acceleration Tolerances. (After Boudurant et al. in Kenneth Brown and Lawrence D. Ely, *Space Logistic Engineering*, Wiley, 1962.)

aftereffects were observed, even when 10 g had been approached—provided that the interval was short. But kept for weeks at accelerations as low as 1.5 or 2 g, animals do suffer permanent physiological changes.

Man is evidently tougher. Experiments show that he can stand as much as 10 g for a short time, and still more if the time is *very* short.* The limit of endurance depends on a number of factors. Immersed in water, which supports his weight and provides a counterpressure against cellular fluid leakage, he can tolerate about 7 g for as long as 15 minutes, but such a system may not be feasible in a spacecraft.

Position is also important. By lying flat, or nearly so, a man minimizes the strain on himself. The supine and prone positions are, respectively, known among engineers as "eyeballs in" and "eyeballs out." In Figure 5.1 we see approximately how much acceleration can be tolerated for how long a time in these postures. Clearly, eyeballs out works best. Just as clearly, 4 g is about the maximum over a period of several minutes.

Even under the best conditions, a man who has been through so

---

* This was first demonstrated by Dr. John P. Stapp (Colonel, U.S. Air Force, ret.) who volunteered as the subject in his experiments.

long an episode of heaviness will probably not be able to do precise work for a while. Accordingly, blastoff and entry into orbit must be controlled by automatic machinery. Luckily, spaceship acceleration does not last long, and to date no astronauts have been hurt.

Free Fall

Once the motors are shut off, the men suddenly find themselves in the opposite condition: free fall or zero-gravity. This prevails until maneuvers begin to put the vessel into orbit and resumes when those are over. Free fall does not mean that the astronauts have left Earth's gravitational field behind them, only that it is acting equally on every part of their ship and themselves, so that there is no resultant weight. We have all noticed the sensation of lightness when an elevator floor or the deck of a rolling ship falls away beneath us. A man in orbit experiences this to the ultimate.

We know from animal experimentation and from astronauts that several days of weightlessness do no harm. Most of the humans reported that zero-gravity was pleasant, with no spatial equivalent of seasickness and no significant effect on the body or—what had worried some psychologists—the mind. However, the Russian cosmonaut Titov admitted feeling indisposed, and in every man exposed to weightlessness the blood did pool in the lower legs to a certain extent. Nature soon corrected these matters after the return to Earth.

We do not know what might come of weeks or months in zero-gravity. What evidence we have suggests it could be extremely bad. Certainly the pulse rate after acceleration takes several times as long to stabilize in weightlessness as it does under normal gravity. Test pilots find that they are slower to rouse from the blackout following a high-gravity loop if a zero-gravity maneuver went before it—and such an outside loop lasts less than a minute. Considering how precise and intricate the fluid balance of the body is, we might have expected this.

Quite possibly an astronaut who has spent a long time in free fall may recover very slowly, or not at all, from the effects of high-gravity maneuvers at the end of his trip. If this turns out to be the case, we shall have to develop some way of counteracting the influence of weightlessness on the circulatory system, for example, by drugs, or else supply weight artificially during the voyage.

Free fall can also cause general physiological deterioration. Materials within the body, such as food, do not always move properly along the intended channels and could lead to cumulative damage; this apparently was the reason for Titov's malaise. Furthermore, man has evolved under conditions of vigorous motion in a gravity field. Since a sick wild animal will soon be a dead wild animal, there is no provision for long nonuse of the muscles. Anyone who has been bedridden, even for a few days, will remember how weak he was on first getting up. If a person is confined to bed for some weeks, the effects are great enough to measure. Circulation becomes markedly less efficient and the heart shrinks. Zero-gravity might well cause the same things to happen.

Indeed, when experiments in simulated free fall were carried out (the subject spent days lying in a bath of warm water, which supported his weight completely), the bones themselves were found to atrophy.

Of course, in cases like these, the patient can recover by building himself back up to normal, but we do not know if free-fall changes become irreversible after a certain time. Many physiologists suspect it.

Perhaps exercises can substitute for weight. The spacemen can pull against springs or oppose one muscle to another for several hours per day. Whether this will be enough to keep them healthy remains to be seen. It also remains to be seen how low a gravity the body can tolerate for an extended time. That of the moon is only one sixth that of the Earth. This may or may not satisfy our requirements.

We have already gathered a certain amount of information about free-fall physiology in such vehicles as X-15 and the Mercury capsules. More will be learned as Projects Gemini and Apollo proceed, but at present there are still too many unanswered questions to permit us to make confident predictions.

Besides the possible biological dangers, free fall has an immediate nuisance value. When there is no weight, there is no pressure differential to produce air currents. An astronaut might even smother in the cloud of his own exhaled breath. So it is necessary to provide pumps or fans. Tools, crumbs of food, and other small objects do not fall to the floor, but float about getting in the way. The spaceman needs rather special rations, such as the famous "meal in a tube" that has been devised. (However, one American astronaut remarked that a ham sandwich would have been just about ideal.) Liquids will not pour, but form mercurylike globs. They must therefore be forced out of flexible containers. Elimination likewise requires unusual equipment.

Pseudogravity

In view of all this, we would like to provide weight inside the ship, at least when space missions of weeks or months are undertaken. We know only two ways by which that might be done. One is for the vessel to maintain acceleration for the whole trip. The nuclear-powered ion jet will, hopefully, be able to do so, but it will not be operational for years to come, and in any event its acceleration will be quite low, maybe too low to be helpful (see Chapter 7).

The other way to supply weight is by spinning the ship. Centrifugal force acts much like gravity. We can, for instance, picture the craft as a hollow cylinder, rotating on its long axis (see Figure 5.2). The crew will be pushed against the inner wall. At any place where a man happens to be standing on that wall, the direction of "down" will be just below his feet, and he can walk all around the cylinder's circumference, always feeling weight, the opposite side of the ship always seeming to be directly above him.

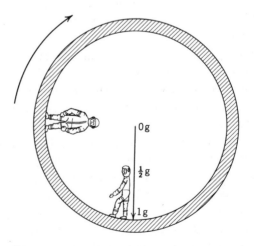

Figure 5.2.   Cross Section of Rotating Cylindrical Ship.

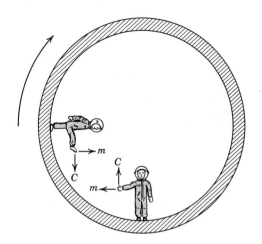

Figure 5.3.   Coriolis Effect.

There are some practical problems.   If the ship is 20 feet in diameter
and rotates once in about three seconds, the centrifugal acceleration
equals 1 g at the wall; but 5 feet inward, where the spaceman's
head would be when he stands erect, it is only one half of 1 g.
Every vertical movement he makes will take him through a nause-
ating series of gravity changes.   Even "horizontal" motion will have
disturbing consequences, due to the Coriolis force.   This is equal to
twice the vector product of the ship's angular velocity and the linear
velocity of the man's motion, and is exerted at right angles to both
(Figure 5.3).   It will not only complicate the simplest actions, but
will add to the vertigo-producing effect of gravity changes.

The bigger the ship, the less noticeable the two phenomena.   One
design which has been proposed rotates the vessel end for end rather
than around its bow-to-stern axis (see Figure 5.4).   This increases
the radius of spin, making less angular velocity necessary to get
a given centrifugal acceleration.   Hence the weight gradient and the
Coriolis force are reduced.   However, as the reader can see, the direction of "down" varies according to one's position inside.

Another suggestion is to build the craft in such a way that once
it is well established in orbit it can be divided into two halves, connected by a cable, which are then set spinning (see Figure 5.5).
If the separation is three miles, the two parts need rotate only once
in about 72 minutes to give 1 g that feels comfortably constant.

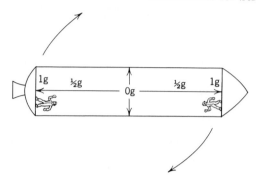

Figure 5.4.   End-for-End Rotation of Ship.

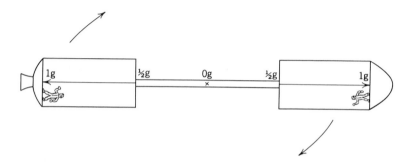

Figure 5.5.   Divided Space Ship.

Naturally, there is a catch to this, too. Willy Ley points out that such a cable, if made of steel, would have a mass of **13,000** pounds.[1] A shorter one would be less heavy, but no matter how it is done there will be a lot of dead weight. Maybe spin is the only solution to the free-fall problem, but engineers hope devoutly that the physiologists can come up with a better one.

This may well happen, or the actual perils of weightlessness may turn out to be less than some people now imagine.

Meteorites

Certainly other dangers have been much exaggerated in the past. Many writers, for instance, worried about meteorites striking and destroying the ship.   In reality, the vast majority of them are tiny sandlike particles.

An approximate graph of mass distribution is given in Figure 5.6 for meteorites in the neighborhood of Earth. From it the reader can see that the chance of a vessel colliding with one as heavy as a gram is extremely small. In any case, such an event need not be fatal. At cosmic speeds the stone would go through the hull like a rifle bullet through a cardboard tube, leaving two neat holes which could quickly be patched.

The smallest meteorites cannot penetrate at all. Those of somewhat larger size pose a greater hazard than the biggest, both because there are more of them and because the damage they can do is less notice-able. A pinprick hole in the ship would cause an air leak so slow that it might not come to the crew's attention until pressure had dropped dangerously and might then be impossible to find. However, monitoring instruments can be devised to warn and indicate. Or, a self-sealing hull can be built. If necessary, the ship can be guarded by a "bumper," a thin metal skin mounted on short studs outside the hull proper. Without any special protection, Earth satellites do not appear to have suffered much from meteorites.

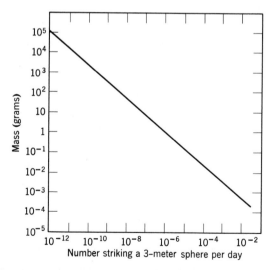

Figure 5.6. Mass Distribution of Meteorites Near Earth. (From a report by F. L. Whipple, in Kenneth Brown and Lawrence D. Ely, *Space Logistics Engineering*, Wiley, 1962.)

Physiological Requirements

Air loss brings up the subject of decompression. What would happen if, for some reason, the spaceman's air suddenly whooshed away from him? Some writers have given a gory picture of the results: lungs forced through the mouth by interior pressure as cells explode. But in fact, the body can stand greater decompression than this, as deep-sea diving experience has proved. What would kill the man is lack of oxygen and the boiling water in his system, as loss of ambient pressure reduces the boiling point below body temperature. So if the hull cracked wide open, he would have only a few seconds in which to take emergency action. A smaller hole means a lower rate of air loss, which would probably give him time enough to save himself.

As for the air within the ship, there is no reason why it has to be at sea-level density. The citizens of Denver manage quite well with less. But the composition is highly important. In the past, when there was more worry than now about decompression, the suggestion was often made that pure oxygen be used, or else helium in place of nitrogen. Helium, being less soluble in the bloodstream than nitrogen, is less likely to produce the agonizing, sometimes fatal "bends" caused by bubbles forming as pressure abruptly drops. Recent research has shown that nitrogen is not really inert. A man can subsist on pure oxygen at high altitudes or a diver can breathe "oxyhelium" for some hours. Over a period of days or weeks, though, nitrogen deprivation leads to collapse of the alveoli in the lungs and possibly to other damage.[2]

The percentages of carbon dioxide and water vapor in the air cannot vary too much from the norm either without bad results, as everyday experience confirms, and there may well be trace substances that are vital over the long haul. The degree of weak ionization (electrically charged molecular fragments) in the atmosphere affects the body and the mind. It even seems that ionization, like temperature, should vary in a cyclical way for optimum health.

How much air, water, and food need be taken along depends on the length of the mission as well as on the demands that will be made on the crew. A man at work needs more of everything than a man at rest. We can safely assume that the requirements will be those of someone doing light work daily; moments of great stress

Table 5.1. Daily Food Requirements of Astronaut
on Light Work Schedule

Oxygen	862 grams (about 2 pounds)
Water	2200 grams (about 5 pounds)
Food	523 grams (about 1.2 pounds)
Total	3605 grams (about 8.2 pounds)

will average out with times of ease. According to Pogrund,[3] an adult under such conditions consumes the amounts given in Table 5.1. In Figure 5.7 we see how this adds up as the weeks go by.

For a short mission the weight problem does not look serious, and no recycling apparatus is contemplated. It would be more massive than the amount of supplies it would save. For a longer expedition water recovery and reuse become essential.

This is simple enough in principle. All that needs to be done, it seems, is to distill the waste water, and just outside the hull there is a whole cosmos of vacuum, plus solar radiation, for such a still to use. As a matter of fact, a 10 per cent water surplus would accumulate on a lengthy voyage, since the body manufactures it

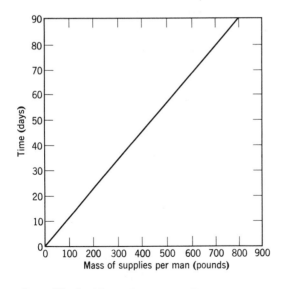

Figure 5.7. Food Supply Requirements Without Recycling.

from nonwater foods along with carbon dioxide in the course of metabolism.

Even so, there are complexities, some of them psychological. The story goes that an engineer in Project Apollo once asked a physiologist how much dissolved material must be taken out of urine to make it drinkable, to which the physiologist replied: "All of it, if you want to stay friends with your astronaut." Simple distillation cannot do this, for many of the undesired compounds are quite volatile. At present, more elaborate methods, for example, ion exchange, are under development.

Certainly the gradual buildup of odorous metabolic by-products cannot be permitted. Quite apart from the annoyance, they are toxic in large amounts and must be removed completely, probably by chemical means.

It is important also to get rid of excess carbon dioxide. This is now done by absorption from the air by such materials as lithium hydroxide, one pound of which can take up 0.74 pound of the gas. For a still longer mission than one that merely requires water recovery, absorption methods involve too much dead weight. A system will be needed to recycle the ship's air, maintain a proper level of carbon dioxide and water vapor, and release oxygen to be breathed again.

As everyone knows, green plants do that job on Earth as they take in carbon dioxide and water, make carbohydrates in their tissues, and give off free oxygen. Cannot a similar balance be struck on a spaceship?

Again, there are many unknowns, as well as blatant practical difficulties. For example, hydroponic (soilless) gardens will not be easy to keep in free fall! But research is going ahead. It appears that some 11 square feet of leaf surface will supply as much oxygen as a person at rest needs each day. Algae seem to be still more efficient, but since they must be spread thinly over a water surface to get the light they need their containers may prove to be too bulky for use in space. Whatever plants are grown, they may well be fertilized by suitably processed human wastes, and they could supplement the food ration.

Turning to that, we may as well forget about "a meal in a pill." The body has to have a certain mass of food every day, which is not made less by being jammed into pills, even if this were feasible.

The digestive system needs bulk if it is to work properly. Space rations can certainly be trimmed of all bone and other waste beforehand and can be given a maximum nutritional content per pound. They can be dried or powdered, both to avoid taking excess water along and to avoid heavy packaging. Pemmican, the old Canadian standby—a dried mixture of meat, fat, and berry juices—might be one good item to have. Naturally, dietary supplements, such as vitamins, can be put into pills, and the herbs and spices that can keep meals from being too monotonous do not weigh much. The total food requirement (exclusive of oxygen and water) for an astronaut seems to be only about 450 pounds per year.

Still, on extremely long missions, such as we hope to launch in the distant future, it would be most economical of weight to recover the food itself; that is, plants, yeasts, etc., could be grown for the men to eat, as well as to maintain the air and dispose of wastes. Much research and particularly engineering development work must be done before this recovery would really be practical, but there is no known reason why it cannot in time be realized. The ship would then be a complete miniature world, self-sustaining like the mother planet herself.

Radiation

Although we can seal a small habitable environment into a spacecraft, there is one part of Earth that we cannot take along. That is the thick blanket of atmosphere which softens and diffuses the sun's light, blocks most of its ultraviolet radiation, and shields us against the charged high-energy particles that fill the Universe.

The experience of astronauts, as well as of men who have gone to the fringes of space in balloons, proves that we need not fear too great an intensity of visible light as such. If we did, it would be simple to use dark glass in our portholes. But when illumination is not scattered by air some confusing and perhaps dangerous things can happen. Shadows become knife-edged and inky black, and the hull or the lunar ground beyond them can be painfully bright. Coming out of such shadow into such brilliance, the spacemen's dilated pupils will take in more light than the human eye is built for. If this occurs only a few times, no harm should be done, but after many repetitions serious eye trouble might develop. It may prove necessary to have a glare filter on every helmet and to slide it down across the faceplate before looking from darkness to sunlight.

Incidentally, man will never see, except on a photograph, what is so often shown in astronomical paintings—the unwinking stars of space surrounding the sun in a black sky above the moon's surface. He dare not look directly at the sun, and his pupils will be so contracted, because of the ground illumination, that the stars will be invisible to him. Of course, he will see them in abundance during the lunar night or in free space if he turns his back to the sun.

More serious is the danger of those radiations we cannot see. Without Earth's ozone layer to block it, the sun's ultraviolet light can kill an unprotected man. Fortunately, any thin layer of opaque material will stop it completely, and glass can be made that will not let it through. The sun also emits X-rays, which are less easily warded off. They are not usually intense enough to do any immediate damage. Nevertheless, spacemen had better minimize their own pressure-suited exposure outside the ship. Its hull will protect them against that particular kind of bombardment: solar X-rays are "soft."

A far more dangerous hazard is created by charged particles—electrons, protons, hydrogen and helium nuclei, heavier ions, and the more esoteric things like mesons. They travel through space at enormous speeds, some of interstellar origin, some ejected by the sun itself. Proton energies in excess of 10 million billion electron volts have been observed. Interacting with matter or with electromagnetic fields, such particles release energy in the form of high-frequency X-rays with great power of penetration and destruction. When they strike a living body, they themselves cause injuries that can be fatal if the irradiation is strong enough.

This harm is wreaked in various ways by mechanisms too complex to discuss here. Cells can be destroyed, especially in the blood, in the bone marrow, and in the retina of the eye. Cataracts can be produced. The affected organism can become predisposed to cancer or leukemia, it can suffer a kind of accelerated aging, or its gonad cells can be changed, so that any offspring it has afterward may carry some hereditary abnormality.

Earth's magnetic field deflects many of the cosmic bullets, and its atmosphere is an armor against still more. Even so, about seven of them go through us every second. Once beyond our planet, can we be safe inside the thin walls of our ship?

The answer to this question depends first on how much hard radiation we can tolerate, second, on how much will actually be encountered, and third, on what precautions can be taken. Let us briefly take these matters up in that order.

Radiation tolerance is a function of numerous factors: they include individual idiosyncracy and state of health. (Under this heading we might also put any protective drugs the organism has been given.) Then there is the kind of radiation: X-rays of different wavelengths, neutrons, electrons, stripped nuclei of different elements, etc. There is the rate at which it is received; a chronic low-level exposure adds up, in time, to the same total dosage as a brief intense exposure but the former does markedly less harm. There are numerous environmental factors, such as temperature, which are not yet very well understood. Finally, the "permissible" dose depends on the total situation. A man who has not yet become a father should not be exposed so much as one who has finished reproducing. In an emergency it is allowable to expose oneself to more radiation than would be the case under normal conditions.

Matters being so complicated, we can here only sketch what is known about tolerance. Radiation dosage can be expressed in various ways, some of which are more convenient for certain kinds of radiation than for others, but the handiest unit is the roentgen. This is the amount of radiation which will produce one electrostatic unit of ions in one cubic centimeter of ordinary matter. On Earth at sea level the average radiation density is about 0.001 roentgen per day, or 0.365 per year. Recently the allowable maximum was set at 0.3 per week, about 40 times as much as the natural irradiation rate. This amounts to some 450 in a 30-year working life. No ill effects have been observed from it, though a different formula has been adopted to reduce the genetic hazard still further.

A dose of 400 roentgens, given instantaneously or over a short period of time, would kill 50 per cent of those exposed to it and make the rest gravely ill. This illustrates the importance of dose *rate*. The universally lethal acute dose is considered to be 600 roentgens. At the other end of the scale, 25 does not seem to do harm, and it takes about 100 roentgens before blood cell damage becomes really serious.

In the light of these data, the maximum permissible emergency exposure is now set at 25 roentgens and the long-term limit at 12 roentgens per year. Standards are subject to change, but these give us an idea of the boundaries.

As for the radiation that will be encountered beyond the atmosphere, it varies enormously with place and time, not only in total amount but in kind. In the inner Van Allen Belt, as many as 100,000 protons per second may pass through a square centimeter with energies of several million electron volts. The Earth's magnetic field causes them to give off X-rays at a rate equivalent to somewhere between 10 and 100 roentgens per hour. Of course, the Van Allen Belts constitute a rather special region. They can be transitted rapidly, to minimize irradiation, or largely avoided by taking off from polar territories.

The normal level of radiation in undisturbed interplanetary space, due to cosmic rays, is much less alarming. Though their energies are stupendous, their numbers are comparatively few. In the 129 days during which radio contact was maintained, the Venus probe Mariner II recorded a total incidence of some three roentgens; this is equivalent to eight or nine per year, and agrees well with earlier estimates, based on terrestrial observations, of 5 to 12 roentgens per year. In short, when there is interplanetary "clear sailing," radiation does not appear to be a formidable obstacle.

Unfortunately, the sailing is not always clear. Not only are there regions of special danger, like the Van Allen Belts, but there are times when space in general becomes flooded with radiation. This happens when the sun emits a great flare from which there sweeps a veritable storm of charged particles and X-rays. The resulting level in Earth's vicinity has been estimated at 30,000 roentgens per hour.[4] Although it dies down again before long, we can clearly see that astronauts caught unprotected in such "weather" would die. Quite apart from this, it is desirable to reduce their exposure under normal cosmic conditions.

Hence spaceships on extended missions require shielding. This will not simply be lead plate, which by itself would actually make matters worse. The reason is that a heavy, high-speed nucleus passes cleanly through the body, doing comparatively little damage. But if it is stopped in an atomic collision—by the interposition of a barrier plate material—it produces a shower of slower-moving secondary particles, which are not only more numerous, but each have biologically more deleterious effect. At the same time, lead does work well against X-rays. (Any substance does, provided you have enough of it.

What counts in blocking off this particular kind of radiation is simply the number of grams per square centimeter of shield area. Lead's high density gives it a desirable compactness.)

The most effective barrier to stripped small atoms, such as hydrogen nuclei, is hydrogen itself because the maximum recoil is achieved when two bodies collide that are of the same mass. According to Newell and Naugle, 12.3 grams per square centimeter of liquid hydrogen will just stop protons of 200 million electron volts energy, whereas it takes 52 grams per square centimeter of lead. On the other hand, because of its low specific gravity, the hydrogen layer must be 176 centimeters thick—nearly 6 feet—as compared to 4.6 centimeters of lead. Aluminum is intermediate, requiring an area density of 32.7 grams per square centimeter, a thickness of 12.1 centimeters.[5] This metal is also a good shield against electrons.

On such grounds, S. Fred Singer—who also first proposed the meteorite bumper that we have mentioned—has suggested a three-ply armor. There would be lead on the outside (though this must have some protection of its own, being soft and easily melted), then the skin of the ship, and finally a layer of a hydrogen-rich material such as polyethylene.

Although this should be adequate most of the time, armor that can ward off the full fury of a solar storm may prove to weigh too much to be practical. Even so, such events need not necessarily prevent spaceships from traveling. A small, very heavily shielded section can likely be built in, a sort of flying fallout shelter within an otherwise lightly clad vessel. There the men could take refuge— uncomfortably but safely—while the storm lasted. Eventually we may solve the problem completely: electric and magnetic forces deflect charged particles, and theoretically such fields can divert charged particles entirely away from the ship. So far this is only a theory and a hope. We must face the fact that the astronauts of the near future are going to be more irradiated than ordinary men on the ground.

Still, as we have seen, this is no reason for crying doom. Even when intense exposures occur, there should be a fair chance of saving the victim. A number of drugs are already known which increase radiation tolerance considerably. They include such simple materials as cobalt, magnesium, and glucose as well as more esoteric ones like colchicine, chlorpromazine, and thiouracil. For example, the 50 per cent lethal dose, that is, the dose which kills half the animals exposed to it, over a 30-day period was increased from 765 to 1120 roentgens by an injection of 1200 milligrams per kilogram of body weight of cysteine.[6] This represents raising the threshold value by 45 per cent! Other drugs have since been found to be still more effective, and research in this field is progressing rapidly. There is also a good prospect of developing treatments that will enable the body to repair a very large amount of radiation damage (in fact, this is how some of the "protective" drugs actually work).

Besides this prospective battery of precautionary and therapeutic measures, we have the practical observation that the health of those men who have gone beyond the atmosphere to date has not been impaired. Although radiation is a real danger, it has been exaggerated by some writers.

Temperature Control

To close this section on a yet more optimistic note, we shall discuss one "obstacle" that has been infinitely exaggerated, since it does not exist at all. That is the terrible cold of outer space.

The truth is that space has no temperature. It is a vacuum, for every practical purpose, and temperature is a property of matter. A ship in orbit will acquire some temperature, but space never will.

How hot or cold the ship gets depends on several factors. To begin with, there is its distance from the sun, but even when quite remote it need not get too frigid. It can cool off only by radiation, unless man can provide additional ways, and radiation is a rather slow process at terrestrial temperatures. Meanwhile the crew's bodies are generating warmth. Out around Jupiter it would no doubt be necessary to install a heating system. Closer in, the problem is, conversely, to get rid of heat.

There are several ways in which this might be done on a long trip (the orbital flights which have been made encountered little difficulty, since about half the time was spent in Earth's shadow). An elementary method is to make the hull shiny on one side (to reflect as much light as possible) and black on the other side (to radiate efficiently). By varying the orientation with respect to the sun, the interior temperature can be regulated. But more sophisticated versions are already available.

They have proved out well in practice with satellites and probes. Though Mariner II, for example, had some difficulties with heat, analysis of data showed that a simple change of paint pattern would have obviated them. Alternatively, or more likely as a supplement, some kind of refrigeration system could be installed. It might be as simple as a valve through which excess water would bleed into space, taking heat with it as it boiled away.

All in all, we can see immense problems ahead, and not a few dangers, but none of the problems look insoluble. As for the peril, that is something that men have always faced, and gladly, when the goal of their journey was a bright one.

5.2 EXOBIOLOGY

The search for life beyond Earth is as noble a quest as man has ever ventured on. Its significance goes far beyond scientific interest, which would exist in abundance, were every planet of the Solar System barren except our own. What is the internal structure of the moon? What are the *canali* of Mars? What strange, violent processes go on in the deeps of Jupiter's atmosphere? But to find life out there—

It would not only illuminate the whole question of our own origin and nature, but it would give us some inkling of our place in the Universe. How rare or common is our kind of life? Any kind? How much do living beings matter, and what role do they play in the history of the Universe? Are consciousness and civilization an accident or a normal phase of evolution? How far beyond us have they gone on other planets?

Although we are not likely to answer these riddles for a long time, if ever, the exploration of the Solar System will be our first serious attempt to do so. The embryonic science variously known as astrobiology, xenobiology, and exobiology has already accumulated a number of facts on which to base our thinking. Let us therefore send our imaginations ahead of the spaceships and consider what the astronauts may find.

Imagination must be kept within limits if it is to serve any purpose other than entertainment. For instance, there is no point in discussing whether human life has appeared elsewhere in the Solar System. We know perfectly well that Earth is the only body circling the sun on which man can live without artificial help. To be sure, we can accept what astronomy tells us about extraterrestrial environments but wonder if radically different biologies may not have developed in them. Do silicate creatures with bloodstreams of molten sulfur romp in the 770°F of Mercury's sunward side? Do organisms, using lipids where we use proteins, swim in liquid hydrogen on Pluto?[7]

Speculation like this is entirely respectable, but at present it has to remain sheer speculation. We do not know enough to say whether such things could be. One of the objects of interplanetary expeditions is to gain some of that knowledge.

However, we do know quite a bit about the chemistry and even the origin of our kind of life—carbon-based, operating in an environment of free oxygen and liquid water. We can, meaningfully if not with absolute certainty, think about variations of its basic pattern which might enable it to flourish on worlds unlike Earth.

But life is not simply plunked down, fully equipped, into ready-made surroundings. It evolves from simple beginnings, and, as it does, it modifies its whole planet. If the first evolutionary steps cannot be taken, it makes little difference whether organisms could eventually adapt themselves to local conditions. They will not be there to do so. Accordingly, in examining the chances of life occurring on some particular world, we must begin by asking how it could get started. How did it commence on Earth?

The Genesis of Terrestrial Life

As yet, the area of our ignorance in this field dwarfs the area of our knowledge, but in the last decade or so we have learned enough to sketch the general outlines of what must have happened and even to put details into certain parts of the picture.

Mathematical analysis has shown that the material composing the planets cannot have been drawn out of the sun by a passing star. Nor can they have been cast out whole in some convulsion. Evidently the Solar System coalesced from a vast cloud of interstellar dust and gas, mostly hydrogen but containing the other elements as well. Solid motes stuck together to form meteorites, which fused to make asteroids, and at last formed planetary spheres. The major planets, Jupiter, Saturn, Uranus, and Neptune, were so big that they retained hydrogen and helium, which still make up the bulk of their atmos-

pheres. The others lacked sufficient gravity to keep these light elements from escaping back to space.

Earth did not remain airless long. Heavier gases and water, which
had been trapped in the rocks, seeped upward. The breakdown of
hydrates and other chemical compounds because of the heat of compression inside the globe supplied more gas. Eventually Earth had
a dense atmosphere of nitrogen, ammonia, carbon dioxide, methane,
water vapor, and minor constituents such as hydrogen sulfide.

Now, when such a mixture is energized, it forms amino acids. The
principal source of this energy on the ancient Earth must have been
ultraviolet light; there was no ozone layer to screen it out. Lightning
and radioactivity may also have contributed energy. The formation
of amino acids in this way has been duplicated in the laboratory.
These compounds, in turn, join to make protein molecules, and other
organic compounds must have appeared similarly. Not long ago
adenine (one of the four units of the DNA and RNA which govern
enzyme production) and adenosine triphosphate (essential to the
energy metabolism of the living cell) were prepared in the same
simple fashion. The natural synthesis of other important materials,
such as fats and sugars, should soon be equally well known to us.

Without free oxygen to destroy these prebiological compounds, and
in the absence of bacteria to devour them, a high equilibrium concentration was possible. So they accumulated in the oceans, in smaller
bodies of water, and, perhaps, on the surface of clay and sand grains.
As their concentration got higher and higher, chemical interaction
between them intensified, yielding more and more complex structures
in ever greater variety. Finally, nucleic acids appeared, molecules
which had the power to reproduce themselves by forcing other molecules to link up according to their own pattern.

In an explosive spread through the nutrition-rich waters these virus-
like microbodies took over the world. Radiation and heat caused them
to mutate, to change in ways that were inheritable. When these
changes conferred an advantage, the new forms increased their numbers at the expense of the older ones. Gradually they developed exterior complexity. Instead of the virus pattern of reproduction—a
mere rearrangement of externally available molecules—a bacterium-
like reproduction pattern of metabolism within the cell evolved.

As yet we are far from complete certainty about the details of
this earliest evolution. For instance, some authorities believe that

the first self-reproducing units were not naked molecules but crude protocells with interior structure. Be this as it may, the "cat and rat farm" process of consuming whatever could be consumed cannot have gone on long. Life would have perished had it not developed ways of making its own food.

That need was met when cells evolved that had the power of photosynthesis, of converting carbon dioxide and water to carbohydrates while releasing oxygen. This corrosive gas reacted with methane, ammonia, and their derivatives, replacing them with carbon dioxide, water, and free nitrogen. Raw rock took up most of the carbon dioxide in forming carbonates. Thus, presumably, we acquired the atmosphere we now have. Meanwhile, other forms had appeared to prey on the one-celled plants—the first animals. Life was fully established and evolution proceeded toward trees, fish, and men.

Grossly oversimplified though this account may be, it does illustrate three general requirements for the origin of life. There must be simple molecules which can interact to form the more complex. There must be an energy source to power this interaction. And there must be a solvent in which the molecules can concentrate and react freely with each other.

The smaller planets, if not the larger ones, should be well supplied with the first of these necessities. Heat, radioactivity, the sun, and lightning, if there is the right kind of atmosphere, furnish energy. As for the solvent, on Earth it was water. On colder worlds it may possibly be liquid ammonia, which has quite similar properties. Given such conditions on a young planet, we can be pretty sure that life will arise.

Are the requirements met anywhere else in the Solar System?

Meteoritic Evidence

The only direct indications of life elsewhere we have so far come from meteorites. A few of them do include rather complex organic materials. This may be due simply to contamination, after they struck Earth, but it seems more likely that the "cargo" was actually brought here.

If so, the organic substances may have been formed in the primordial nebula, before the planets had consolidated themselves. Hoyle has suggested that a great deal of chemical activity went on there.[8]   On the other hand, they may be the remnants of extraterrestrial germs.   If a large enough meteorite strikes a planet, it can actually throw smaller rocks into space.   If the planet is lifebearing, those rocks will presumably contain microbes in their pores.

Thus shielded from solar radiation, germs in spore form can survive in space for as long as a million years (i.e., we know some terrestrial ones that could).   If, during this time, the meteorite which carries them happens to land on another world, there seems to be no reason why they cannot emerge.   The passage through an atmosphere may not heat up the interior of the stone sufficiently to hurt them, provided that the stone is big enough to survive through ablation.   In this way life might appear in a place in which it could not originate; it might then be able to adapt itself.   Thus we must not be too dogmatic about the sterility of worlds like the moon.

Luna

Our satellite certainly looks dead.   During the two-week lunar day temperatures rise to more than 200°F, while the sun floods an airless country with radiation that would soon break down any large organic molecule.   Nevertheless, much of the lunar surface is covered with a layer of dust which may in places be quite deep.   This offers protection.   So do chasms and caverns, in some of which there may be ice that occasionally liquefies.   Thus there could be a good deal of organic matter on the moon.   This may have originated entirely in the primordeal nebula.   Yet we can conceive that some of it is alive—microbes from Earth, changed to fit the harsh lunar environment.

As a matter of fact, life might even have originated there as it did here.   Though now without any air to speak of, the moon must once have emitted gas and water; Carl Sagan has estimated that this atmosphere may have lasted for 10 or even 100 million years.[9]   Since we now think that the initial development of life on Earth was comparatively fast, it is not beyond the bounds of possibility that there was time for primitive lunar organisms to appear.   If so, they may have been able to adapt as the air bled away into space and still be alive in the dust, digesting minerals like some of our own anaerobic bacteria.   If they became extinct, they will have left traces that we can identify.

Maybe none of this is true, but we cannot ignore the chance. And so it is supremely important for us to sterilize our space probes, lest terrestrial germs contaminate other worlds and destroy a Golconda of scientific data.

Now we turn to the planets.

Mercury and Venus

Closest to the sun lies Mercury, a tiny globe, only 3100 miles in diameter, virtually airless, forever keeping one blistered face to the light of the sun and the other—dark, though warm enough to suggest a thin atmosphere—toward outer space. How could life, even approximately as we know it, exist there, let alone develop in the first place? We must not answer that question too glibly. Doubtless Mercury also has caves and dust layers. Between the bright and the dark hemispheres there is a region in which the libration of the planet makes the sun rise and set in an 88-day cycle. We can dream a strange saga—microbes from Earth or Mars hurled by a meteorite to the moon, evolving to fit its environment, and then being carried by another meteorite to Mercury's "twilight zone." Wildly improbable, yes; but who knows?

Next out, at 0.72 astronomical units, is Venus, very nearly Earth's twin in regard to mass and size. Though Venus gets almost twice the solar radiation we do, this need not make the suface intolerably hot, especially since clouds perpetually veil it, reflecting back more than half the energy. For a long time romancers were free to depict a tropical jungle, lapped by oceans that swarmed with fish, rimmed by cool grassy highlands.

But we have learned to our disappointment that this is not the case. The spectroscope has revealed the atmosphere of Venus to hold immense quantities of carbon dioxide, estimated at 5 per cent of the total; a bare trace of water vapor has lately been detected, but no oxygen. Along with radio studies, spectroscopy also indicates that this atmosphere has a ground-level pressure more than 10 times that of ours. Data collected on the Earth and by the spectacular U.S. space mission Mariner II show that the surface temperature is probably around 800°F—as bad as Mercury's dayside.

The clouds are still generally believed to be water, with some carbon compounds to give them their yellowish tinge. The reason we find so little vapor is that it is frozen out in the cold upper air of Venus. But there can be no liquid water down below, and no hypothetical oceans could have lasted long.

The temperature is high because the thick air, particularly the carbon dioxide, acts as a heat trap rather like a greenhouse. We do not know why Venus should have kept so fatally much atmosphere. Earth, even though it is slightly larger and much farther from the sun, did not. Perhaps the moon's gravitational pull caused most of our secondary atmosphere to escape, back when the moon was closer than it is now, or perhaps energetic solar particles kicked our "surplus" air into space. Venus does not seem to have much—if any—magnetic field, so that there must be less interaction with such particles than occurs here. Perhaps for some reason the planet originally outgased a great deal more than Earth. The whole subject is still, in Churchill's words, "a riddle wrapped in a mystery inside an enigma."

Despite these uncertainties, we can say that Venus is almost surely barren. Of course, microbes of extraplanetary origin may exist in the upper, cooler layers of her atmosphere. It is not too likely, but it is the very most we can reasonably hope to find. Unless we can someday mount a project to change the whole atmosphere of this world—such schemes have been outlined[10]—Aphrodite's planet is ironically named.

Mars

Some 40 million miles beyond Earth, at closest approach, lies Mars: an altogether different case from Venus. It not only seems possible that there is Martian life, it is probable.

This cannot be identical with our kind of life. Small, with a gravitational pull only 40 per cent of Earth, Mars has lost most of its atmosphere. The ground-level pressure must be less than one tenth of ours. What air remains is believed to be mostly nitrogen, traces of argon, and a surface concentration of carbon dioxide about 13 times as great as we have. Exceedingly small amounts of water vapor have recently been detected. At noon on the equator, temperatures may go as high as 70°F and in the polar midwinter to —150°F. Still, this is not much worse than what has occasionally been measured in Siberia and Antarctica. Experiments have been made to see if terrestrial microorganisms and plants can survive simulated Martian conditions. Though the results are somewhat controversial, they do suggest that certain varieties can.

There are several direct lines of evidence for the existence of life on Mars. The dark areas which cover one fourth of the surface exhibit seasonal color changes, as if they were vegetated. Their reflection spectrum indicates the presence of organic molecules. Polarimetric readings show that in spring they are swarmed over by microbe-sized particles, which may well *be* microbes. Now and then these regions change outline, like living forests or plains. At the same time, their essential constancy argues the presence of plants. If they were merely blotches, the great dust storms which have been observed on Mars would soon cover them. Something is forever renewing them, pushing up above the dust; if this were a volcanic phenomenon, it should liberate more water vapor than we have observed.

Furthermore, in its past Mars must have had thicker air and extensive bodies of water. As we have seen, life ought to arise under such conditions. The environment would not deteriorate too fast for evolution to keep pace, for organisms to adapt to an attenuating atmosphere and a drying soil. Besides, there could still be quite a bit of water. The polar caps are thin, perhaps mere hoarfrost, but shallow muddy swamps may remain; and there may be glaciers, buried under dust, from which water is slowly released. The vapor from such areas would be almost undetectable spectroscopically, since the high-velocity winds known to occur on Mars would quickly disperse it, and it would soon precipitate again in the cold.

On such grounds most writers suggest a sparse population, chiefly primitive lichenlike growths. But, as Frank Salisbury has shown, this cannot be.[11] A landscape covered with lichens would not behave like the dark regions of Mars. Furthermore, these alga-fungus combinations are not primitive at all, but most complex, dependent on a biological milieu and an atmosphere such as Mars cannot supply.

Indeed, the Martian life must differ from ours in many ways. We have not observed the reflection spectrum of chlorophyl from the dark areas. This does not by itself rule out the presence of that photosynthesizing compound; it could be masked by other materials, as it is in many terrestrial plants. But photosynthesis as we know it would lead to more oxygen and less carbon dioxide on Mars than is the case.

We can say with fairly good assurance that Martian biology is based on carbon compounds like our own and that it originally used water as a solvent. Whether it still does, or has converted to something else, is a moot point. There is no reason why it cannot. Cells can retain water inside themselves and evolve a structure that is not injured by freezing solid every night. They can even provide themselves with antifreezes (e.g., alcohols).

Vegetation on Mars might well split oxygen out of iron oxides, which are presumably abundant. This element might then be taken in with the food, rather than the breath, by those animals that are almost sure to be found wherever there are plants. As one alternative to this cycle—among others—metabolisms based on the intake of nitrogen are chemically possible.

In fact, as Salisbury has pointed out, there is no a priori reason why Mars has to be thinly populated. If life is there, well adapted to the surroundings, it should flourish rather than just barely hang on. Here at home only those regions that are densely overgrown look dark from a high altitude. Yet the rest is not empty. So perhaps the light reddish three quarters of Mars has as much life per acre as an Arizona desert.

Given that, it is even possible that large animals exist and that one of their branches has developed intelligence comparable to our own. If so, they cannot have a civilization more advanced in the mechanic technologies than ours or they would be visiting us (unless they have done so in the past and afterward lost interest). But they may have far exceeded us in other fields, such as art and philosophy. Even if they are savages, they can still have cultures as rich, with as much to teach us, as some we have found in Africa. Contact with nonhuman ways of life and thought could be the greatest stimulus that man will have ever encountered.

I do not press this point very hard because, of course, it is highly speculative. No matter what we find on Mars it will explode the boundaries of our experience outward.

This is where the more conventional thinkers stop. Beyond Mars the planets are too cold and alien for life; or so we are told. But this is not necessarily so.

True, the tiny asteroids that make a belt between Mars and Jupiter are unlikely to have any population. At most, there may be some organic matter on them, possibly some adapted microbes that originated elsewhere. If we wish to get quite fantastic, we can imagine these organisms evolving, becoming multicellular, and finally covering their bleak little rock with curious plants and nonbreathing animals. But the probability of finding any such things is small. The chances are that man's interest in the asteroids will be confined to the mineralogical domain.

Jupiter

Five times as far from the sun as Earth, more than 318 times as massive, Jupiter, the king planet, looks like the strangest of them all. It was big enough to keep most of its hydrogen and helium, which therefore dominate its atmosphere. Methane and ammonia vapor have also been detected. The clouds which band it may get their colors from free radicals, molecular fragments that could never last under terrestrial conditions; or the colors may be due to sodium dissolved in ammonia. The atmospheric pressure at the surface (if Jupiter has a definite surface) must be comparable to that in our ocean depths, or even greater. The temperature has been measured at about —200°F, for Jupiter gets only some 4 per cent of the sunlight that Earth does.

Until lately no serious thinker proposed that Jovian life could ever arise, but now many scientists are not quite so sure.

Were Earth airless, it would be, on the average, a good deal colder than it is, but our carbon dioxide and water vapor retain heat. We have seen what this has done to Venus, which has still more carbon dioxide. It turns out that methane and ammonia act similarly. The temperature we have measured on Jupiter is that of the stratosphere. It must be warmer farther down.

Perhaps it even gets warm enough for water to be a liquid, in which case two prerequisites for life exist, a solvent and an abundant supply of simple compounds. As for energy, the sun does supply some; so do lightning and the intense synchrotron radiation from charged particles caught by the Jovian magnetic field. Whether a sufficient amount of this energy gets down to the surface to spark the development of life, we do not know. But we cannot say it is impossible, especially since prebiological evolution could conceivably take place more slowly than it did on Earth.

If the Jovian surface is so cold that all water is frozen, ammonia should still be a liquid, and, as I have remarked before, the physico-chemical properties of liquid ammonia are closely akin to those of water. There should be a gradual accumulation of organic molecules in such an ocean, and they should interact to form more complex materials. There are certain objections to the idea that this process would continue until something appeared that could properly be called alive, but in the present state of our knowledge these objections are not overwhelmingly strong.

If there is life on Jupiter, it cannot use free oxygen as we do. However, we have no proof that it cannot use hydrogen. We can, for instance, imagine plants that convert methane and other simple gases into higher unsaturated hydrocarbons.[12] To do this, they would need energy; and not much solar energy can penetrate to the bottom of the Jovian atmosphere. They would also have lightning and radiation to help them. Life might proceed at a slower tempo than ours, but it would still proceed. As another possibility, living things might float about in the air at a level where the density is still so great that the organism's weight is supported but where some sunlight can reach.

Animals would then eat the plants, breathe in hydrogen, and use this gas to recreate the original unsaturated compounds with an energy release. If we let numbered R's stand for various organic radicals, a typical equilibrium can be shown schematically:

$$R_1R_2C{=}CR_3R_4 + H_2 \rightleftharpoons R_1R_2HCCHR_3R_4 + \text{energy}$$

This is only one of several conceivable mechanisms which have been outlined. Today we cannot be sure if any of them occur in fact anywhere in the Universe. But there is no clear reason why they should not. At any rate, we ought to see for ourselves. Though we have no idea how to land men on Jupiter, it has numerous moons. After establishing a base on one of them, the expedition could send probes to gather data.

As for the planets farther out, we are as yet too ignorant even to speculate coherently. The possibilities we have already considered prove to my own satisfaction that we cannot simply write them off as possible habitations, and whether or not they have life, each is a unique and fascinating world, a reservoir of mysteries and a lure for explorers of the coming era.

Extrasolar Planets

Then there are the planets of other stars. Unless we make some revolutionary new discovery in physics, we will not visit them in the near future, nor will we ever visit a large percentage of them. If a spaceship traveled at just under the speed of light, which modern theory says is the ultimate speed, it would still need more than four years to reach the closest star, Centauri Proxima. Of course, such a spaceship is as far beyond our present capabilities as an orbital flight was beyond Columbus. Yet that much progress has been made already!

Given a ship which travels at nearly the speed of light, the crew would experience less transit time than one might think. Theoretically, an interstellar trip could be made in months, days, or hours by the ship's clock—though when the crew returned, they would find that a time had passed at home approximately equal to the time required for light to make the passage back and forth.

To describe this more fully, let us imagine two observers moving at constant speed with respect to each other. Quite arbitrarily we will say that one is stationary. His clock measures a time interval T_0, whereas the clock of the "moving" observer measures a time interval T. If we are willing to neglect acceleration effects, we can compare these intervals by letting the one start out, travel at constant speed v to some distant point, brake, return at the same speed, and brake again. It then turns out that

$$T_0 - T = T_0 \left[1 - \left(1 - \frac{v^2}{c^2} \right)^{-\frac{1}{2}} \right],$$

where c is the velocity of light.

Thus, suppose that a spaceship has gone a distance of 10 light years, and back, at three quarters the speed of light. The observer who stayed at home will measure the time T_0 for the round trip as $2 \times \frac{4}{3} \times 10$, or 26.6 years. The spaceship's crew will have experienced only a time T of 17 years.

If the spaceship makes its round trip at a steady speed, but in a continuous closed curve—that is, without any stops—then

$$T_0 - T = \frac{1}{2} T_0 \frac{v^2}{c^2},$$

and in the case we are considering, a total distance of 20 light-years, covered at $\frac{3}{4}c$, T equals only 19.1 calendar years.

In any event, the closer one can approach the speed of light, the smaller his T becomes with respect to the T_0 of the outside universe. Admittedly, the problems involved in any attempt to do so are so formidable that they may never be overcome.

But if only slower craft were available, which would take a hundred years or so to make an interstellar crossing, some exploration would still be feasible. The crew might spend the time in suspended animation, or they might take their wives along in a giant, self-contained vessel, embarking on a journey that their descendants would finish. Various other ideas have also been discussed. Maybe one day one of them will become a reality.

Or maybe we will simply establish radio contact with beings who dwell on a planet of another star. If such beings exist, at a distance that is not too great, we could build the necessary equipment today. A mutual language could be worked out and, slowly, many volumes of information could be exchanged, out of which we might get whole new insights, arts, sciences, philosophies, and ways of life.

The question is, how likely are there to be intelligences and civilizations comparable to our own out yonder?

Although a great deal of research remains to be done, current scientific opinion is that a large number of stars—maybe a large majority—have planets. The process by which the Solar System originated cannot have been unique; rather it is typical of the way in which stars form. The markedly slower rotation of main sequence stars of class F5 and later, compared to that of the giants, indicates that they, like the sun, have given up most of their angular momentum to smaller companions. Finally, four extrasolar planets have already been found in our neighborhood—not with a telescope, but through their gravitational effects on the motion of their suns. Those of 61 Cygni, 70 Ophiuchi, and Lalande 21185 are monsters, ten or more times more massive than Jupiter, but the one circling Barnard's Star has only about 1.5 Jovian masses. All give strong support to the idea that bodies comparable to Earth exist.

Our survey of the Solar System indicated, if it did not prove absolutely, that the range of conditions under which life can develop is wider than once thought. Granted, most stars are dim red dwarfs. But it does not follow that every one of their worlds is frozen to death. We have seen how an atmosphere warms a planet and also how life might occur at far lower temperatures than we are used to. Besides, the fraction of stars that are similar to the sun is not too discouragingly small. We know of half a dozen in our own neighborhood, within 16 light-years, out of a total of 55. Within 50 light-years there are more than a hundred more or less sunlike stars.

The entire Milky Way galaxy contains some hundred billion stars. A conservative estimate, based on the dogma that life is possible only under reasonably Earthly conditions, is that 3 to 5 per cent of them have one planet each on which there is life. My personal guess is that more than half of them have. Let us take the lower figure. This one Galaxy, out of the uncounted millions that there are, holds several billion lifebearing worlds. There should be a dozen or so within comparatively easy radio range of us, even though a radio signal might take many years to reach them.

We do not know how many of them have intelligent inhabitants. If we assume that intelligence is a natural development in evolution, not a mere accident, and if we assume that the Solar System is about average (it does seem to be just about half the age of the galaxy, with man a newcomer, less than a million years in existence), there should be thinking creatures on half the populated planets. That is to say, there are, in this single Galaxy, *at least* a billion races equal or superior to ours. Out of this enormous number surely some have machine civilizations and some of these have gone beyond our achievements.

So the chances are that, here and there in the Universe, radio beams are probing outward, seeking contact with unknown brothers. Some day we will build instruments that can hear them and will answer, or we may go out ourselves.

This is a lucky generation, standing on the threshold of such an adventure.

References

1. Willy Ley, *Rockets, Missiles, and Space Travel.* New York: Viking, 1951, p. 314.
2. Ari Shternfeld, *Soviet Space Science* (tr. by the Technical Documents Liaison Office). New York: Basic Books, 1959, p. 207.
3. Robert S. Pogrund, "Physiological Aspects of the Spaceman," in Kenneth

Brown and Lawrence D. Ely (eds.), *Space Logistics Engineering*. New York: Wiley, 1962, p. 83.

4. *Ibid.,* p. 99.

5. *Ibid.,* p. 100.

6. *Ibid.,* p. 108.

7. Poul Anderson, *Is There Life On Other Worlds?*. New York: Crowell-Collier, 1963, p. 103. The original suggestion is Isaac Asimov's.

8. Fred Hoyle, *Frontiers of Astronomy*. New York: Harper, 1955, p. 95.

9. Carl Sagan, *Organic Matter and the Moon*. Washington: National Academy of Sciences—National Research Council (Publication 757), 1961.

10. *Idem.,* "The Planet Venus." *Science,* **133** (March 24, 1961), pp. 857–58.

11. Frank B. Salisbury, "Martian Biology," *Science,* **136** (April 6, 1962).

12. John G. Meitner, "Does Space Travel Herald a New Milestone in Evolution?" *Astronautik,* **2,** 321 (1961).

CHAPTER 6

Semiconductor Electronics— Computers, Communications, Controls, and Navigation Systems

Phil Adamson

Hughes Aircraft Company

Contents

Semiconductor Electronics—Computers, Communications, Controls and Navigation Systems

6.1 INTRODUCTION

Electronics is the art of switching, controlling, or otherwise modifying a strong electric current, by the action of some other, usually weaker "signal" current. This is accomplished through the medium of a "control circuit" in which the two currents are brought together in the proper relationship.

In most applications the strong current undergoing control becomes modified so as to have the same intensity variations (high-and-low) and the same rhythm (long-and-short or on-and-off) as the signal current. This process of "magnifying" the signal current is called *amplification*. The entire accomplishments of radio and television communications, the fantastic success of electronic computers, and the achievements of remote control of spaceships can be effected and explained in these terms.

For decades the key device in all electronics circuits was the electron tube, or *vacuum tube*—commonly known as the "radio tube." Specialized tubes exist for the various electronic modes, but the same principles govern all modes; choice of operating mode is made through the design of the control circuit, which is usually external to the tube itself.

In a vacuum tube the "strong" current mentioned earlier is made to flow between two elements, a (negative) *cathode* and a (positive) *plate*. The controlling signal is impressed on this current by means of a third element, the *grid*.

At first glance the very idea of controlling an electric current by a vacuum tube may seem to be a contradiction, since electricity will not normally flow through a vacuum. However, a flow of electricity is always a flow of electrons, and in the vacuum tube a "cloud" of electrons, known as a *space charge*, can be formed around the cathode simply by heating it. This causes electrons to "boil" off into the space surrounding the cathode. The cathode is connected

203

through an external circuit to the negative terminal of a power supply, and the plate of the vacuum tube is connected to the positive terminal. Thus the plate is given a positive charge, and according to the laws governing electrical charges the plate must then "attract" electrons from the cathode to itself. The flow of electrons from the surface of the cathode through the vacuum to the plate constitutes an electric current.*

For amplification and all its variants the *grid* is needed. The grid is simply a perforated piece of metal (or a wire mesh) that does not interfere with the flow of electrons between cathode and plate *so long as the grid is electrically neutral.* If, however, the grid is given a slight positive charge, it will attract electrons from the cathode and accelerate them on their way to the plate. If a slight negative charge is placed on the grid, it will *repel* electrons back toward the cathode and diminish or cut off the stream of electrons to the plate. If the charges on the grid fluctuate between negative and positive, the flow of current in the tube will fluctuate in step. A source of such fluctuating charges would be the weak *signal* current impressed on the grid. The grid then acts as a sort of "valve," varying the flow of the main current in step with the fluctuations of the signal.

The fluctuations of the signal are a reflection of the *information* the signal current contains. Since the tube's main current now fluctuates in the same manner, it, too, carries the same information but in *amplified* form. A weak signal has become a strong signal.

Although electronics based on the vacuum tube has grown to a fantastic extent in applications to communications and computers, the full potentialities for the development of *airborne* use were not realized because of the great weight and large size of devices composed

---

* In the tube this current can only flow *one way,* from cathode to plate. Even reversing the connections to the power supply, so as to make the plate a "source" of electrons and the cathode an "attracter" of them, will not reverse the current (it will only shut it off). This is because a high temperature is needed to "boil" electrons out of the tube elements to get the current flow started. The plate is simply what its name implies—a piece of metal or other good conductor (such as graphite). The cathode is either a glowing filament (similar to the filament in an incandescent lamp bulb) or a metallic sleeve surrounding the filament; in either case it is *hot*. In some applications a vacuum tube may consist only of these two elements. These applications are variants of the process of *rectification,* in which an *alternating* current can be converted to a pulsating *direct* current. This is because of the feature of one-way current flow.

of large numbers of tubes, their associated circuits, and their power supplies. Also, tubes generate great amounts of *heat,* and the necessary heat-dissipation can only be accomplished by increasing the weight and bulk of the equipment. The difficulties experienced with the design of airborne equipment are, of course, compounded when equipment for use in space is contemplated.

The recent development of an entirely new family of switching devices, the *semiconductors*—which are several orders of magnitude smaller than tubes—has provided a radical departure. Moreover, semiconductors do not produce the large quantities of heat associated with the operation of vacuum tubes. Semiconductors of various kinds can perform practically all vacuum tube functions at a much higher degree of relative and absolute efficiency. These new devices and their uses in communications, in computers, in navigation, and in guidance equipment for space vehicles are described in the following sections of this chapter.

6.2 SEMICONDUCTORS

Fundamentals of Conductance

The existence of the class of materials which form the basis of solid state technology has been known for more than a century. An Englishman, Michael Faraday, observed that the resistance of silver sulfide decreased as the temperature was increased. Before that time all electrical conductors were thought to exhibit an increase in resistance when subject to an increase in temperature. This experiment provided the first direct evidence that distinctly different classes of electrical conductors existed.

Other materials were tested. The electrical resistance of various materials was found to cluster in three groups which were called conductors, semiconductors, and insulators. Some typical resistance values are shown in Table 6.1. The semiconductors were found to exhibit electrical properties quite distinct from those of the conductors. Investigation of these phenomena resulted in the discovery of the transistor in 1948.

Semiconductors can be made into devices which exhibit the important property of conducting electricity much better in one direction than in

Table 6.1.   Typical Resistance Values

Group	Material	Resistance (ohms/cm^3)
Conductor	Silver	10^{-6}
	Aluminum	10^{-5}
Semiconductor	Germanium	10^2
	Silicon	10^4
Insulator	Mica	10^{12}

others.   The ratio of front-to-back conductance, or inversely of back-to-front resistance, can be in the high thousands.   In this way a *semiconductor material resembles a vacuum tube in its most important characteristic:* the property of conducting *significant* amounts of electricity in one direction only.   This immediately introduces the possibility of control of any current flowing through the material.

Many control functions can be carried on by semiconductor devices which consist essentially of tiny crystals weighing a small fraction of a gram.   The only currents involved are the input signal current and the "strong" current which is to be modified.   No need exists for additional supplies of electricity just to heat up a cathode, or to provide power for some auxiliary grid.   Thus power supplies can be much smaller, and the generation of heat is greatly lessened as well.   Also, because of the extremely small size of semiconductor devices in relation to the magnitudes of currents they handle, heat-dissipation problems are simpler.

Because semiconductors can operate effectively at much lower voltages than tubes (being "current-operated" devices rather than "voltage-operated" devices) a great number of other problems, including those of adequate electrical insulation for circuit components, are also more easily dealt with.   This means very small "external" circuit components can be used.

The end result of all these advantages is equipment which can be highly complex and sophisticated, but of greatly reduced size and weight, and having a greatly reduced total power demand and only minor problems with heat.

Transistors and diodes, as we know them today, are made from semiconductors.   There are many semiconductor materials, but at the present time most devices are made of germanium or silicon, both of which are hard brittle crystals by nature. In their natural state they are impure and do not exhibit the nearly pure crystalline structure of high quality diamond.

Semiconductor technology is often called *solid state* technology. This term suggests that semiconductor devices make use of solid material rather than of gas or a vacuum as in standard electron tubes. The unique electrical properties result from modifications of the solid material itself. The electric current flows directly through the material in a fashion similar to current flow in a conductor.

It is necessary to understand how electric charges move through solid material. A so-called solid material is not truly solid, but only partly so. It is composed of separate atoms, with empty spaces between the atoms. Each atom consists of a number of electrons clustered about a central nucleus. Electric current flow is the movement of electrons from one atom to another. The outside band of electrons in each atom is the most mobile and is called the valence band.

In a good conductor, such as a metal, there are many mobile valence electrons. In an insulator all valence electrons are tied up in the chemical bonds which hold the crystal together. Such immobilized electrons cannot contribute to electrical conductivity. In a semiconductor, *some* of the valence electrons can be freed easily.

In the structure of single crystals of pure germanium and pure silicon the atoms are arranged in an ordered array. This arrangement is referred to as a diamond lattice, since the atoms are oriented in a latticelike structure similar to that found in high-quality diamond crystals. A definite and regular pattern exists among the atoms according to the principle of space equality: the greatest number of atoms that can surround any single atom at equal distance and still be equidistant from one another is four. Figure 6.1 is a two-dimensional presentation of a germanium lattice structure. It could just as well represent a silicon lattice, since the silicon atom is similar to the germanium in that it also contains four electrons in its outer valence band. In this configuration no excess electrons are free to drift throughout the crystal as electric charge carriers. This configuration is a perfect and stable diamond lattice of single-crystal structure and, ideally, would be a perfect insulator.

A semiconductor device is manufactured by adding controlled

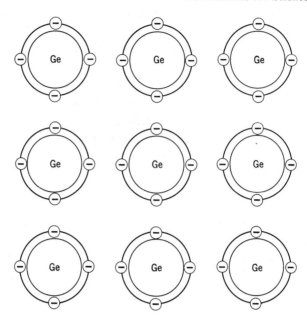

Figure 6.1.   Germanium Lattice Structure.

amounts of impurities to extremely pure germanium or silicon. These impurities provide *donor* or *acceptor* atoms to permit electrical current flow through the crystal as already described. A donor atom is one which has an "extra" electron available, whereas an acceptor atom is one which has an open space—an electron *hole*.

One of the most important principles involved in the operation of semiconductor devices is the principle of space charge neutrality. In simple terms, the principle states that the total number of positive charges (holes plus donor atoms) in any region of a semiconductor must equal the total number of negative charges (electrons plus acceptor atoms) in the same region, provided that there are no large differences in voltage within the region. Use of this principle can frequently result in a simpler and more accurate interpretation of the operation of semiconductor devices. For example, in explaining the characteristics of one type of semiconductor, it is usually stated that the function of the donor atoms is to produce free electrons in the crystal. However, using the principle of space charge neutrality, it is more accurate to say that the function of the donor atoms is to provide positive charges within the crystal which permit an equal number of free electrons to flow through the crystal.

Carriers—holes and electrons—can move through a semiconductor by two different mechanisms: diffusion or drift. Diffusion occurs whenever there is a difference in the concentration of the carriers in adjacent regions of the crystal. The carriers have a random motion due to the temperature of the crystal, so that carriers will move in a random fashion from one region to another. However, more carriers will move from the region of higher concentration to the region of lower concentration than will move in the opposite direction.

In practice, perfect single crystals are not possible. Even in highly purified semiconductor crystals charge carriers are present to move about freely, making the crystal a poor conductor rather than a nonconductor. At the start of the manufacturing process transistors require as near perfect *single-crystal* material as possible, that is, crystals that exhibit an orderly arrangement of equally spaced atoms, free from structural irregularities such as grains and grain boundaries found in *polycrystalline* structures. Polycrystals do not readily allow charge carriers to flow freely. Unlike single crystals, they are not easy to produce with any regularity. Furthermore, among polycrystals, surface structure varies considerably from crystal to crystal; this makes production of transistors to definite specifications difficult.

If a semiconductor is heated or subjected to a light source, the electrons in the crystal can absorb energy. An "excited" electron is free to move through the crystal and conduct current in much the same way as electrons in metals. This process of conduction is called n-type conductivity; the n stands for negative charges carrying current.

Examination of the region in which the electron originated shows a "hole." A neighboring electron may occupy the hole, thereby creating a new hole. The hole can travel through the crystal lattice in the opposite direction to the electron flow. This conductivity is called p-type conductivity since the electron holes act as positive charges.

Drift of carriers occurs whenever there is a difference in voltage between one region of the semiconductor and another. The voltage difference produces a force on the carriers, causing the holes to move toward the more negative voltage and the electrons toward the more positive voltage. For the n-type material the electrons enter the

semiconductor at the negative electrode, move through the semiconductor, and leave through the positive electrode, passing then through
the connecting circuit wire to the positive terminal of the battery.
In accordance with the principle of space charge neutrality, the total
number of mobile electrons in the semiconductor is determined by
the total number of acceptor atoms in the crystal.

Diodes

If a p-type region and an n-type region are formed in the same
crystal structure, a device known as a diode results. The boundary
between the two regions is called a *junction;* the terminal connected
to the p-region is the anode, and the terminal connected to the n-region
is the cathode. A diode is shown in Figure 6.2 for the two conditions
of applied voltage. In Figure 6.2b the anode of the diode is at a
positive voltage with respect to the cathode and the diode is said
to be forward-biased. In this case the holes in the p-region will
flow across the junction and recombine with electrons in the n-region.

Similarly, the electrons in the n-region will flow across the junction
and recombine with the holes in the p-region. The net result is
a large current through the diode for only a small applied voltage.
In Figure 6.2a the anode is at a negative voltage with respect to
the cathode and the diode is said to be reverse-biased. The holes
in the p-region are attracted away from the junction toward the
anode terminal and the electrons in the n-region are attracted away
from the junction toward the cathode terminal. Consequently, no
carriers can flow across the junction and no current will flow through
the diode. (Actually, a small leakage current will flow because of
the few hole-electron pairs which are thermally generated in the
vicinity of the junction.)

There is a region near the junction in which there are no carriers;
this is called a depletion layer. The charges of the donor and acceptor
atoms in the depletion layer generate a voltage that is equal and
opposite to the voltage which is applied between the anode and cathode
terminals. As the applied voltage is increased, a point will be reached
at which the electrons crossing the junction creating leakage current
can acquire enough energy to produce additional hole-electron pairs
on collision with the semiconductor atoms. This mechanism is called
avalanche multiplication. The voltage at which it occurs is called

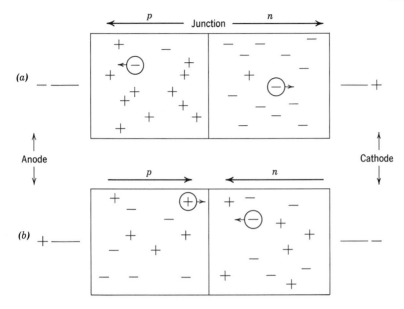

Figure 6.2. Diode.

avalanche voltage or breakdown voltage of the junction. If the voltage is increased above the breakdown voltage, large currents can flow through the junction, and, unless limited by the external circuitry, this current can result in overheating and consequent destruction of the diode.

Transistors

One of the most important semiconductor devices is the transistor. There are two types, PNP and NPN. An NPN transistor is formed by making a thin p-region between two n-regions, as shown in Figure 6.3. The center p-region is called the *base;* it is less than 0.001 inch thick. One junction is called the *emitter* junction and the other, the *collector* junction. In most applications the transistor is used in the "common emitter" configuration, as shown in Figure 6.3, in which the current through the output or load, R_L, flows between the emitter and collector while the control or input signal, V_{BE}, is applied between the emitter and base. In the normal operation the collector junction is reverse-biased by the supply voltage, V_{CC}, and the emitter junction is

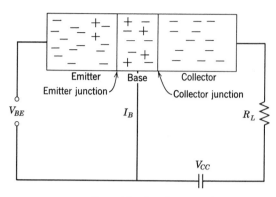

Figure 6.3. Transistor.

forward-biased by the applied base voltage, V_{BE}. As in the diode, electrons flow across the forward-biased emitter junction into the base region. These electrons are said to be emitted or injected by the emitter into the base. They diffuse through the base region, flow across the collector junction, and then pass through the external collector circuit. Transistor action is one of injection, diffusion, and collection.

If the principle of space charge neutrality is used in the analysis of the transistor, it is evident that the collector current is controlled by means of the positive charge (hole concentration) in the base region. As the base voltage, V_{BE}, is increased, the positive charge in the base region will be increased, which in turn will permit an equivalent increase in the number of electrons flowing between the emitter and collector across the base region. The ratio of the collector current to the base current is known as the *current gain* of the transistor. It is written $h_{FE} = -I_C/I_B$. Thus a current of one ampere flowing in the base circuit will produce 10 amperes in the collector circuit if the current gain is ten. It is this characteristic that permits a transistor to replace a vacuum tube as an amplifier.

Semiconductor devices have no theoretical failure modes, while tubes can fail from many causes. When the device is used, nothing is used up or worn out. Potential high reliability makes these devices extremely desirable for long critical space missions. A second desirable characteristic is their small size; a third is the lower operating power level.   Truly, semiconductor devices have been a key factor in making man's dreams of space conquest a reality.

6.3   COMMUNICATIONS

From the modest beginning made by Marconi in 1894 in transmitting information over long distances without wires, telecommunication has become a routine but necessary part of everyday life. Radio communication anywhere on Earth is an accepted event. Television pictures are in every home.   Newspapers receive text and pictures from sources at great distances.   Computers on opposite sides of a continent converse with ease.   How do we extend these numerous communications modes to include "off-Earth" contacts?

All wireless communications services have one thing in common: it is necessary to detect, at a receiving station, energy sent by a transmitting station.

The basic components of a wireless communication system are a transmitter, a receiver, and a channel for energy flow from the transmitter to the receiver.   These are shown in Figure 6.4.   This description applies to any communications system.   The most significant differences between systems have to do with the *range* of the system (the distance between the transmitter and the receiver) and the *amount of information* that the system must carry as a function of time.

Information capacity of a communications system is often expressed in *bits* per second.   A bit is a single unit of information represented

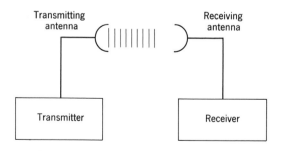

Figure 6.4.   Schematic of Wireless Communication System.

by an "on" or an "off" condition of the signal. A teletype machine generates a small number of *bits* per second; the 100 words per minute speed of routine teletype operation represents about 50 bits per second of information. This computation is made by considering 100 five-letter words per minute and noting that each letter is represented by a six-bit on-off code. Codes of this character are called Morse codes after Samuel Morse, the inventor of the telegraph.

A television picture requires a much larger amount of information: millions of bits per second. The number of bits may be roughly calculated by considering how the picture is built up on the television screen. The picture consists of 525 lines extending across the screen. Each of these lines is subdivided into light and dark segments; each segment represents a data "bit" and there are about 200,000 such bits in the entire picture. The picture is electronically erased and reproduced to enable motion to be reproduced smoothly. Multiplying 200,000 by 30, gives 6 million bits per second.

A telephone coversation falls midway between television and teletype in quantity of information. Approximately 10,000 bits per second are required.

What sort of information might be sent from a spacecraft? If the spacecraft carries people, it would be desirable to communicate with the occupants to give them directions in case of equipment failure, to help them make nonroutine maneuvers, or to permit the transmission of scientific data. It may be desirable to transmit—or to telemeter—some data to the ground automatically. Such data might relate to the condition of the spacecraft, provide an indication of malfunction of equipment on it, or provide detailed data relating to the astronauts themselves, such as their physiological states and responses. Finally, it may be desirable to transmit television pictures of areas explored, of the spacecraft, of people in the spacecraft, or of the instruments in the spacecraft.

If the spacecraft is a communications satellite, it may transmit or handle large quantities of any of the data just described. One such satellite presently being developed will handle 1200 telephone channels. One television channel is equivalent to hundreds of telephone channels, whereas almost 100 teletype (or telemetry) channels may be carried on one telephone or voice channel. Twelve hundred telephone channels across the North Atlantic would increase the number of channels now available from New York to London approxi-

Figure 6.5. A Synchronous Communications Satellite. (Courtesy of Hughes Aircraft Company.)

mately four times. A diagram of a communications satellite, Syncom, is shown in Figure 6.5.

Dr. Claude E. Shannon of the Bell Telephone Laboratories has advanced a theory regarding the maximum amount of information expressed in bits per second with a constant rate of error which can be passed over a communication channel between a transmitter and receiver in the presence of noise. The maximum capacity of such a communication channel is found to be

$$\text{capacity} = W \log_2\left(1 + \frac{P}{N}\right),$$

where W = band width of the channel,
  P = signal power at the receiver,
  N = noise power at the receiver.

Signal power, P, is a measure of the loudness of the desired signal; a louder signal is one with more power. Noise power, N, is a measure of the loudness of the noise; a noisier receiver or a louder noise exhibits greater noise power. Bandwidth is a term applied to the band of frequencies which a transmitted signal is using. This characteristic can be observed in an AM radio. Tune the dial very slowly and it can be observed that each station occupies about 10 kilocycles, or 10,000 cycles on the dial; 10,000 cycles is then the bandwidth of the signal.

Available bandwidth is a function of *frequency*. It is easy to understand the dictum of communications theory that bandwidth cannot be greater than frequency: the highest conceivable bandwidth for a signal of, say, 15,000 kilocycles is 15,000 kilocycles. In practice, the actual bandwidth is always less than the frequency, but higher frequencies always permit use of larger bandwidths than lower frequencies, ultra-high-frequencies permit practical bandwidths many thousands of kilocycles wide.

Some interesting general conclusions can now be reached by an examination of the equation. As the signal at the receiver is increased (resulting in a louder output signal) we can pass more bits per second (more information) but with the same number of errors. As the noise is increased, less information can be carried on the channel. Likewise, if the bandwidth of the channel is reduced, the channel capacity is reduced. Thus a given quantity of information (at a given error rate) can be passed through the channel by adjusting the three variables appropriately, and signal power may be exchanged for noise power or bandwidth.

The foregoing equation shows the fundamental problem in space communications: the effective energy at the receiver. The problem of providing sufficient energy at the receiver can be divided into general areas: the amount of energy available in the space vehicle, the degree to which the energy can be directed toward the ground receiver, the efficiency of the receiving system in detecting this energy in the presence of noise, and the distance that must be covered.

Radio waves can be described by the same mathematical expressions that describe light waves, so let us consider a system in which light energy is transmitted over a distance to a receiver, such as a human eye. How far away can you see a standard light bulb mounted on a post in your front yard? It depends on many factors: is it day, or night? How sensitive are your eyes? How dark is the background against which you are viewing the light? How much fog or dirt is in the air between you and the light? How powerful is the light bulb? Is there a reflector behind the bulb to concentrate the light in the desired direction toward you? Is the light white or of a single color? Each of these questions has counterparts in the space communications system.

Referring to Figure 6.4, we see that in order to determine the amount of energy at the receiver (the P in the previous equation) it is necessary to know the amount of energy radiated by the transmitter, the exact way in which the energy is directed toward the receiver, and the losses in the path or channel between the transmitter and receiver.

The path or channel losses will be considered first. We observe that as we move away from our hypothetical lamp on the post the light gets dimmer. If we double the distance, the observed intensity will decrease to one fourth—the inverse square of the distance. This effect is described by the law of the "inverse squares."

$$P_r = K \frac{P_T}{R^2},$$

where P_r = received power,

  K = a constant,

  R = the distance from the observer to the transmitter,

  P_T = transmitted power.

Thus, if no devices are used to direct the transmitted energy toward the receiver for a particular distance R between the transmitter and receiver, the selection of transmitted power determines the received power. To increase the received power, we must increase the transmitted power or use a reflector to concentrate more energy in the direction of the receiver. Such a reflector can be included in the transmitter's antenna system.

The signal power that can be transmitted from a spacecraft is limited by the amount of power on board available for communication equipment and the amount of surface of the spacecraft available for cooling. Figure 6.6 shows the power available on several early spacecraft. The radiated signal power is actually a rather small portion of the total power available and is usually on the order of a few watts.

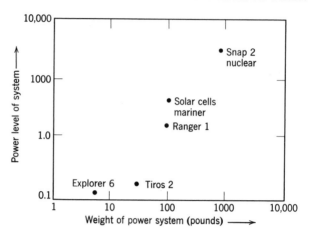

Figure 6.6.   Power Levels of Several Spacecraft.

The common method of increasing the amount of energy to be radiated in a chosen direction is the use of a reflector as part of the antenna system.   (Signal power is *generated* by the tubes or semi-conductors in the transmitter but must be *radiated* by an antenna connected or "coupled" to the transmitter proper.)   The antenna reflector is exactly analogous to the reflector behind the filament of an automobile headlamp; without the reflector the antenna would radiate its power in all directions.   The reflector concentrates most of the power in a fairly narrow beam in the chosen direction.   In this way it makes the effective radiation equivalent to that of an omnidirectional system of many hundreds or even thousands of times the power. Thus a 10-watt transmitter can be made to radiate, in one direction, the amount of power equivalent to that of a 10,000-watt transmitter radiating in all directions.   Such a directional antenna system is said to have a *gain* of 1000 (i.e., 10,000/10).

There are practical limits to the narrowness of the antenna beam that can be achieved.   These relate both to the size of the antenna* and to the problem of keeping it correctly aimed.

The size of rigid antennas for spacecraft is limited by the diameter

---

* Beam width is an inverse function of system size: in general, the narrower the beam, the larger the reflector system must be.   This applies strictly to antennas using parabolic reflectors and, with modification, to antennas using other types of reflector.

of the metal or plastic shroud that protects the spacecraft during launching. Erectable or inflatable antennas are limited to 30 or 40 feet by surface-pointing accuracy requirements and by obstruction of the field of view for other instruments on board the spacecraft. Two typical antennas are seen in Figure 6.7 on the Surveyor spacecraft: a high-gain unit and an omnidirectional unit.

The performance of earth-based antennas is limited by the cost of achieving the desired performance. A circular antenna with a diameter of 85 feet presently costs about one million dollars. Such an antenna is shown in Figure 6.8. To keep the cost within reason, these antennas are built with lightweight structural materials. This makes them sensitive to normal stresses expected in operation; for example, wind loading and nonuniform sun heating may cause significant structural deformation. Even nonuniform deflection due to

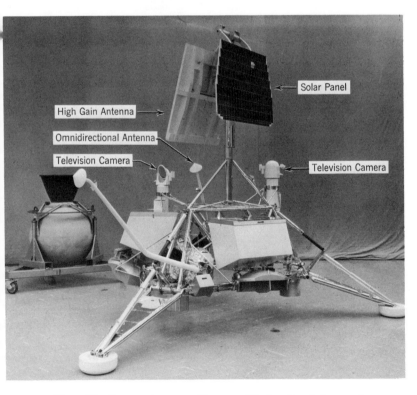

Figure 6.7. Surveyor Antennas. (Courtesy of Hughes Aircraft Company.)

Figure 6.8. Sixty-foot Steerable Antenna.

gravity as the antenna system is turned may be noticeable in antenna performance. The electrical center of the beam may not remain aligned with the mechanical center of the antenna.

The practical limitation to ground antenna gains is presently about 10,000. Such an antenna has an antenna beam width of about $\frac{2}{10}$ degree and must be pointed in the desired direction to an accuracy of $\frac{2}{100}$ degree ($\frac{2}{100}$ degree is the angle sustended by a lead pencil at 40 feet!).

In the optical analogy, the lightness or blackness of the night and the amount of dust or dirt in the atmosphere affected the reception of the signal. The extraneous signals created can be called "noise."

The radio signal from the spacecraft must compete with a variety of noise. Man-made interference may create noise in a frequency band substantially above that in which natural noise such as that caused by lightning occurs. Power-line corona, diathermy machines, automobile ignitions, and mobile transmitters pose noise problems.

When a radio is tuned to a very weak station, we hear many extraneous disturbances. These disturbances may consist of short bursts or impulses created by the ignition of passing cars or they may be due to lightning or other atmospheric interference. A steady background noise, called "thermal noise," will always be heard. Some of this thermal noise is generated within the receiving system itself.

To space communications, noise is not only a disturbance, it creates errors in received signals, and it may, under some conditions, make effective communication impossible. Fortunately, however, man-made interference, as well as lightning interference, drops sharply in strength at the higher frequencies.

Thermal noise is generated in any device that produces power losses. Thermal noise results from the random motion of electrons in the device. The amount of noise in a communications system is measured by comparing the noise output of the particular device with the amount of noise generated by a resistor held at a specific temperature. The noise in the resistor increases as the temperature is increased according to the following equation:

$$P_N = 4kTB,$$

where k = Boltzmann constant,

T = temperature of the device in degrees Kelvin above absolute zero,

B = effective bandwidth.

Thus temperature provides a measure of the noise power—changing the temperature of the resistor until it generates the same noise power as the noise source to be measured.

It is interesting to note that increasing the bandwidth not only increases the amount of information which may be passed over a channel but also the amount of noise observed in the channel.

The Earth itself is a source of natural radio noise. The Earth temperature is well above absolute zero so that the Earth generates noise in a space communications system. Solar energy causes the Earth to heat; the Earth then acts as a radiator at the ambient temperature, radiating over a wide range of frequencies. If an antenna were aimed directly at the Earth, the noise seen would be many times larger than that inherent in a practical receiving system. The common solution to the problem of Earth noise is to have the receiving antenna point away from the Earth. Special antennas so designed are called low-temperature antennas.

Even though an antenna is highly directional and is not normally pointed at the ground, a small fraction of the energy radiated by the Earth will still be received by the antenna. It has been calculated that a well-designed, narrow-beam antenna whose main beam is directed away from the Earth will receive a noise-temperature contribution of about 22°K.

For a complete receiving system a figure of merit may be defined as follows: M = antenna gain/system noise temperature. The system noise temperature is equal to antenna noise temperature plus the receiver noise temperature.

The sun and the sky provide other noise sources. The sun is very noisy, but the energy is localized to a small portion of the sky. Therefore systems and experiments are designed in which the antennas do not point directly at the sun.

The moon is heated by the sun much like the Earth. It produces noise in the system proportional to its temperature and the fraction of the antenna beam intercepted by the moon's image.

The noise due to rain, water vapor, and other atmospheric matter will depend on the amount of this material included in the beam, and also on the frequency.

We commonly think of the sky as completely devoid of radio sources and, therefore, as a dark background against which the desired signal can be viewed. When the sky is examined at the frequencies we must use, it turns out to look very much like a starry night sky with bright points of energy. An accepted map of the heavens at a wavelength of 480 megacycles is shown in Figure 6.9. Such a map would be completely different at a different wavelength. This corresponds to suggesting that stars have different colors and that different stars are seen through various colored filters.

Although the sky may look very black or noise-free to radio waves when the antennas are looking between stars, the interference level may be quite high if the spacecraft happens to be directly in line with a star. This situation requires an increase in spacecraft trans-

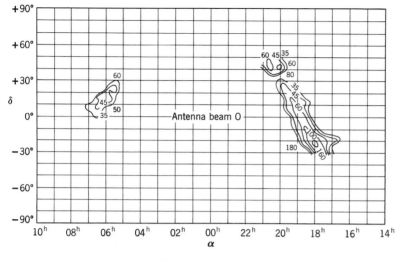

Figure 6.9. Map of the Radio Sky Background.

mitter power; it cannot be met by increasing the receiver's sensitivity.

Table 6.2 is a calculation of the system's noise temperature experienced by the receiving system at the Jodrell Bank 250-foot radio
telescope at the University of Manchester in a particular experiment.
Note that the side-lobe Earth noise is about one eighth of the total
noise. Note also that the natural noise (cosmic and atmospheric
absorption) is only about one-fifth that of the system noise. This
shows the improvements that can be made with better system components such as antennas and receivers.

Since the size of the antenna structure on the spacecraft is strictly

Table 6.2.   System Noise Distribution—Jodrell Bank

Cosmic noise	45°K
Side-lobe or earth noise	30°K
Atmospheric absorption	10°K
Plumbing loss	45°K
Receiver and preamplifier noise	120°K
Total system noise	250°K

limited by dimensions of the spacecraft, every effort must be made to compensate by decreasing the internal noise in the system. Among the modern devices used for this purpose are the parametric amplifier and the maser. The maser may provide internal noise in the radio receiver as low as one eighth that obtained with conventional techniques.

A maser operates by permitting crystal atoms to absorb locally-generated microwave radiation and release energy at the signal frequency. Amplification can then be obtained from the atoms with extremely low system noise. A maser, however, has the disadvantage of requiring extremely low operating temperatures; most are refrigerated by use of liquid helium. The parametric amplifier lacks this disadvantage but its low-noise performance is not quite as good.

Systems have been operated providing a noise temperature of about 50°K. A 10°K system could be built when refrigerators become available to provide practical operation for the maser at about 1.5°K.

A space communication system can be devised that will meet any space mission requirement. For low-altitude satellites with reasonable transmitter weights very large amounts of information can be transmitted. Since radiated power from the spacecraft is roughly proportional to weight, we can show that with 10 pounds devoted to the transmitter and antenna system it is possible to send a television picture from a satellite in a 500-mile orbit to a 60-foot antenna on the ground. For transmission from the moon a 200-pound antenna and transmitting system is capable of transmitting a television picture from the moon to the Earth. If only 10 pounds can be devoted to the antenna-transmitter combination, the maximum information capacity of the equipment will drop to that equivalent to two telephone conversations. In the exploration of Venus or Mars a 200-pound system would provide approximately one voice channel, whereas a 10-pound transmitter would permit approximately one teletype channel when transmitting to a 250-foot-diameter antenna on Earth.

In conclusion, consider an interstellar mission with a 10-ton transmission system and a 1000-foot receiving antenna on the Earth's surface: it is barely possible to receive from the nearest star, Proxima Centauri. With this system the information rate is so low that the teletype could be operated at only 1/10,000 of the design speed. Some improvement can be made in information rate by placing the receiving antenna in a satellite orbit around the Earth. If this is done, the low-noise properties of the maser amplifier may be utilized. A 10-ton transmitting system received by a 1000-foot antenna at an altitude of about 5000 miles above the Earth's surface would provide an information rate 100 times that of the previous example and thus would permit a teletype channel to be operated at 1/100 design speed. If it were possible to locate communication repeater stations along the way, it would be possible to permit transmission of one teletype channel or 100 bits per second to Proxima Centauri. Thus it appears that as communication techniques are improved it will be possible to achieve communication at high information rates throughout the entire Solar System, since the distances involved would be only tiny fractions of the distance to Proxima Centauri.

6.4 CONTROL

Airplane flight began with manual and semiautomatic controls. The pilot read the instruments and applied corrections. He compensated for deviations from desired performance and he performed a manipulative correction of control surfaces, valves, and switches. He served as feedback link and as error-detector, controller and corrector. He decided what the reading was, what it meant, what should be done about it, and whether the correction was satisfactory.

Rapid improvements in the performance of airplanes caused the pilots to fall behind.

It was necessary to find a way to relieve them of routine operating chores and free them for decisions involving judgment. Instruments which previously had only measured now controlled as well. Power amplification helped to replace muscles.

The advent of space flight increased the difficulties for the pilot. Not only did many corrective decisions have to be made almost instantaneously, but the environment became more unfriendly to man. Electronics was pressed into service for control; just as with communications, practical space-flight control was based on the technology of solid state devices.

Feedback Controls

The first feedback control system not involving human beings as part of the system was the flyball governor for controlling the speed of steam engines, introduced in 1788 by James Watt. Since that time feedback control systems have come into common use. The power steering on an automobile is an excellent example. As the steering wheel is turned, the front wheels are forced to move until they are again aligned with the position of the steering wheel.

A feedback control system is designed to maintain a prescribed relationship between the *actual state* of a system and an arbitrarily varied *desired state,* using the difference between the states as a means of control. The standard definition of a *servomechanism* is a feedback control system in which the controlled element is mechanical position. Thus a servomechanism positions with respect to an input signal capable of supplying only negligible power. It performs its function by detecting the difference between the actual position and the desired position. Recently, the word "servo" has become generally accepted as meaning any feedback control system.

Feedback control systems have many uses in space. They may be used as part of an analog computing system, as a voltage or frequency control system, or as temperature, position, or velocity control systems. They are used to orient the large ground antennas already described.

A block diagram of a feedback control system is shown in Figure 6.10. The input may be a quantity, such as voltage, speed, position, or temperature which the output is expected to follow. The output is seen to be equal to the error signal multiplied by the amplifier gain A. This is expressed as

$$eA = c,$$

where c is the output from the system, A is the gain of the amplifier, and e is the error signal. Thus, if the error signal is 1 volt and

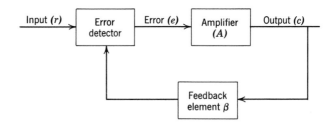

Figure 6.10.   Block Diagram of Feedback Control System.

the amplifier gain A equals 100, the output, c, equals 100 volts. The error detector takes the difference between the input, r, and the feedback voltage, c. The error, e, is written as

$$e = r - c\beta,$$

where β is the fraction of the output appearing at the error detector. Now divide both sides of the previous equation by A.

$$e = \frac{c}{A}.$$

Place the last two equations equal,

$$e = -c\beta + r$$

$$= \frac{c}{A},$$

multiply by A,

$$-Ac\beta + Ar = c,$$

transpose,

$$+Ac\beta + c = Ar,$$

factor out c,

$$c(A\beta + 1) = Ar,$$

divide both sides by $r(A\beta + 1)$,

$$\frac{c}{r} = \frac{A}{A\beta + 1},$$

and divide the numerator and the denominator of the right-hand term by A,

$$\frac{c}{r} = \frac{1}{\beta + 1/A}.$$

Then, if A is much larger than β, perhaps 100 times,

$$\frac{c}{r} \simeq \frac{1}{\beta}.$$

Thus, if the gain of the amplifier is high, the gain of the system is dependent only on the characteristic of the feedback element. Amplifiers with precise characteristics can be constructed with precision elements only in the feedback path β.

Servomechanisms

Servomechanisms are used to position mechanical elements. A pictorial diagram of a servomechanism is shown in Figure 6.11; its block diagram is shown in Figure 6.12. The function of this servomechanism is to reproduce the angular position of the command shaft at some remote location. The angular position of the command shaft is "converted" to a voltage proportional to its position by means of a potentiometer. The position of the output shaft is "converted" to a voltage proportional to its position by means of another potentiometer, fed from the same voltage source as the first potentiometer. The difference between the voltages from the two potentiometers is the error signal and is a measure of the lack of correspondence between the two shafts. This difference voltage is connected to the amplifier in such a way that if the difference is positive the motor will move in one direction; if the difference is negative, the motor will run in the opposite direction. When the control and output shafts have identical angular positions, the error signal is zero, and the motor stops.

Although a properly designed servo will not have sustained oscillations for any position of the input shaft, many units have *damped* oscillations. Because of the inertia of the servo motor, the controlled shaft does not stop instantaneously at its final position. When a sudden change, called a step function, of position is applied to the

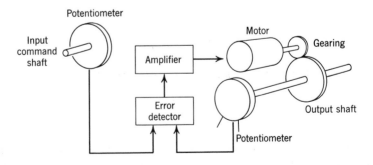

Figure 6.11.   Schematic of Servomechanism.

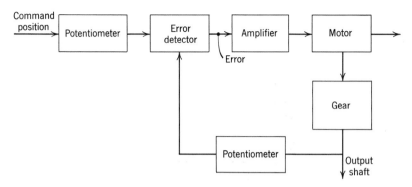

Figure 6.12. **Block Diagram of Servomechanism.**

input shaft, the motor accelerates and gradually rotates the output shaft to a position approaching that of the command shaft. This input is shown graphically in Figure 6.13. When the shaft positions are identical, the error voltage is zero. The momentum of the controlled shaft and the motor rotor causes the position of the controlled shaft to overshoot its desired value. When it has done so, the voltage from the potentiometers reverses polarity and causes a torque in the opposite direction to come to bear on the controlled shaft. The motor slows down, reverses, and again crosses a point of zero-actuating signal. A small momentum still exists, and the system again overshoots; the system may then reach its ultimate position. This whole operation is completed in a few tenths of a second. The action called underdamped response is shown in Figure 6.13b.

If the action is slowed by adding corrective elements to the feedback network β, the result shown in Figure 13c may be reached; this situation is called overdamping. *Critical* damping permits the output to reach its final position in the least time with no oscillation.

Servo systems commonly use circuit elements that perform computations. The error detector subtracts one input from another to find the difference between them. An operational amplifier, as used in one type of analog computer, operates by connection of an addition network to the feedback amplifier; the output of the system is the sum of the inputs. A servomechanism with an additional potentiometer mounted on the output shaft becomes a multiplier in a similar analog computer.

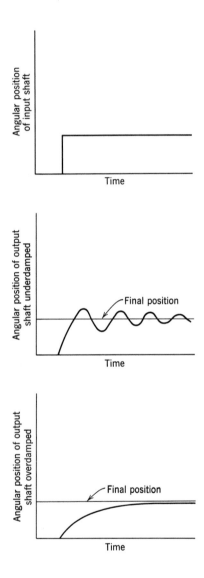

Figure 6.13.   Damping of Servomechanism.

6.5   COMPUTERS

Two types of computer are in common use today—analog and digital. Although the distinction between them is blurred in some instances, analog computers perform by making physical models of the desired computation, whereas digital computers work with numerical representations.

An example will make the distinction clear.   Assume that we desire to solve the equation

$$d = vt;$$

that is, distance, d, is equal to velocity, v, multiplied by time, t. One method of solving the equation might be to search the physical laws for an equation of similar form.   Such an equation might be

$$E = IR;$$

that is, voltage, E, is equal to current, I, times resistance, R.   If the current in an "analog" circuit is varied in proportion to the velocity v and the resistance R in the analog circuit is varied in proportion to the time t, the voltage drop E across the resistance is a measure of the distance d.

A second method of solving the equation in an analog fashion would be to construct a multiplier with servomechanisms.   If one shaft position is proportional to velocity V, a potentiometer is mounted on the shaft, and a voltage input proportional to the time t is applied across the potentiometer, the voltage output from the potentiometer will be equal to V times t, or d.   The potentiometer mounted on the output shaft of the servomechanism thus represents a "multiplier."

A third method of solving the problem is to measure v and t in terms of digital numbers and multiply the two numbers.   Of course, if the output is required in the form of a shaft position, the resulting digital representation of distance d must be converted to a shaft position with additional equipment.

The digital computer has a number of design advantages over the analog computer.   The digital computer can achieve very high accuracy in computation because additional accuracy is obtained by merely carrying another column of numbers.   No increase in accuracy of the parts making up the device is required. The digital computer is also easier to up-date for changes in requirements, since it can be made to solve a new problem by merely providing the computer with a new set of instructions in its memory circuits. An analog computer is likely to require rewiring or machining of a cam or similar mechanical modifications to make it perform a new job. The digital-computer technology is beginning to provide speeds of response comparable to the analog-computer technology. However, the digital computer is often more complex and more costly. Thus both digital and analog computers are commonly utilized aboard a spacecraft.

Although the principles involved in digital computers have been known for many decades, it is only since World War II that electronics technology has developed to the point where it has been possible to build practical digital computers. Digital computers are composed of circuits called *gates* and *flip-flops*. The term "gate" is derived from the physical analogy: a gate permits the passage of a person or thing only when it is open. In a digital computer a gate performs precisely the same function. A pulse or a wave of electrical energy is permitted to pass when the gate is open. An ordinary wall switch might be considered a gate. When the switch is on—and *only* when it is on—the electric current is permitted to pass.

In digital computers gates are usually composed of semiconductor devices and resistors. An elementary gate may have the form shown in Figure 6.14. The arrow-type symbols in the gate indicate semi-

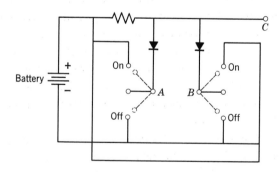

Figure 6.14.   Elementary "and" Gate.

A	B	C
0	0	0
1	0	0
0	1	0
1	1	1

Figure 6.15.   Truth table $(A \cdot B = C)$.

conductor diodes. Earlier it was shown that a diode is a device which permits the passage of electric current in only one direction. The gate shown has two inputs, A and B, and a single output, C. If input A or B is connected to the plus side of the battery, it is said to be "on." If it is connected to the minus side of the battery, it is said to be "off." When the output terminal C is positive, the output is on.

The operation of a gate can now be considered. If only input A is turned on, by connecting it to the positive side of the battery, there is no change in the output level C, since it is connected to the negative side of the battery through diode B. However, if B is also turned on, that is, connected to the positive side of the battery, the output C is also turned on. This action is described in Figure 6.15, called a "truth table." Either A or B can be either on or off, and in the truth table this condition is designated by one or zero, respectively. Output C can also be on or off. The truth table then shows the output for all possible combinations of inputs. Note that only if both inputs are on is the output on.

In the middle of the nineteenth century George Boole developed an algebra which has been applied to the design of computers from gates. This algebra is unusual in that it permits numbers to have only two values: one and zero. An expression to describe the truth table which we have just developed for the gate can thus be written as $A \cdot B$ equals C. By substitution, in this equation, it can be shown that the truth table satisfies it exactly; that is, only when both A and B are equal to one does an output exist. A gate such as we have described by this equation, $(A \cdot B = C)$ is called an "and" gate.

Other gate configurations are possible and are used. A common one is the "or" gate. Such a gate is shown in Figure 6.16 with

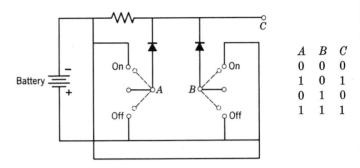

	A	B	C
	0	0	0
	1	0	1
	0	1	0
	1	1	1

Figure 6.16. Elementary "or" Gate and Truth Table (A + B = C).

the corresponding truth table.   The equation for the "or" gate is written $A + B = C$.   Note here a characteristic of Boolean addition, $1 + 1 = 1$, and that only when there is no input present on either A or B is the output C equal to zero.

The gates just described can be combined into a device that adds. To understand such a device, it is necessary to understand binary numbers, which are the numbers commonly used in digital computers. As we start counting in decimal numbers, we count (1), (2), (3), (4), (5), (6), (7), (8), (9). To describe a number that is greater than nine, a second column of numbers is started. Ten is written by putting a one in the second—or tens—column and changing the nine to zero in the first—or ones—column, (10). Describing quantities of increasing size, we then count (11), (12), (13), (14), etc. On reaching 99, the same problem recurs. Again we replace the nines in the first two columns with zeros and add a one in the third, or hundreds, column (100). We see that a number such as 376 can then be read as:

$$
\begin{aligned}
& 3 \times 100 \qquad\quad\ 3 \times 10^2 \\
+\, & 7 \times\ \ 10 \quad \text{or} \quad +7 \times 10^1 \\
+\, & 6 \times\ \ \ 1 \qquad\quad +6 \times 10^0.
\end{aligned}
$$

When added together, these numbers equal 376.   The decimal system, then, is based on powers of the number 10.

Binary numbers are created in exactly the same fashion, except numbers are built on powers of two.   We count (0), (1).   A number bigger than one cannot be written in a single column. Therefore the one is replaced by a zero and a one is placed in the second column as in the decimal example. This gives us the number two. To count three, the zero in the first column is changed to a 1 (11). To increase this number (11) by one, we must now introduce a third column, change the numbers in the first two columns to zero, and add a one in the third column making (100). This gives successive powers of 2, as follows: $2^0 = 1$; $2^1 = 2$; $2^1 + 2^0 = 3$; $2^2 = 4$. Each column represents a successively higher power of 2.

A comparison of decimal numbers with binary numbers is shown in Figure 6.17. Note, however, that binary numbers can be expressed in the same fashion as decimal numbers. Take the binary number 111. This may be read as one times one, plus one times two, plus one times four, or 1×2^0, plus 1×2^1, plus 1×2^2. This, of course, equals "seven" in the decimal system.

A truth table can be written to express the addition of two binary

Decimal	Binary
0	0
1	1
2	10
3	11
4	100
5	101
6	110
7	111
8	1000
9	1001
10	1010
11	1011
12	1100
13	1101
14	1110
15	1111
16	10000
17	10001

Figure 6.17. Comparison of decimal and binary numbers.

numbers.   From examination of the examples, the rules are observed to be

$$0 + 0 = 0$$
$$0 + 1 = 1$$
$$1 + 0 = 1$$
$$1 + 1 = 0.$$

This last rule is similar to the decimal addition of 5 plus 5, which equals zero, plus a "carry" in the next column.   Let us now proceed to the development of a composite gate that will follow this set of rules.   Comparing the truth table for the addition operation with the previous truth tables shows that the "or" gate performs most of the operations required.   The "or" gate gives a correct answer for the input combinations 00, 01, 10, but gives 1 rather than 0 for 11. Thus some modifications must be made in a simple "or" gate to make it operate as an adder.

A	$\bar{A}$
0	1
1	0

Figure 6.18.   Truth table (A, not $\bar{A}$).

The concept of "not," or the complement of a binary number, must be used to solve this dilemma.   If the signal A exists, then the signal $\bar{A}$ or (A-complement) does not exist.   A truth table for this function is shown in Figure 6.18.   Now a new truth table may be written. Here $\bar{A}$ is combined with the signal B with the use of an "and" gate. The truth table for this operation is shown in Figure 6.19.   Figure 6.20

$\bar{A}$	B	C
1	0	0
1	1	1
0	0	0
0	1	0

Figure 6.19.   Truth table ($\bar{A} \cdot B = C$).

A	$\bar{B}$	C
0	1	0
0	0	0
1	1	1
1	0	0

Figure 6.20.   Truth table (A · $\bar{B}$ = C).

then shows the truth table for the signal A times $\bar{B}$.   When these two truth tables are combined in an "or" gate, the resulting function is the precise function required for addition.   This may be written in symbolic or Boolean form as $\bar{A}B + A\bar{B} = C$.   This expression is described precisely by the truth table in Figure 6.21, which also defines the rules for binary addition.

A	$\bar{A}$	B	$\bar{B}$	C
0	1	0	1	0
0	1	1	0	1
1	0	0	1	1
1	0	1	0	0

Figure 6.21.   Truth table ($\bar{A}B + A\bar{B}$ = C).

Having seen how the machine may be made to add two numbers, it is but a modest extension to see how it can multiply.   In the decimal number system, when the number 376 is multiplied by 2, this operation can be performed by adding 376 to itself; thus multiplication is seen to result from a series of additions.   To multiply 376 by 32, the number 376 is added to itself 32 times.   This would be rather time-consuming for large multipliers.   The time required can be substantially decreased by remembering a property of the decimal number system.   We remember that when we step over a column we increase the value of the number by a factor of 10; thus the multiplication by 30 can be accomplished by merely moving the columnar relationship of the numbers of one column to the left and adding the resulting number to itself three times.   This is shown in Figure 6.22.   Division can be performed in a similar manner by using subtractions.

Having reviewed the techniques by which numbers may be added, multiplied, subtracted, and divided, we can consider the elements of

MULTIPLY 376 BY 30   DECIMAL
                                                                        376
                                                                     × 30
1. Add 376 to itself 0 times   0000
2. Move 376 one column to left   3760
3. Add to itself 3 times   3760
                                                                     7520
                                                                     3760
            Product   11280

                                                                     BINARY
1. Add 1101   1101
2. Shift multiplicand one column to left   101
3. Note 0 multiplier plus digit   1101
4. Shift multiplicand   0000
5. Add   1101
            Product   1000001

Figure 6.22. Multiplication.

a digital computer. A digital computer mechanism consists of a memory, or store, and an operating arithmetic element. The store may consist of cards, magnetic tape, paper tape, magnetic cores, or a magnetic drum. The arithmetic element is a complex of gate circuits. Each memory has its place in computer technology and probably every device will be used in either ground or airborne computer equipment for space flight. The general operation of the computer is similar for each. A number is selected from the permanent store and transferred to an operating store. A second number may be called from the memory and transferred to another operating store. A command is given to perform the required arithmetic operation. The result is then placed back in either a temporary store or the permanent store.

Punched cards are easily visualized as a storage medium, but magnetic-tape or magnetic-drum stores can be employed in a similar fashion. Instead of holes punched in a material, magnetic patterns are introduced on the surface of the material in a manner similar to that used in a tape recorder. These patterns can then represent numbers just as holes in a punched card can represent numbers. The magnetic pattern is stored by changing the condition of each small magnetic region of the material. In a magnetic core memory, the small magnetic regions are individual magnetic rings, perhaps 0.02 inch across. The advantage of this type of memory is the extremely rapid access. The memory may have a number requested from it and supply that number in less than one ten-millionth of a second.

6.6 NAVIGATION

Fundamentals of Position Measurements

Space navigation, like space communications, has much in common with its Earth-based counterparts: airplane, ship, and vehicle navigation. Each requires a knowledge of the vehicle's location and its trend of motion. Variations in the technology used occur in determining the actual vehicle position and in the kinds of control applied. A general navigation problem is shown in Figure 6.23.

An automobile is equipped with an odometer which measures the distance traveled along the actual path of the vehicle. If this datum is combined with a compass reading to determine direction of travel, the exact path can be drawn on a map of the area. If the destination

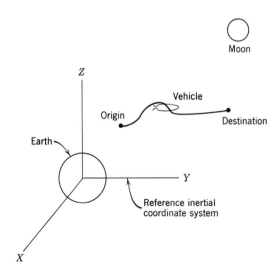

Figure 6.23.   General Navigation Problem.

is known on the same map, steering commands can be computed to reach the required point.

If the odometer is not working, it is possible to draw the path by computing the distance traveled from observation of a speedometer, a compass, and a clock or stopwatch. The following equation is used:

$$d = vt,$$

where d = the distance traveled,
v = the velocity observed on the speedometer,
t = the elapsed time.

The procedure is to start the stopwatch, observe the speedometer, observe the direction of travel of the compass, stop the stopwatch, perform the computation to determine distance, and measure off the distance indicated at the observed direction on the map. Repeating this process continually as long as the vehicle is moving will permit the path to be drawn on the map.

It is also possible to determine position by measuring acceleration. If a device for measuring acceleration is mounted on the vehicle, velocity can be computed by the following equation:

$$v = at,$$

where a is acceleration and t is the time interval over which the acceleration was observed. A process similar to that described for determining position from velocity will again permit a path or course to be drawn on the map.

The guidance of a ship is accomplished in a slightly different way: the position of the ship on the Earth's surface is determined directly by observation of sun or stars. This position can be plotted directly on a chart or map. Successive points on the path are obtained in the same fashion. This technique is called celestial navigation and has been used by seafarers for centuries. Steering signals are easily derived to reach the destination. If the position cannot be determined directly by celestial navigation, "dead reckoning" is used. "Dead reckoning" consists of assuming a constant speed computed from past position measurements. This speed is then used to estimate the distance from the last measured position by multiplying it by the time elapsed since the last measurement.

The principle of direct position finding in interplanetary space is similar to direct position finding on a ship. If a planet could be observed at some particular time to appear coincident with a star, the space vehicle must be on a line joining the star and planet. If another planet could be observed simultaneously in coincidence with another star, another line of sight is established; the actual position of the vehicle is obviously at the intersection of these lines.

Since it is seldom possible to find planets lined up with stars, what actually is done is to measure the angle between a planet and a star in the same general area of the sky. This observation locates the vehicle on the surface of a cone having its vertex at the planet and an apex angle equal to twice the observed angle. A second observation on another planet-star combination determines another cone, intersecting the first one in a curved line. A third observation on another-star-planet pair determines a third cone which intersects in a point the curved line locus already determined; the intersection is the position of the space vehicle.

This method of position determination is very rough by Earth standards. Errors of 20,000 miles will not be uncommon in the middle of an interplanetary voyage. This distance corresponds to changes in direction of about one minute of arc—a convenient size for changes in course.

All of the foregoing methods of determining position, course, and speed require calculations to determine the proper steering signals. A space voyage to a celestial body requires that a calculation be made to show whether the craft and its intended destination—which also moves—are traveling on courses that intersect and whether they will arrive at the intersection at the same time. If not, further calculation is required to show whether the course or speed of the spacecraft (or both) should be changed and by how much. The calculations are elaborate and cannot be made in the required time without a good digital electronic computer.

Each of these descriptions has included the basic requirement for a navigation system; the vehicle position must be known at all times and the destination must be known in the same coordinate system, that is, on the same map.

To meet these requirements, an inertial space guidance system must consist of an attitude reference to identify directions, a device for measuring acceleration, a computer, and a clock. The attitude reference is a mechanical device carried within the vehicle; it permits determining the direction of acceleration. At the present time, attitude references employ gyroscopes. Accelerometers measure the acceleration of the vehicle. The computer calculates velocity and position from these accelerations and the effects of gravity and steering commands. The clock furnishes time information to compute motions of the Earth or other bodies in space.

Accelerometers

A simple accelerometer may consist of a weight on a horizontal surface connected to a spring (Figure 6.24). Ignoring the effects of friction and dynamic effects, if the suspension is subject to an acceleration a along the axis of the spring (the input axis), the spring will change in length and exert a changed force on the weight. The acceleration is measured by the force in accordance with the following equation:

$$a = \frac{F}{m}$$

Since spring deflection, from its at-rest position, is proportional to F, which is due to the acceleration, the spring deflection is proportional to the acceleration a. We thus have a device to measure

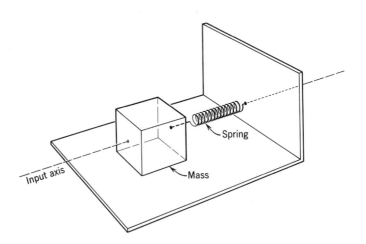

Figure 6.24. Accelerometer.

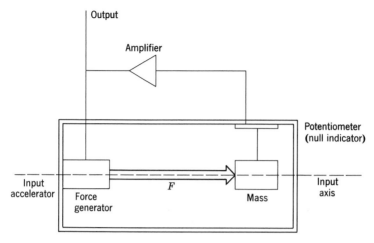

Figure 6.25.   Single Axis Accelerometer.

acceleration in terms of spring deflection. This device is called a single-axis accelerometer.

The practical single-axis accelerometer (Figure 6.25) operates by applying force to a mass inside a case so that the acceleration of the mass is equal to the acceleration of the case. The force used to accelerate the mass along the input axis is measured in terms of some physical quality proportional to force. In the previous example it was a spring. In Figure 6.25 the force is obtained by applying current to a magnetic coil. The current is obtained by feedback from a position sensor sensitive to relative motion between the mass and the case. The force is then altered to keep the position sensor at the null or zero position. The required change of force is proportional to, and is a measure of, the acceleration. The equation for the device is

$$a = \frac{F}{m} + g, \text{ where g is the acceleration of gravity.}$$

Note that the device measures not acceleration but the difference between measured acceleration and acceleration due to gravity. Gravity must be computed in a space vehicle, for it is continuously changing.

An accelerometer mounted vertically on the surface of the earth measures the upward "thrust acceleration" of the support on the case of the instrument. Gravity acceleration is computed as a downward quantity. An accelerometer which is freely falling (e.g., one mounted in a satellite) will have zero output. This result can be obtained from the foregoing equation by noting that for a freely falling body (i.e., acceleration $a = g$)

$$\frac{F}{m} = -g.$$

Accelerometers can determine only net accelerations; that is, the measurements include also the effects of any local gravity field. Thus, to measure absolute spacecraft acceleration in a region containing gravity fields, some method must be used for calculating gravity independently. If the path of the vehicle is known, the effects of the gravity can be precalculated. If the path of the vehicle is difficult to predict, it is necessary to compute gravity in flight.

Gyroscopes

Some of the characteristics of a gyroscope may be seen by examining the operation of a toy top. When a force attempts to tip the axis of the top, it reacts by swinging the plane of its rotation in a direction at right angles to the force. In other words, a torque applied perpendicular to the spin axis causes the spin axis to rotate about an axis which is perpendicular to both the spin and torque axes. This rotation is called precession.

Gyros are sometimes said to operate in inertial space. When a gyro is mounted on the surface of the Earth, its spin axis is subject to a torque due to its rotation around the center of the Earth. The spin axis could line up with the gravitational field if the spin axis were not rotating with the surface of the Earth. However, when the gyro is used in a space vehicle, it tends to maintain its original orientation with reference to the center of the Earth while the Earth turns beneath it. The usefulness of the gyroscope in navigation devices results from this characteristic.

Gyroscopes commonly come in two types, with a single degree of freedom and two degrees of freedom; Figure 6.26 shows a single degree of freedom gyro. Note that it looks like a top mounted in

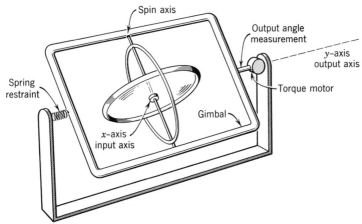

Figure 6.26.   Single Degree of Freedom Gyroscope.

bearings in a frame called a gimbal. The gimbal is pivoted in a second set of bearings in such a way that the spin axis of the wheel is perpendicular to the axis through the gimbal bearings. This second axis is called the output axis.

The output from the gyro is measured by the amount—or angle—of rotation of the spin axis about the output axis. When the output angle is zero, the spin axis reference is zero. The angle between the spin axis reference and the actual spin axis is called the output angle. The spin axis is perpendicular to the output as well as the input axis. The position of the input axis is measured with reference to the case. The principal input quantity is the rotation of the case about the input axis relative to inertial space. The torque so created on the output axis is balanced by the spring restraint torque proportional to the output angle. The output is proportional to the angular rate of rotation of the input axis in inertial space. The accuracy of the device is determined by the amount of friction in the bearings and by the unbalance in the wheel.

Any stray torques will cause a precession or "drift." This drift represents a loss in attitude reference and is an error. Drifts arise from gimbal unbalances and friction in the gimbal bearings. The prime problem in gyro design is to make these items as small as possible.

A torque generator is used to apply known torques to the gimbals

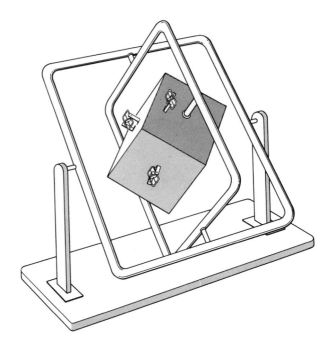

Figure 6.27.   Three Axis, Stable Platform Gimbal System.

of a gyro. It is similar to an electric motor which is not permitted
to rotate more than a small fraction of a revolution.

Torque generators are used to adjust the position of a gimbal ini-
tially, as well as to keep it in its original orientation when an input
is applied. They are a rotary equivalent of the force generation used
in the accelerometer.

A torque motor may be mounted on the output axis of the gyro
just described. The current in the unit will be adjusted to keep the
output angle zero; the gyro then operates as a null device. The
torque provided by the motor and thus the electric current driving
the motor are the output from the gyro. The null mode of operation
keeps the output axis always exactly perpendicular to the input axis
and the spin axis. It provides higher accuracy due to the elimination
of errors resulting from lack of orthogonality.

In order to navigate in space, it is necessary to use a model of
the original attitude reference system. Such a device is commonly

called a stable platform. This employs gyros to serve as error indicators to keep the platform from rotating in its position in inertial
space. Thus the platform maintains a constant attitude, against which
changes in spacecraft attitude can be measured. Accelerometers are
mounted on the platform so that they measure acceleration directly
in terms of the model attitude system. Position can then be computed,
since both acceleration and direction are known.

An unusual thing about a stable platform is that the components
of which it is composed use natural physical phenomena for control
purposes. They take dynamic measurements, translate them into electric signals, and then transform these signals into mechanical power.
Thus they are analog computers because they represent geometry
physically.

Figure 6.27 shows a three-axis, stable-platform gimbal system. The
controlled member supports three single degree of freedom accelerometers and three single degree of freedom gyros. The input axes of
the three accelerometers form the instrumented model of the inertial
coordinate system. The gyro units sense any angular deviation of
the accelerometer coordinate system from the initial inertial coordinate
system and produce signals which are converted into currents to the
gimbal torque motors. The resultant torques are applied to the controlled member to realign the model coordinate system to its original
position in inertial space (with reference to the center of the Earth).
A block diagram of a single axis of the stable platform is shown
in Figure 6.28.

The controlled member of the platform is supported on three single-
axis gimbal drives. Because the orientation of the vehicle with respect
to the accelerometer axis will change during flight, the gimbal drive
axes will, in general, not be orthogonal. It is therefore necessary
to have complex trigonometric transformations in the circuit for each

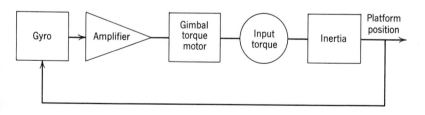

Figure 6.28.   Block Diagram of a Single Axis of the Stable Platform.

torque motor in order to produce the proper currents in the torque motors to permit accurate maintenance of attitude of the controlled member.

A stable platform provides the function which is normally provided by the navigator taking a star sight; he absorbs the motions of the deck by flexing his body so that a stable support is provided for the sextant. In the case of a stable platform, the motions of the vehicle are filtered out so that they do not appear on the controlled member or inner axis. Thus the accelerometers measure acceleration in a stable coordinate system unaffected by the motion of the vehicle.

To achieve the prerequisite accuracy of flight, a stable platform must be accurately aligned just before the start of the flight. One approach is to move the three gimbal angles to the required values by energizing the torque motors. Another approach is to level the platform by use of the accelerometers and to orient it in azimuth by optically sighting on a mirror mounted on the platform from a theodolite external to the vehicle.

In addition to steering the space vehicle, it is necessary to keep it in the correct attitude. The purpose of a vehicle control system is to maintain the vehicle's attitude at some particular value. Attitude of a space vehicle is a problem that requires constant attention. The forces required to move the vehicle are often very small; they may even result from radiation pressure from the sun.

Since an attitude reference (the stable platform) is available on board the spacecraft, the orientation of the platform's gimbal system may be used to generate a measurement of the error in the vehicle attitude. A command signal can be generated. This signal is amplified and sent to a servomechanism which may operate a small thrust motor or may otherwise cause a change in vehicle orientation. Attitude control systems must be carefully designed, since the attitude required for re-entry to keep a spacecraft's heat shield in proper orientation is very precise. Automatic control has been commonly used to achieve the necessary precision, although failure of the automatic system has sometimes required manual re-entry procedures to be employed in manned spacecraft.

CHAPTER 7

Rocket Propulsion

Egan J. Rattin

Aerospace Corporation

Contents

Rocket Propulsion

7.1 INTRODUCTION TO ROCKET PROPULSION SYSTEMS

Propulsion Requirements

Civilization, over the relatively brief span of its existence, has developed many forms of propulsion, all of them described by Sir Isaac Newton's third law of motion, which states that "to every action there is an equal and opposite reaction." The propulsion of bodies through fluids utilized this principle, from the early swimmer in water to the latest aircraft in the atmosphere. Sailing vessels obtain their propulsive force by utilizing the reaction of the wind on their sails. The jet plane gulps a quantity of air into its engines, accelerates this gas by heating it (through combustion with fuel) and ejecting it at a higher velocity through the rear opening of the engine. The reaction of the jet of hot air and combustion products leaving the engine accelerates the airplane forward. The propeller of the piston-engined aircraft and the screw of the motor boat essentially do nothing else but take a quantity of fluid from their surroundings and, accelerating it backward, obtain forward thrust. The reader will note that all of the examples cited so far have used a fluid from the surrounding environment to provide the propulsive force. This operating mode is, of course, quite feasible for vessels or vehicles operating either on the surface of the Earth or within the atmosphere of the Earth. There is, however, no reason why propulsion described by Newton's third law, or reaction propulsion, cannot be used in a fluidless environment such as the essentially empty space surrounding our Earth and other bodies of the Solar System or the Universe. Reaction engines operating in such an environment, however, have one essential difference with those operating within the Earth environment: they take with them into space all the fluid that must be ejected in order to provide forward thrust. Engines operating solely with on-board reaction fluid are called rocket engines. Within this class of engine exists a great variety of subcategories differentiated by the kind of fuel used, the velocity with which the fuel can be ejected, and the duration of the ejection process. By varying these three major parameters, a great family of rocket engines has been developed to fit the variety of propulsion requirements experienced in modern missile and space flight.

Space boosters and missiles have certain special requirements in common and thus employ rocket engines which are basically very similar but vary only in size. The type of powerplant for vehicles of this type is determined by the fact that they must provide sufficient power to lift the vehicle off the surface of the Earth; that is, they must be able to overcome the attraction of gravity. In addition to providing sufficient propulsive force or thrust to lift the vehicle itself, the engine must also lift a heavy payload, or cargo, which the vehicle must deliver either onto a target elsewhere on Earth, into an orbit around the Earth, or into interplanetary space. These engines must also be capable of accelerating the vehicle with sufficient force to achieve the terminal velocity required for the mission. For example, a long-range ballistic missile such as an ICBM must achieve a velocity of about 25,000 feet per second in order to meet its mission requirement. In order to obtain orbits around the Earth, velocities in excess of 25,000 feet per second must be obtained. In order to escape the gravitational attraction of the Earth altogether, and enter planetary space, velocities in excess of 35,000 feet per second have to be obtained—"escape velocities." In order to lift a vehicle from the Earth's surface, the upward thrust of the rocket motors must be at least equal the weight of the vehicle plus payload, and it should exceed this value by a suitable amount to provide the margin of thrust required for acceleration of the vehicle to the required velocity. Rocket engines for this class of vehicle are therefore capable of delivering large amounts of thrust. These engines are also associated with a fuel supply which is limited to the specific requirements of the mission.

Vehicles operating outside the Earth's atmosphere and having attained either orbital or escape velocities through the use of separate booster stages have somewhat different propulsion system requirements. An interplanetary vehicle, for example, once having attained escape velocity, no longer needs to utilize thrust to overcome the gravitational attraction of the Earth but now requires a rocket motor which can accelerate it to higher velocities in order to shorten its trip and which can, if the mission requires it, decelerate it at

its terminal point to permit a safe landing. Interplanetary distances
being what they are, the travel times of such a vehicle are reckoned
in months or even years, in the instance of a journey to Mars.
As will be shown later, this time factor permits the powerplant of
such a vehicle to be considerably smaller in thrust output but in turn
requires that the thrust or accelerating force be applied over a long
period of time. Vehicles already in orbit around the Earth or some
other planetary body require propulsion only to counteract the very
small decelerating effects caused by the very tenuous matter present
in space and by radiation from the sun. They may also require propulsion if they wish to change orbit or to re-enter the planetary atmosphere for a landing on the surface. Again, these propulsion requirements call for considerably less thrust than that originally required
to boost the vehicles into orbit. As a consequence, the rocket motors
utilized by orbiting vehicles are much smaller but of longer duration
than those used in the booster vehicles.

It was stated before that among the many propulsion devices utilizing the principle of reaction force, only the rocket motor contains the
reaction fluid required for its operation. Because matter in space
is so tenuous, it is unsuitable for collection and use as a reaction
fluid; vehicles operating in this environment must therefore take their
reaction fluid with them. It is for that reason that space flight had
to await the development of large, reliable, and relatively economical
rocket motor systems. This does not imply that the invention and
utilization of rocket motors has in itself opened the Universe to exploration. Rocket motors also have inherent limitations which, at
the time of this writing, severely restrict man in his attempt to learn
about space and the Universe. These limitations relate to the energies
available for accelerating the reaction fluid and which thus put a
limit to the speed of the vehicle. As shown later, structural considerations also limit the maximum velocities that space vehicles may
reach. Last, but not least, we may speculate about velocity limits
set by the basic physical principles of the Universe; according to
current theory, the speed of light appears to be the highest attainable
velocity. We have not yet learned to what fraction of the speed
of light we may accelerate a space vehicle before experiencing a
new barrier, which at present is theorized to consist of infinite mass
and thus would require infinitely large thrust forces to provide motion.

History of Rocket Propulsion

Seemingly contradictory to the statement made earlier that space flight had to await the development of rocket propulsion is the fact that rockets have been known to civilized man for perhaps as long at eight centuries. At about 1200 A.D. the Chinese were said to have used a weapon which made use of a rocket device to propel an incendiary arrow. The rocket propellant which may have been used in this weapon was probably similar to an incendiary material already used in the Greek Byzantine Empire. Early Arab sources also indicate that war rockets in the form of arrows were known to them, and it is quite likely that the Arabs learned their art from the Chinese. Later in the thirteenth century mention is made of rockets in warfare both in Germany and in Italy. By the fifteenth century several types of rockets were known to have been developed by European military engineers. For a number of centuries the use of rockets seems to have lain dormant, until the Napoleonic wars when the British engineer Congreve manufactured for military use a variety of rockets using solid propellants. The British fleet used these rockets in the bombardment of Copenhagen and succeeded in burning down a large part of the city. We are already familiar with the use of naval rockets against shore targets during the British-American War of 1812 and in the bombardment of Baltimore. Early nonmilitary uses of the rocket included distress flares and line-shooting rockets in rescue operations from floundering vessels at sea.

A number of claims are made for the origination of the liquid rocket principle. Among them was that of Pedro Paulet, a Latin American who actually operated a small liquid rocket engine in the nineteenth century. The Russian claim for a first in this field is based on Professor Ziolkowsky's writings, in which he proposes the use of a liquid propellant motor for space travel. Both in Europe and the United States experimental work with liquid rockets began in the decade following World War I. Robert Goddard in the United States and Herman Oberth in Germany experimented with rockets using liquid oxygen in combination with fuels such as alcohol or gasoline. More intense interest in the liquid rocket motor and its use in warfare was, however, found in Europe, and as a consequence the first practical liquid-rocket-powered missile, the V-2, was developed in Germany during World War II. At the same time (1940 to 1945) the United States pioneered some very successful work in solid propulsion which led to the wartime development of bazookas, barrage rockets, and 4.5-inch aircraft rockets, which were extensively and successfully employed during World War II. Much of the technology developed by German engineers in connection with the use of liquid-rocket-powered missiles for warfare was later used by both the United States and Russia in the development of rocket motors suitable for booster and space propulsion.

Because of this long history of rocket propulsion we must therefore modify our earlier statement to the effect that space flight was not only dependent upon the development of practical rocketry but also upon the development of rocket motors with sufficient thrust to lift vehicles from the surface of the Earth into outer space. Many correlary technologies were, of course, also required before space flight could be achieved. New materials were necessary to contain the very hot rocket gases, guidance and control systems had to be developed to permit the aiming of the rocket, and last but not least a willingness on the part of government was necessary to spend the vast sums of money required to take man into space.

Principles of Rocket Propulsion

The rocket motor is basically a simple device when compared to other thrust-producing devices such as reciprocating or electric motors. Its development problems more frequently relate to materials of construction and combustion chemistry rather than to complicated me-

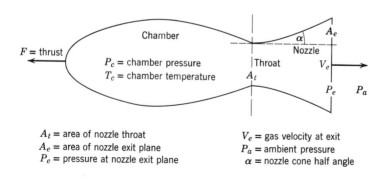

A_t = area of nozzle throat V_e = gas velocity at exit
A_e = area of nozzle exit plane P_a = ambient pressure
P_e = pressure at nozzle exit plane α = nozzle cone half angle

Figure 7.1.   Schematic of Rocket Motor.

chanical design or complex operation. The rocket motor consists essentially of a chamber in which propellant is burned to produce combustion gases at high temperatures, which are then exhausted through a nozzle to the rear. The high-velocity gases moving to the rear produce the forward thrust in accordance with the phenomenon described by Newton's second law of motion (see Figure 7.1). Variations of this basic motor design exist in the form of nuclear and electric rockets and are described later.

The force which propels the rocket motor forward is called thrust and is a function of the momentum of the fluid expelled from the motor to the rear according to the following relation:

$$F = \frac{\dot{\omega}}{g} C, \qquad (7.1)$$

where F = thrust,

$\dot{\omega}$ = weight flow rate of fluid ejected,

C = effective velocity of fluid ejected (see Equation 7.2, below),

g = a constant equal to the acceleration of gravity, 32 ft/sec^2 (this value is used throughout this chapter).

As may be seen, thrust can be increased by either increasing the flow rate or the fluid velocity or both. Chemical propulsion and nuclear propulsion devices produce exhaust gas velocities ranging up to 8000 feet per second and can therefore provide higher thrust only by increasing weight flow and thus increasing the size of the engine. Electric rocket motors, however, operate with particle velocities in excess of 50 miles per second and can produce useful thrust with minute weight flows measured in micrograms per second.

A nozzle is used with rocket motors as an amplification device operating on the velocity component of thrust. The effective exhaust velocity C is described by

$$C = v + \frac{(P_e - P_a)A_e g}{\dot{\omega}} \qquad (7.2)$$

where v = actual fluid velocity,

P_e = gas pressure at exit plane of nozzle,

P_a = ambient atmospheric pressure,

A_e = cross-sectional area of the nozzle exit plane.

When P_a is less than P_e, the effective exhaust velocity can be increased by either increasing P_e or A_e or both. A commonly used method for increasing C is to increase the exit area of the nozzle. This may be done by increasing the length of the nozzle rather than by increasing the angle of the conical nozzle section, since the latter method will permit exhaust gas to be ejected in directions differing from that of the desired flight of the vehicle and its energy will be lost to the desired thrust direction by the factor λ which relates to the nozzle cone angle, 2α, by

$$\lambda = \tfrac{1}{2}(1 + \cos \alpha). \tag{7.3}$$

Rocket propulsion systems are often characterized by the "total impulse" they can provide as a measure of their performance potential. This quantity, often designated I_T, is the product of the thrust and operating time, or

$$I_T = Ft, \tag{7.4}$$

where t = total burning time.

An important concept in measuring performance of both propellants, as well as engines, is the use of *specific impulse*, or the impulse obtained per unit weight of propellant. This is designated I_{sp} and is related to thrust and total impulse as follows:

$$\frac{I_T}{W} = I_{sp}, \tag{7.5}$$

where W = the total weight of propellant used during the time t, or $\dot{\omega} \times t$.

Specific impulses of a variety of liquid and solid propellants are shown in Tables 7.1 and 7.2, and it is noted that liquid propellants have generally higher values of I_{sp} than solid propellants.

Table 7.1.   Solid Propellant Characteristics*

	Theoretical I_{sp}† (lb-sec/lb)	Burning Rate (in./sec)	Density (lb/in.^{3})
Double-base	220	0.40	0.056
Polyurethane composite	235	0.22	0.062
Polybutadience composite (with aluminum additive)	250	0.50	0.064

* Data from March 1959 *Astronautics* and ARS Paper 973-59.

† I_{sp} at sea level and P_e = 1000 psia.

Table 7.2.   Liquid Propellant Characteristics*

Propellant Mixture (Oxidant-Fuel)	Theoretical I_{sp}† (lb-sec/lb)	Mixture Ratio (lb oxidizer/ lb fuel)	Combined Density (lb/in.³)
Oxygen-kerosene	280	2.2	0.0036
Oxygen-hydrogen	380	3.5	0.009
Nitric acid-kerosene	260	4.0	0.048
Nitrogen tetroxide-hydrazine	280	1.1	0.043

* Rocketdyne Publication 573-A-2.
† I_{sp} at sea level and $P_c = 1000$ psia.

Gas velocities obtained from rocket motor exhaust nozzles are related to specific impulse because both are related to thrust. The effective velocity, C, can be expressed as

$$C = I_{sp}g, \qquad (7.6)$$

where g has a constant value of 32 ft/sec².

The gas generated in the chamber portion of the rocket motor as a result of the combustion of propellants moves at relatively low velocities in the chamber. It rapidly accelerates as it reaches the nozzle and moves at the local velocity of sound as it passes the throat of the nozzle. In the conical expansion section of the nozzle, the gas accelerates to supersonic speeds and will reach *effective* velocities in excess of 10,000 feet per second in chemical and nuclear rockets.

Specific impulse can also be calculated analytically from knowledge of the thermodynamic properties of the propellants, and chamber and exit gas pressures. The mathematical relationship for theoretical I_{sp} reduces to

$$I_{sp} = A \sqrt{T_c/M}, \qquad (7.7)$$

where A = a quantity related to various thermodynamic properties
        of the propellant gases,
   M = the average molecular weight of the exhaust gases,
   T_c = the chamber temperature.

It can readily be seen that the more desirable propellants will have low molecular weight combustion products and will produce high chamber temperatures. Atomic hydrogen with a molecular weight of 1 would therefore make an ideal propellant if means could be found to heat it to high temperatures. Molecular hydrogen, H_2, with a molecular weight of 2, is more practical to produce and handle. As a consequence, nuclear rockets and electromagnetic rockets use this substance as a propulsive fluid, and chemical rocket propellants are chosen so as to obtain a high hydrogen concentration in the reaction products in the form of either free H_2, water (H_2O), or both.

7.2 CHEMICAL ROCKET PROPULSION SYSTEMS

Solid Rockets

Historically, solid rockets were known and received practical application long before the advent of the liquid rocket. As mentioned previously, records of the use of solid rocket devices were found to date as early as the twelfth century. Although discussions of the principle of liquid rocketry can be found in the technical literature of the latter part of the nineteenth century, experimental work with liquid rockets and their practical application in both warfare and space exploration had to await the coming of the twentieth century.

PROPELLANTS

A solid rocket derives its name from its use of solid propellants. A great variety of these propellants have been in use over the past centuries and have had in common the prime requirement for a solid rocket propellant which is that it contain its own fuel and oxidizer in intimate mixture so that no atmospheric oxygen is required for either initiation or sustained combustion of fuel. The term "oxidizer" is used here in its true chemical definition of a material capable of reacting with a "reducing" element or compound, i.e., a fuel; thus the term oxidizer covers oxygen itself and applies also to materials such as fluorine and chlorine, among others. In addition, the combustion of the propellant should be as energetic as possible and result in low molecular weight reaction products in order to produce high specific impulse.

Double Base. Earlier propellants, for example, mixtures of pitch or tar fuels with saltpeter as oxidizer, were quite low in impulse. The advent of double-base powder for military guns made it possible to produce rockets possessing higher specific impulses. Double-base powder is essentially a mixture of nitrocellulose and nitroglycerin; trace amounts of various chemicals are added for the purpose of adjusting burning rates and physical properties of the propellant, and in order to reduce the inherent sensitivity of this mixture to accidental detonation. Many millions of pounds of double-base propellant were produced and used in the two major wars of this century in a variety of applications ranging from mortars to the recoilless rifle, and from the bazooka rocket to the shore-bombardment rockets used by the Navy during its Pacific campaigns. Air-to-air and air-to-ground rockets introduced during World War II also made use of double-base propellants. Table 7.1 contains a listing of some of the rocket propellants used during and since World War II together with values of specific impulse.

Double-base propellants can be made into rocket grains by two basic methods. One involves the extrusion of propellant into various shapes, which later can be assembled into a rocket grain. These shapes include rods, tubes, and cruciform cross-sectional shapes. Another method, developed subsequently for the purpose of producing more complicated and larger shapes not suitable for extrusion, was the solventless casting process. In this process the grain mold is first filled with the nitro-cellulose powder, usually in the form of a very fine ball powder; upon subsequent addition of nitroglycerin containing various additives, followed by heating, a uniform solid propellant mixture results, similar to the preparation of Jello molds. Nearly all the double-base rocket motors exceeding 6 inches in diameter are now produced by this casting method.

Double-base rockets offer a major availability advantage: the raw materials required are plentiful, and the many powder factories supporting the Armed Forces can not only be called upon to provide the basic rocket propellant, they can also manufacture these rockets. As a consequence, U.S. Army or Navy arsenals produced most of the double-base rockets in use during World War II and even today produce the vast majority of such rockets still being utilized by the Armed Forces. Another advantage is that double-base propellants have higher specific impulses than most other solid propellant compositions available. The major disadvantages of this type of solid propellant is its apparently greater sensitivity to detonation and its poorer physical strength when compared to composite propellants (see later).

Many advances have been made in recent years in improving the physical strength of double-base propellants. The very large rockets being developed for space-flight application and having diameters in excess of 10 feet, with lengths ranging up to 100 feet, are loaded with composite propellants in order to avoid detonation hazards which would be disastrous with rockets of this size.

Composites. Composite propellant derives its name from the fact that it is a nonhomogenous mixture of two chemically dissimilar materials: the fuel constituent of such propellants is usually a polymeric organic material, e.g., a synthetic rubber with a high ratio of hydrogen to carbon, which forms the binder or matrix in which the oxidizer is embedded; oxidizers have ranged from saltpeter in the very early rockets to potassium perchlorate which was used extensively during World War II. Currently, ammonium perchlorate is the oxidizer used in the majority of composite propellants. Three major classes of fuels are used in composite propellants. These are polyvinylchloride

Figure 7.2. Solid Propellant Being Poured from Mixer into Transfer Can. (Courtesy of Thiokol Chemical Corporation.)

formulations, polyurethane polymers, and several variations of poly-butadiene polymers.

The propellant is prepared by mixing the oxidizer with the fuel while the latter is in a viscous state. The resulting material in pasty, semiliquid form is then cast into the rocket motor case around the core mold. On subsequent heating the paste solidifies ("cures"), and the resulting propellant is similar to tire rubber. Figure 7.2 shows composite propellant being poured from a mixer into a transfer can from which the propellant will later be poured into the motor case.

ROCKET MOTORS

A solid rocket consists essentially of four major components: the first is the motor case which contains the propellant and the hot gases during the burning of the propellant. The second is the propellant itself, which in most instances is cast into the case in fluid form and then "cured" (polymerized) into a solid rubbery mass by the application of heat and the addition of curing catalysts to the propellant mass. The cured propellant within the motor case is called the "grain" and can be obtained in a variety of shapes through the use of a casting mandrel or core. As will be discussed later, the shape of the casting core is determined by the requirements in thrust and duration of burning time for which the motor is to be designed. The third major component is the nozzle. As explained earlier, the nozzle provides amplification to the thrust of the motor as a function of the length of the nozzle and the cone angle of its expansion section. The fourth major component required for the operation of a solid rocket is the igniter, which provides the heat energy required to ignite the propellant grain. Igniters contain either mixtures of pyrotechnic materials such as aluminum powder and potassium perchlorate, or rocket propellants similar to that of the motor. They are ignited themselves by electric squibs which utilize the electric heating of a thin wire to set off a mild explosive, which in turn causes the burning of the main igniter.

Other components are the thrust termination device, which is used on some rocket motors for the purpose of precisely cutting off thrust for trajectory control, and the thrust vector control devices which provide steering by changing the direction of the motor thrust. This is accomplished in a variety of ways, such as moving the nozzle itself or by introducing specially shaped solid objects into the nozzle

exhaust stream to deflect the gases. Another frequently used system
for thrust vector control which is receiving greater acceptance in recent
times is the liquid injection system, which involves the introduction of
a stream of liquid at an appropriate section of the exhaust nozzle
and which thus brings about a deflection of the exhaust gas stream
to provide steering.

Figure 7.3 shows a cross-sectional view of a solid motor using gim-
balled nozzles for thrust vector control. The igniter is seen at the
head-end and the propellant grain is indicated by crosshatching.

Figure 7.4 shows a rocket motor being removed from the pit in
which the propellant was cast and "cured" into the case. The core
or mandrel has been removed and the shape of the grain perforation
is clearly visible at the top (this "top" is actually the aft end of
the rocket motor and the nozzle will be attached there).

During the development program, and also as a quality control
measure after the motor has been accepted for production, solid motors

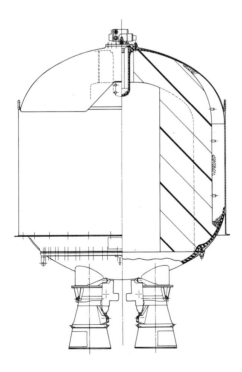

Figure 7.3. Cutaway of Solid Motor with Movable Nozzles. (Courtesy of Thiokol Chemical
Corporation.)

Figure 7.4. Solid Motor Being Removed from Casting Pit (aft end removed). (Courtesy of Thiokol Chemical Corporation.)

are tested by firing them in a static test facility in which important characteristics such as thrust and burning time can be precisely checked. Figure 7.5 shows such a test firing. The heavy white smoke is characteristic of solid propellants in which ammonium perchlorate is the oxidizer. Upon combustion,* dry hydrochloric acid is formed,

---

* The decomposition of ammonium perchlorate proceeds according to

$$2NH_4ClO_4 \rightarrow 3H_2O + 2HCl + N_2 + 5(O)$$

$\qquad\qquad\qquad\qquad\qquad\qquad\quad \downarrow$ to combustion of fuel.

Figure 7.5. Test Firing of Large Solid Motor in Test Cell. (Courtesy of United Technology Center, Division of United Aircraft Corporation.)

which absorbs moisture from both the atmosphere and the exhaust gas and then condenses to produce a white cloud of moist hydrochloric acid.

ROCKET MOTOR DESIGN

The hot gases providing thrust are, in the instance of the solid rocket, produced by the burning of the propellant surface. This burning proceeds quite rapidly in a direction perpendicular to the surface, with the surface regressing at rates up to one inch per second. The thrust, F, of a solid rocket is then dependent upon various parameters which form the following relationship:

$$F = A_b r \rho I_{sp} \qquad (7.8)$$

where A_b = the propellant surface area capable of burning,
$\quad\ r$ = the burning rate,
$\quad\ \rho$ = the density of the propellant,
$\quad I_{sp}$ = the specific impulse.

For a given propellant with fixed I_{sp} and ρ, thrust can be tailored to the needs of the mission by changing the propellant burning surface or the burning rate. The former can be done by casting grains with different cores, while the latter is adjusted by varying the composition of the propellant or by changing the operating pressure of the motor; propellant burning rates change with chamber pressure according to

$$r = a(P_c)^n, \qquad (7.9)$$

where a and n are constants characteristic of specific propellants, and P_c is the operating pressure of the motor.

Because many liquid rockets can be fueled only just immediately prior to firing and since such fueling is lengthy, military missiles were increasingly based upon solid rockets during the last decade. By now all new American missiles are based upon solid rocket power, because of their instant readiness. The biggest of these solid missiles are the Polaris and Minute Man. Figure 7.6 shows some of the solid motor core designs currently in use and indicates the variety of burning surfaces that can be used to control thrust.

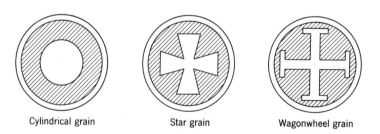

Cylindrical grain   Star grain   Wagonwheel grain

Figure 7.6.   Cross Section of Several Solid Motor Grain Designs.

Liquid Rockets

After Dr. Goddard pioneered its development in the United States during the 1920's, the liquid rocket engine received its biggest boost with the advent of the German V-2, and has reigned supreme from that moment in all ballistic and space applications until about ten years ago. Only as late as 1962 were serious attempts made to apply large solid rocket motors to the space missions previously performed by liquid motors.

BOOSTERS

The liquid rocket engine is based upon a considerably more complex mechanism than the solid rocket motor. It also consists of a chamber in which propellants are burned and a nozzle through which the exhaust gases are ejected at high velocity. However, the propellants are stored external to the combustion chamber and are introduced through a device known as an injector; the injector resembles a showerhead and adjusts the incoming propellants (the fuel and oxidizer) in the right proportion and dispenses the mixture into a spray so as to sustain stable combustion within the chamber. A pump is necessary to pump the propellants from the storage tank to the injector; a gas generator is provided together with a turbine which drives the pump. (The gas generator frequently makes use of the same two propellants used in the main rocket motor, but burns them in a different mixture ratio in order to reduce the temperature of the exhaust gases to make them suitable for use with the turbine.) Since the chamber and the nozzle require cooling, a flow system is used which requires one of the two propellants to pass through a hollow shell around the nozzle and the chamber in order to act as a coolant. A number of control devices are associated with this liquid engine system, all of them designed to maintain programmed thrust and to assure reliable starting and stopping of the engine. In order to provide the suction pressure required by the pump, gas pressurization systems with associated controls are used to pressurize the main tanks in which both fuel and oxidizer are stored. Sensing devices are installed at various critical portions of the engine, the pump, and other components, for the purpose of giving indication of incipient trouble which might lead to a catastrophic failure and to provide closed-loop control. The resulting

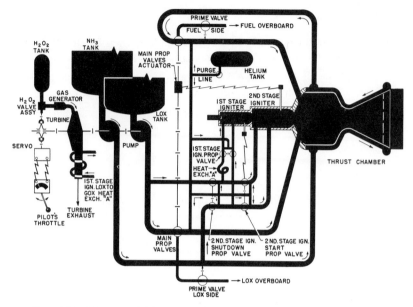

Figure 7.7.   Schematic of X-15 Engine.   (Courtesy of Thiokol Chemical Corporation.)

engine contrasts sharply with the simplicity of a solid rocket motor (contrast Figures 7.3 and 7.8).

Figure 7.7 shows a schematic view of the liquid rocket engine used to propel the X-15 research aircraft. It uses ammonia and liquid oxygen for the main propellants but employs hydrogen peroxide in the gas generator to drive the turbine pumps. By throttling the peroxide flow to the gas generator, the pilot can control the speed of the propellant pumps and thus the thrust derived from the motor. Figure 7.8 is an external view of this engine.

Figure 7.9 shows a cut view of a typical injector. The pinholes in the face of the injector lead to separate chambers behind the face in which the oxidizer and fuel flows are kept separated until they join as fine sprays in the combustion chamber. One set of holes is drilled to shallow depth to connect with radial tubes opening from the center chamber; the other set of holes connects with a plenum chamber located below these radial tubes. The holes are drilled in a slant direction so as to bring about impingement and mixing of the propellant streams emerging from the different sets of holes.

Liquid engines of very large sizes are now required to boost the

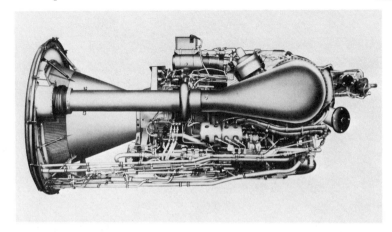

Figure 7.8.   X-15 Liquid Rocket Engine.   (Courtesy of Thiokol Chemical Corporation.)

space vehicles intended to carry man to the moon.   Figure 7.10 shows
a comparison of two such engines.   The smaller engine in front is
the H-1 engine intended for the first version of Saturn, which will
use eight of these engines in the first stage.   Flight tests of this
stage have already been successfully completed.   The thrust of this
cluster of eight engines is destined to be equaled by 1965 by a single

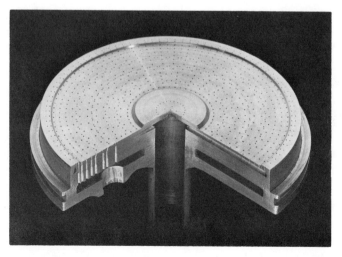

Figure 7.9.   Liquid Rocket Injector.   (Courtesy of United Technology Center, Division of United
Aircraft Corporation.)

Figure 7.10. Size Comparison Between F-1 and H-1 Liquid Rocket Engines. (Courtesy of Rocketdyne Division of North American Aviation.)

engine, the F-1, in order to provide a simpler and more reliable system. The F-1 is the larger engine behind the H-1 in Figure 7.10. It produces a thrust of 1.5 million pounds and is the largest liquid rocket engine known to be in development. This engine will be used in advanced versions of the Saturn in a five-engine cluster.

PROPELLANTS

A variety of propellant systems may be used with liquid rocket engines. In all cases the liquid oxidizer and the liquid fuel are stored in separate tanks and are mixed only just prior to combustion in the injector of the combustion chamber. Some oxidizers and fuels will ignite spontaneously on contact with each other; these propellants do not require a separate ignition system and are called hypergolic propellants. Other fuels and oxidizers do not ignite spontaneously upon contact and thus require spark plugs, glow plugs, and other sources of heat, such as solid propellant starter cartridges, to provide ignition. Some of the "liquid" propellants possessing very high energy content are gases at normal ambient pressures and temperatures. As a consequence, they must be condensed and stored in liquid form at very low temperatures in the missile or space booster. Materials such as oxygen and hydrogen fall into this category and are called cryogenic propellants. Other materials such as chlorine trifluoride or nitrogen tetroxide require only some pressurization in order to liquefy and do not need to be cooled below ambient temperatures in order to maintain their liquid state. Considerations of both energy content and cost have led to the adoption of several standard liquid propellant systems. Liquid oxygen and kerosene, constituting the fuel on the Atlas, Titan I, and Thor missiles, has received the greatest usage so far. The use of hydrazine and nitrogen tetroxide in the Titan II missile represents a propellant system which can be stored at ambient temperatures in the missile. More recent developments by NASA have included the utilization of liquid hydrogen and liquid oxygen as a propellant system of very high energy. Table 7.2 shows the properties of a few representative liquid systems.

The choice of a liquid propellant for a particular application involves such complex factors as performance, cost, storage time in the missile tanks, requirement for quick fueling and quick reaction, etc. Cryogenic propellants, although frequently used, offer a great many difficulties. Liquid oxygen, for example, is a very reactive material and cannot be allowed to contact metal surfaces containing impurities such as oil, grease, or other combustible materials, since reaction with such materials often results in combustion or explosion. In addition, liquid rocket tanks loaded with cryogenics such as liquid oxygen or liquid hydrogen will be at temperatures of approximately -300 and $-400°F$, respectively. Unless adequately protected by insulation, such tank surfaces condense moisture and other condensable materials in the air or, in the case of liquid hydrogen, condense air itself. The ice which thus forms on the tank surfaces adds to the weight of the missile at takeoff and is wasteful of fuel. In addition, the cooling of the tank surface indicates that heat is leaking into the missile tanks, thus causing the vaporizing of the propellant stored within. Such vaporization could result in the missile leaving the ground with tanks not completely filled and unable to meet its mission requirements. In the instance of liquid oxygen these problems are solved to some degree by constantly replenishing the oxygen boiling off from the tank with fresh liquid oxygen until just prior to take-off, and by reducing the amount of time between fueling of the rocket and takeoff to the bare minimum. Even under those conditions, the initial takeoff of a liquid-oxygen-fueled rocket is generally accompanied by the flaking off of substantial quantities of ice which have formed on the missile's exterior surfaces.

Liquid hydrogen, because of its considerably lower liquid temperature and its consequent ability to liquefy air in contact with uninsulated tank walls, must be stored in missile tanks insulated from ambient atmosphere by either efficient insulating materials or by a vacuum jacket. This adds to the mass fraction of the vehicle and therefore reduces flight efficiency as well as increases vehicle cost. In spite of these difficulties, cryogenics continue to be used in liquid rocket propulsion systems for two major reasons. The first one is the considerably higher specific impulse which they offer and the second reason relates to their comparatively low cost. Liquid oxygen, for example, can be bought at a price of less than two cents per pound. Liquid hydrogen sells at approximately 50 cents per pound. The kerosene fuel used with liquid oxygen in some of the booster systems, such as Atlas, Titan I, and Saturn, costs approximately two cents per pound delivered to the launch site. The storable propellant systems mentioned earlier, such as hydrazine and nitrogen tetroxide, will, on the other hand, run to considerably higher costs. Hydrazine costs about one dollar per pound and the oxidizer costs seven cents per pound.

The liquid propellant system possessing the highest specific impulse is a combination of fluorine and hydrogen. Both propellants are cryogenic, but fluorine is considerably more reactive with materials of construction than is liquid oxygen. For this reason fluorine is not in operational use as yet, but some engine development has been carried out. Methods are available to improve the specific impulse of presently used liquid rocket systems. For example, it is possible to add a metallic fuel in finely divided form to the fuel constituents of a propellant system. Metals not only have a high heat of combustion but they also exhibit considerably higher density than any liquid fuel, and as a consequence more energy can be packaged in the same volume, an important factor in vehicle design. Metallic additives which could be used are such materials as aluminum, magnesium, or beryllium. They are generally used together with a jelling agent whose function it is to keep the finely divided metal particles in suspension within the fuel, thus preventing it from settling out on prolonged storage.

SPACE ENGINES

Liquid rocket systems suitable for use in orbiting or interplanetary space vehicles are similar in concept to those used for booster vehicles but differ in some design characteristics. For example, propulsion systems used for course or steering correction during interplanetary flight must be capable of long storage in outer space and of repeated restart and stop operation. Similarly, a system required to reduce the velocity of a space vehicle prior to landing on another planetary body requires long storage capability and also the capability of varying its thrust to permit a smooth landing. Propulsion systems used to maintain a space vehicle in orbit around a planetary body also require long storage and multiple restart capability and must be able to operate at very low thrust levels. Propellant systems chosen are therefore mostly so-called storable systems, such as hydrazine and nitrogen tetroxide, which do not suffer losses due to vaporization of the propellant and do not deteriorate due to aging or radiation.

A number of semicryogenic propellants are available for space propulsion purposes. These are propellants that require only moderate pressures within the storage tanks to maintain them in the liquid state but do not need tank insulation to prevent propellant boil-off. Many schemes are used to maintain the temperature range at which such propellants are stored in space vehicles at an acceptable level. Temperature control on the propellant tanks in space can be accomplished by the use of reflecting paints applied in special patterns on the missile exterior surfaces. Such schemes control the absorption of solar radiation as well as the emission of heat from the tanks to the dark of space in such a way as to maintain the propellant contained within these tanks at a reasonable temperature equilibrium.

The cooling requirements of space engines also differ from those of booster-vehicle powerplants. As discussed earlier, thrust is a function of the expansion ratio of a nozzle. As the ambient pressure decreases, additional thrust can be obtained by making the nozzle longer and increasing the exit diameter. In the vacuum of outer space it would therefore be desirable to have engines with large expansion area nozzles. However, space engines generally operate at low thrust levels so that the propellant flow rate to the engine and through the engine cooling jacket is low. The problem of cooling these very large, high-expansion-area nozzles becomes a difficult one under those conditions because not enough rocket fuel coolant is available to circulate through the entire area exposed to the hot combustion gases. As a consequence, space engines will frequently make use of two other methods of cooling, either ablative cooling or radiation cooling or a combination of both. Ablative cooling exists when heat is absorbed by an expendable solid material lining the engine; the absorbed heat serves to vaporize or "ablate" some of the lining which is then expelled through the nozzle in gaseous form.

Radiation cooling is used in those engine components where it is possible to radiate sufficient heat away from the component so that the resulting equilibrium temperature of the material is still within its safe structural limits. For example, the rocket motor chamber of a liquid space engine may be lined with an ablative material which vaporizes at a uniform rate during combustion; the original thickness of the liner is designed to retain sufficient lining for the entire combustion cycle of the engine. Such ablative liners are also used in the throat of the nozzle and a portion of the exit cone. The remainder of the exit cone is often made of materials, such as titanium or molybdenum, which exibit fairly high strength even at elevated temperatures. The hot combustion gases flowing through such an exit cone will then heat it to a temperature level at which the heat input to the nozzle from the hot gases equals the heat loss

Figure 7.11. Small Space Engine with Ablative Chamber. (Courtesy of United Technology Center, Division of United Aircraft Corporation.)

by the nozzle to outer space by radiation. The nozzle material will then be at a temperature level where the structural strength of the material is still sufficient.

Figure 7.11 shows a small rocket motor chamber lined with ablative material after a test firing. The injector is at the right and the nozzle is not shown. The uneven thickness of the ablative chamber liner is a result of the fact that most of the combustion and the highest gas turbulence are found near the injector, thus increasing the heat transfer to the walls at that location. The injector itself is cooled by the liquid flowing through its passages.

7.3 NONCHEMICAL ROCKET PROPULSION SYSTEMS

Nuclear-Thermal Propulsion

As we have seen from the previous discussion, a rocket motor derives its forward thrust from the rearward expulsion of hot combustion gases. In the chemical propulsion systems the heating of these gases is accomplished by a chemical reaction between fuel and oxidizer which liberates sufficient heat to bring the product gases to the desired high temperature. The advent of nuclear energy in recent decades has added another method of heating gases for expulsion through a rocket nozzle. This method depends upon the utilization of a nuclear reactor as a heat source. A propellant for such a system is then any fluid that is heated by the reactor and expelled at very high temperatures (without having undergone any chemical changes in the heating process). Hydrogen is a suitable gas for this purpose because, as shown earlier, the specific impulse of a propellant is inversely proportional to the molecular weight of the gases being ejected through the nozzle. On this basis, hydrogen, with a molecular weight of 2, can be exceeded in performance only by the unstable atomic hydrogen which has a molecular weight of one, or by subatomic fragments. Nuclear-reactor technology has proceeded to the point at which development work on a nuclear rocket appears feasible. As a consequence, the United States, and probably also Russia, has in being at the present time development programs aimed at producing such a rocket for interplanetary space flight.

Several problems must be solved in connection with this type of propulsion system. The first, and most important problem, relates to the massive weight of nuclear reactors caused by three essential characteristics of such devices. First, the source of the heat energy is the fuel element in the reactor—consisting of an isotope of uranium, a very dense metal. Second, the control system required to keep the fission reaction at a safe rate consists of dense metal rods able to absorb neutrons produced by the fission of the uranium isotope. Third, all nuclear reactors operating within certain distances of human personnel must be shielded by other fairly dense materials in order to prevent radiation danger to life and also to increase reactor efficiency. As a consequence the ratio of weight to thrust produced is higher for the nuclear rocket engine than for chemical propulsion engines. At the same time, the energy output of the reactor, and therefore the maximum temperature of the gas being heated in the reactor, must be kept at a level tolerable to the materials of the reactor itself. As a consequence, hydrogen gas being ejected from a nuclear rocket nozzle will be considerably lower in temperature (2000°F) than the exhaust gases of a chemical rocket (5000°F). Since temperature is directly related to specific impulse, the impulse efficiency of a nuclear rocket, although still higher than that of chemical rockets because of the lower molecular weight of its exhaust gas, is still only half of what it would be if its exhaust gas temperatures approached those of chemical rockets.

A nuclear rocket consists essentially of a liquid hydrogen storage tank, a pump and gas generator/turbine combination, to pump the hydrogen through the nuclear reactor, the nuclear reactor itself, and an exhaust nozzle. As in the chemical rocket, there are, of course, also pressurization systems for the hydrogen tank and various control devices which regulate the flow of hydrogen and the power output of the nuclear reactor. Because of the high mass of the reactor, nuclear power plants do not exhibit high thrust-to-weight ratios. This, together with their radiation hazards, makes them more suited for use in outer space than in Earth-to-orbit operations. It is very likely, therefore, that nuclear rockets will be used only in upper stages of large space vehicles, with the nuclear rocket stage being used to provide the propulsive power required to travel from Earth orbit to orbit around other planetary bodies in the Solar System. Figure 7.12 depicts a model of the Nerva engine being developed by NASA as the first nuclear engine to be tested in outer space.

Nuclear reactors are, of course, still expensive, and, because of safety

Figure 7.12. Nuclear Rocket Engine. (Courtesy of Aerojet General Corporation.)

hazards, operations involving nuclear rockets must be conducted with extreme care, also adding to the cost of using such rockets in space flight. Their main advantage lies not only in their higher specific impulse but also in the fact that they can be started and stopped at will and are able to produce power for long periods of time. These advantages must be balanced against the disadvantages of higher cost and greater hazards to the personnel of space vehicles on which they may be used.

Electric Propulsion

A number of space propulsion applications exist in which only very small thrust levels are required. These applications include requirements for keeping satellites in their programmed orbits by providing corrective thrust to overcome orbit-disturbing forces such as are produced by collision with the very tenuous hydrogen atmosphere in space or by radiation pressure from solar radiation. Another application would be that of propelling a small space vehicle over the vast distances between the planets of the solar system. Travel times for such missions exceed many months in total duration and thus permit the required terminal velocity to be built up by the continuous application of a small thrust force over longer periods of time. This contrasts strongly with the propulsion requirements to lift a body from a planetary surface into outer space, where high thrust levels for a short period of time are required. For both former classes of missions, electric propulsion devices are well suited. Such devices make use of the fact that thrust is a function of momentum and that momentum is the product of the mass of the matter being accelerated times its velocity. The same momentum can therefore be obtained, whether a large quantity of mass is being accelerated slowly or whether a very small quantity is being accelerated to very high velocity. Electric propulsion engines use this principle by creating small quantities of an ionized, or electrically charged reaction mass, which can then be accelerated to high velocities by suitably placed electromagnetic or electrostatic fields and ejected from the motor. Another category of electric propulsion engine exists which is, however, really a modification of the nuclear-thermal rocket engine, with an electric arc substituting for the reactor as a heat source. The true electric rocket engines are then of essentially two types, the electromagnetic and the electrostatic engines, both of which operate on the principle of ejecting rearward comparatively small quantities of ionized mass at very high velocities.

All electrically operated rocket engines have a high power requirement. According to current planning, power will be provided by systems consisting of small nuclear reactors and a thermocouple device

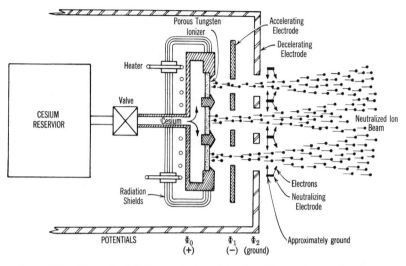

Figure 7.13. Schematic of Cesium Ion Engine. (Courtesy of Electro-Optical Systems, Inc.)

which provides direct conversion of the reactor heat to electric power. The technology of these power-producing devices depends therefore as much upon levels that can be obtained with electric rocket engines as it does upon the technology of the engine itself. Because of the low efficiencies involved in both the production of power by such means and the utilization of this power in providing thrust, it is likely that for some time to come the thrust levels for engines of this type will remain comparatively small, perhaps only fractions of a pound.

ELECTROSTATIC PROPULSION

A schematic of an electrostatic rocket engine is shown in Figure 7.13. The operation of this engine involves the following steps: a metal, such as cesium, which has a high density and, at the same time, a low ionization potential, is vaporized by the use of electric heaters. The metal gas atoms thus obtained are then brought to a very high temperature at which thermal ionization occurs; in this process an electron is removed from each gas atom and an ion carrying an electric charge is produced according to

$$\text{Cs(gas)} \xrightarrow{\text{very high temperature}} \text{Cs}^+ + e^-.$$

Figure 7.14. Cesium Ion Engine Ready for Test in Vacuum Chamber. (Courtesy of Electro-Optical Systems, Inc.)

Accelerating electrodes are used to drive these ions to very high velocities and to eject them to the rear of the engine, thus producing thrust. In addition to cesium, other alkali metals suitable for this application because of low ionization potentials include rubidium, potassium, and sodium.

Electric power is required for two purposes in engines of this type. First, the metal must be vaporized and ionized. Second, electric power is required to produce the electrostatic field which accelerates these ions. Specific impulses which may be obtained with engines of this type range from 6000 seconds to as high as 20,000 seconds. Higher impulses can be obtained, but in the current state of technology they would require electric power sources that are impractical for space-flight applications because of their great size and weight. Figure 7.14 shows an experimental cesium ion engine and the vacuum chamber in which it will be tested. Figure 7.15 shows the engine in operation. The luminous ion beam is clearly visible. An engine

Figure 7.15.   Cesium Ion Engine Test Firing.   (Courtesy of Electro-Optical Systems, Inc.)

of this size produces thrust measured only in millipounds, but it is the forerunner of larger engines to come.

ELECTROMAGNETIC PROPULSION

In this type of engine, electric heating is used to ionize a gaseous propellant which is then accelerated with electromagnetic fields to the rear to obtain thrust. The hot gas may be produced by passing a suitable gas at low pressure through an electric arc. Specific impulses obtainable from such devices will range from 1000 to 20,000 seconds. Thrusts in the order of one pound have already been obtained with laboratory devices. However, it is anticipated that early flight engines will produce thrust levels of only a fraction of a pound.

ELECTROTHERMAL PROPULSION

Propulsion devices falling into this category consist essentially of a chamber and a nozzle. The chamber contains the electric arc device which serves to heat the reaction gas, which is in turn expelled through the nozzle without the benefit of additional acceleration obtainable from the magnetic fields used in the engines already described. Hydrogen is usually used as a working fluid in these devices because of its low molecular weight and appropriate thermal properties.

Summary

It is apparent that even after the successful development of nuclear-thermal propulsion and various electric propulsion methods, chemical means of propulsion will still be extensively employed. In addition to providing the booster-stage power (i.e., first-stage rockets) for nuclear-powered upper stages, chemical rocketry will be useful for providing power in maneuvers requiring short-duration/high-thrust performance. Conversely, electric propulsion will be most useful—if available—for long-duration/low-thrust performance requirements, while nuclear propulsion will be most useful—again, if and when available—in the intermediate power spectrum, that is, at low-to-very high thrust levels.

These general aspects and other specific characteristics of the various propulsion means are abstracted in Tables 7.3 and 7.4

7.4 PERFORMANCE OF ROCKET PROPULSION SYSTEMS

It was mentioned earlier that the only function of the rocket propulsion system is to provide the missile or space vehicle with a terminal velocity adequate for its chosen mission. This is accomplished by developing thrusts which are sufficiently large to overcome the gravity forces and air drag forces which decelerate the vehicle while in the atmosphere. Terminal velocities are related to the range of the warhead if the booster is to be used in a ballistic missile application, or to the orbiting altitude if the booster is employed to launch a satellite. Terminal velocities of ballistic missiles range from about 15,000 to 25,000 feet per second. Orbital velocities range from 25,000

Table 7.3.   Characteristics of Chemical Propulsion Techniques*

Charac-teristics	Type of Propulsion System							
	Solid	Liquid (Cryogenic)		Liquid (Storable)		Hybrid		
Fuel and Oxidant Premixed	Yes	No		No		No		
		Liquid Oxidant	Liquid Fuel	Liquid Oxidant	Liquid Fuel	Liquid Oxidant	Solid Fuel	
Propellant examples	Mixture of solid oxidant and a solid fuel, e.g., ammonium perchlorate and synthetic elastomer binder	Liquid oxygen (LOX); liquid fluorine	Kerosenes (RP-1, JP-4); liquid hydrogen	Nitrogen tetroxide; nitric acid; chlorine trifluoride (CTF)	Amines; unsymmetrical dimethyl hydrazine (UDMH); hydrazine	Nitrogen tetroxide; liquid fluorine; chlorine trifluoride (CTF)	Synthetic elastomer binder; plastic binder	
Typical burning times	0.2 to 120 seconds	0.5 to 3 minutes		0.2 to 200 seconds		?		
Typical thrust levels (in pounds)	1 to 1,000,000	50,000 to 2,000,000		100 to 300,00		?		
Typical specific impulse range (in seconds)†	200 to 300	275 to 400		275 to 325		250 to 300		
Advantages	Simplicity; reliability; storability, i.e., instant readiness; inexpensive development	Best known, historically; thrust can be modulated during flight; engine can be checked out prior to flight. Inexpensive propellants		Storability; thrust can be modulated during flight		Thrust can be modulated during flight		
Disadvantages	No thrust modulation during flight, expensive propellants	Cumbersome fueling; no standby or storage capability; complexity, expensive developments; high failure rates		Expensive propellants, limited experience with simple models (pre-packaged)		No experience as yet		
Present use	Military	Small and large missiles, e.g., Sidewinder, Falcon, Polaris, Minuteman	Large missiles, e.g., Thor, Atlas, Titan I		Small and large missiles e.g., Bullpup, Titan II		None	
	Space	Small auxiliary units; large boosters under development, e.g., Titan III	Large boosters, e.g., Atlas; giant boosters under development, e.g., Saturn		Small auxiliary units, possible boosters, e.g., Titan II		None	
Projected use	All major missiles will use this power source; possible use as giant space boosters, e.g., "solid" Nova after late 1960s	No more development for military applications; use in large space boosters, anticipated for mid- and late 1960s		Many applications for small units for missiles and for space auxiliary engines		Depends on further developments		

* Reprinted by courtesy of the Stanford Research Institute, Menlo Park, California.

† Specific impulse, I_{sp}, is the length of time (in seconds), during which one pound of propellant can deliver one pound of thrust. It is a convenient measure of propellant efficiency.

Table 7.4.   Characteristics of Nonchemical Propulsion Techniques*

Charac- teristics	Nuclear-Thermal Propulsion	Type of Propulsion System		
		Nuclear-Electric Propulsion		
		Electrostatic	Electrothermal	Electromagnetic
Example	Nuclear propulsion	Ion propulsion	Arc jet propulsion	Plasma jet propulsion
Possible reduction to practice	1970s	Late 1960s	1970s	1970s
Mode of operation	A propellant† is heated in a nuclear reactor and is expanded through a nozzle	A propellant† is thermally ionized and the ions are accelerated electrostatically through an exit nozzle by electrically charged grids	A propellant† is heated in an electric arc and expanded through a nozzle	A propellant† is ionized by electric arc heating; this propellant "plasma" is then accelerated through a nozzle by a magnetic field
Typical specific impulse range (seconds)	800 to 1000	5000 to 20,000	1000 to 2000	2000 to 20,000
Typical operating times (continuous)	Minutes	Months	Days	Weeks
Advantages	Most useful thrust range for upper rocket stages (similar and superior to applications of chemical propulsion)	Most useful thrust range for small accelerations of very long duration (for deep space travel); thrust modulation during flight		
Disadvantages	Hazards from abortive launches; restricted to very large units; currently no thrust modulation during flight appears practical	Cannot operate in atmosphere; reliability difficult to achieve; devices are heavy and inefficient as yet; still in laboratory stage		

* Reprinted by courtesy of the Stanford Research Institute, Menlo Park, California.

† A "propellant" in these nonchemical propulsion techniques may be any fluid which is suitable and stable for the particular thermal or electrical means of expansion; thrust is produced here by expanding the fluid through a nozzle, but expansion is not effected by combstion.   For example, hydrogen by itself is a good propellant for nuclear-thermal propulsion.

to about 35,000 feet per second.   Velocities in excess of this value are required to escape Earth orbit and travel to the moon and other planets.

The forces acting on the vehicle in the direction of the flight path can be summed up as follows:

$$m \frac{dv}{dt} = F - D - mg \sin \theta, \qquad (7.10)$$

where m = the instantaneous mass of the vehicle,

$\quad v$ = velocity of the vehicle

$\quad F$ = thrust,

$\quad D$ = drag,

$\quad \theta$ = angle of the flight path to the local horizon.

This equation can be manipulated to yield for the case of vertical flight

$$\Delta v = \bar{c} \ln \mu - gt - D_1, \qquad (7.11)$$

where Δv = the velocity gained by the vehicle at completion of burning,

$\quad \mu$ = the mass fraction of the vehicle (see below),

$\quad D_1$ = a function of the drag,

$\quad t$ = time of rocket motor burning,

$\quad \bar{c}$ = the effective exhaust velocity averaged over the flight time; $\bar{c}$ varies with the altitude in accordance with Equation 7.2 because of the variation of the ambient pressure (see also Equation 7.13).

The mass fraction μ is a measure of the efficiency of booster-vehicle construction. It is defined as

$$\mu = \frac{W_0}{W_f}$$

$$= \frac{W_e + W_p + W_L}{W_e + W_L}, \qquad (7.12)$$

where W_0 = vehicle weight at take-off, including payload,

$\quad W_f$ = vehicle weight at burnout,

$\quad W_p$ = weight of the propellant burned during time t,

$\quad W_e$ = weight of the vehicle at time t when burning has been completed,

$\quad W_L$ = weight of the payload.

These equations permit us to discuss the essential characteristics of the propulsion system, and the performance of such a system, if Δv is to be maximized. The importance of specific impulse was already discussed. It relates to $\bar{c}$ by

$$\bar{c} = I_{\text{sp}}g \qquad (7.13)$$

It is therefore obvious that we will wish to find propellants with as high a value for I_{sp} as possible. In addition, we see that μ increases with a higher fraction of the propellant weight, W_p, to total weight, W_0. The increase in this ratio can be brought about in two ways, both of which are common practice in the aerospace industry. The design of the engine and the fuel tank structure can be refined in order to reduce W_e, or empty weight. Materials of construction should possess the highest strength per unit weight; for example, fiber glass can be used for tanks or for solid motor cases. More precise engineering design methods are used to match the strength of the material to the exact loads at various parts of the structure, thus reducing the weight of material of many components. The other approach involves the increase of the density of propellants so that the same volume of tank will contain a higher weight of the propellant. In addition to choosing propellants with higher basic densities, additives such as metal powders are used to increase density. In the case of liquid propellants, the use of metal powder must be accompanied by the addition of gelling agents which keep the powder in uniform suspension and prevent separation and settling of the solids.

Gravity losses, shown as gt in Equation 7.11, are reduced by increasing the acceleration of the vehicle by increasing thrust. This serves to reduce the required burning time, t. Shaping the flight path so that the angle θ becomes smaller will also minimize the effect of gravity in reducing Δv.

Finally, a number of approaches are available to reduce the drag loss D_1. These also include the shaping of the trajectory so as to pass through the denser portion of the atmosphere as quickly as possible, in addition to better aerodynamic design.

Flight performance for vehicles operating in outer space is considerably simplified by the absence of appreciable gravity or drag forces. This reduces Equation 7.11 to

$$F = m \frac{dv}{dt} \text{ (or } ma).$$ (7.14)

Since, for uniform acceleration,

$$\Delta v = at,$$ (7.15)

where a = acceleration,

$$a = \frac{F}{m}$$ (7.16)

or

$$\Delta v = \frac{Ft}{m}. \qquad (7.17)$$

When flight times are long, such as in interplanetary flight or in permanent earth orbits, the thrust F can be kept quite small if the motor operation time t is increased to yield the desired terminal velocity. Electric propulsion units are able to provide long operating times, albeit at low thrust levels, and can therefore be applied to many such missions.

CHAPTER 8

The Spacecraft and the Payload

Lawrence D. Ely

Aerospace Corporation

Contents

The Spacecraft and the Payload

8.1 INTRODUCTION

A spacecraft is that part of a complete space vehicle which is designed to accomplish some special mission in space. If it is unmanned, it may be filled with special instruments and equipment to obtain scientific information about space. If manned, the spacecraft will be provided with the means of affording comfort and sustenance to the inhabitants.

The other major part of a space vehicle is the launch vehicle. This is the part of the space vehicle that provides the required primary thrust and guidance.

The major parts of a typical space vehicle are shown in Figure 8.1. The spacecraft shown in this figure is a typical unmanned spacecraft with the solar cell paddles that are extended after the spacecraft is in space.

If the mission to be performed by a spacecraft is the exploration of deep space, the spacecraft may be boosted to the required velocity for the mission and be set on the desired path by the primary propulsion and guidance systems of the launch vehicle. At this point the spacecraft may be separated from the launch vehicle to continue on its way to perform the desired mission. All of the special instrumentation, electric power supply, and equipment necessary to accomplish the mission after separation of the spacecraft must be carried in it.

If the mission is one that requires an orbit of the Earth, an additional propulsion stage must be provided for final injection into the Earth orbit. This propulsion stage can be designed as a part of the spacecraft.

Spacecraft are sometimes erroneously referred to as the payload part of a launch vehicle. The *payload*, however, is only that part of a spacecraft which can be referred to as useful load. It consists of the special equipment and instruments necessary to accomplish the mission but does not include the basic structure, propulsion, and electronics in the spacecraft. An analogy can be made with a pickup truck to illustrate payload clearly: payload is the weight or useful

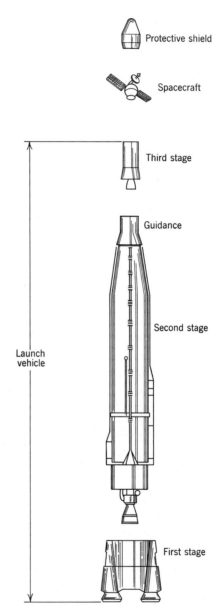

Figure 8.1.   Major Parts of a Typical Space Vehicle.

load that may be put in the body. It does not include the body itself, engine, tires, or wheels; that is, it does not include the parts of the truck necessary to transport or support the useful load.

Some spacecraft must carry a small propulsion and guidance capability for the purpose of correcting the flight path by altering the velocity and direction of motion after separation from the launch vehicle. Some power may also be necessary to obtain the desired spacecraft attitude or to obtain the desired terminal trajectory at the completion of the mission. The desired attitude may be achieved by low-thrust units that can provide a thrust to pitch, yaw, or roll the spacecraft. It is also necessary to provide a source of electric power for the operation of certain instruments and equipment.

The primary purpose of the launch vehicle is to place the spacecraft on the required trajectory or orbit for the mission to be performed. To accomplish this, the launch vehicle, sometimes called the booster, utilizes several large primary propulsion units together with the required fuel, and guidance and control systems. The required velocity is thus achieved in several steps or stages. More than one stage is used as such an arrangement is more efficient than a single stage. Multiple staging permits the used stages to be discarded (i.e. jettisoned, after burnout of their propulsion units), thus reducing the weight remaining to be accelerated. The type of primary propulsion units to use and their size are dependent on the mission and the weight of the spacecraft to be launched (see Chapters 4 and 7).

Spacecraft may be divided into three main categories, according to their objectives:

1. Those designed to orbit the Earth to accomplish the tasks that are now performed less efficiently from the surface of the Earth. Examples of such tasks are world-wide communications, meteorological research, weather forecasting, astronomical and geophysical observations, and navigation (see Chapter 2 for details).

2. Those designed as a means of transportation for man from Earth to any other celestial body and return.

3. Those designed as deep-space probes to explore the environment at or near solar planets and the environment of space between the Earth and these planets.

In order to accomplish these objectives with a high degree of reliability, it is necessary, first, to obtain a large amount of scientific information about the environment of space to design the spacecraft properly. For manned missions it is also necessary to obtain information about man's ability to survive the various conditions to which he will be subjected during space flight. To obtain the necessary design information, a logical sequence of missions has been planned and early missions have already been accomplished. First, unmanned spacecraft have been used for probes high into the Earth's atmosphere, Earth-orbital missions, and deep probes into space—the Moon and Venus. The second phase in many space programs may include animals. Unmanned spacecraft contain equipment and instruments with which to obtain the information and telemeter it to the Earth. The third phase involves manned spacecraft which have been used for suborbital and orbital flights and are next planned for missions to the moon and return. The size of the manned spacecraft will gradually increase as launch vehicle capability becomes greater. A large amount of ground research is under way to support the space-flight activity. The major research areas are hypersonics, flight mechanics, structures, materials, instrumentation, and data acquisition. The objective of this research is to provide the technical background required for the exploration of space, either for the detailed design of the spacecraft or for generating new and novel concepts of space flight.

8.2 TYPES OF SPACECRAFT

The general appearance and design details of a spacecraft are determined by (1) the nature of the mission, (2) whether the spacecraft is manned or unmanned; and (3) the conditions of re-entry: speed, deceleration, and duration. To a large extent, these factors will determine the weight, size, and shape of the spacecraft. The size and weight will be fixed by the duration of the flight and by the equipment and instruments that must be carried to accomplish the mission. The external shape will, of course, be such that the contents are adequately supported and protected. Whether the spacecraft will present a streamlined, drag-resistant appearance will depend on the conditions under which the Earth's atmosphere is encountered.

If the mission of the spacecraft is such that most of it is performed outside the Earth's atmosphere, the designer will need to pay very little attention to drag resistance. This is true of Earth satellites and nonreturn missions to celestial bodies with little or no atmosphere. In these cases the spacecraft is in the Earth's atmosphere only during the brief ascent phase; consequently, the drag force is relatively low. Any spacecraft that has a requirement to re-enter the Earth's atmosphere must be designed for high resistance as well as for protection against high temperatures. This resistance or drag force may be calculated from the formula $D = C_D(\rho/2)SV^2$. From this formula the drag force, D, is obtained in pounds, where C_D is a dimensionless drag coefficient which is dependent on the shape of the spacecraft, ρ is the density of the atmosphere expressed in slugs per cubic foot, S is a

Figure 8.2. Early Development Model of Navy Navigational Satellite. (Courtesy of U. S. Air Force.)

Figure 8.3.   TRACC Spacecraft.   (Courtesy of U. S. Air Force.)

representative cross-sectional area in square feet, and V is the velocity in feet per second.

It can easily be seen from the size and shape of early spacecraft that maintaining low resistance has not been a dominant factor in the design of spacecraft.   Other considerations are overriding, such as the requirement for certain space experiments and the requirement for auxiliary power, in many instances obtained from solar cells. The variety in the size and shape of spacecraft and space stations designed for special missions is illustrated in Figures 8.2 through 8.5.   Figure 8.2 illustrates an early development model of a Navy navigational satellite.   Figure 8.3 shows a TRACC spacecraft to obtain additional data on the Van Allen Belts.   Figure 8.4 is an artist's concept of an Earth-orbital space station, and Figure 8.5 is an artist's concept of a spacecraft design for nuclear systems maintenance.

Many early spacecraft, launched with ballistic missile boosters, were rather small.   Later, booster stages were added to provide increased

Figure 8.4. Design of Future Earth-Orbital Space Station. (Courtesy of Douglas Aircraft Company.)

thrust and improved performance. This resulted in launch vehicles such as the Thor-Delta, Thor-Able-Star, Thor-Agena, Atlas-Able, Atlas-Agena A, and Atlas-Centaur. Titan III, developed by the U.S. Air Force, is the Free World's first complete space launch system designed as such from the beginning. Saturn, developed by the National Aeronautics and Space Administration, is another example of a specially designed space launch vehicle. Nova, still another, example, is at present not yet beyond a design concept, but if developed it will be capable of launching thousands of pounds into space.

Space Missions

Missions are planned and development is under way that will permit man to probe farther into the vastness of space. The first missions have been kept as simple and uncomplicated as possible in order

Figure 8.5. Design of Future Spacecraft Performing Nuclear Systems Maintenance. (Courtesy of Astro-Nuclear Laboratory, Westinghouse Electric Company.)

to keep the probability of success high.   However, even the simplest missions require rather complicated instrumentation and equipment in order to accomplish the missions.

Earth-orbital missions can be divided into three types:

1. Instrumented scientific satellites to obtain geophysical and astronomical data.

2. Unmanned satellites to provide communications, weather, navigation, and other commercial services.

3. Manned satellites to gain information and experience with which to design spacecraft for lunar exploration and the exploration of solar planets.

The satellites of (1) and (2) are well under way. Many missions have already been accomplished. Spacecraft for these are continually being refined and more sophisticated missions will be accomplished in the future.

Project Mercury is the first phase of the program mentioned in (3). From the flights that have been accomplished the operational capability of the Mercury spacecraft has been proven, as well as some of the capabilities and limitations of the astronauts. A two-

man spacecraft has been used for the second phase of the program—
Project Gemini. Project Apollo, the third phase, will carry three
astronauts; this phase will make manned circumlunar flights and
manned lunar landings possible.

A comparison of the size of the Mercury and Apollo spacecrafts
is illustrated in Figure 8.6.

In preparation for manned Earth-orbital flights, successful ballistic suborbital flights were made by Navy Commander Alan Sheperd
on May 5, 1961, and by Air Force Captain Virgil Grissom on July
21, 1961. On November 29, 1961, a successful two-orbit flight was
achieved with a chimpanzee named Enos. On February 20, 1962,

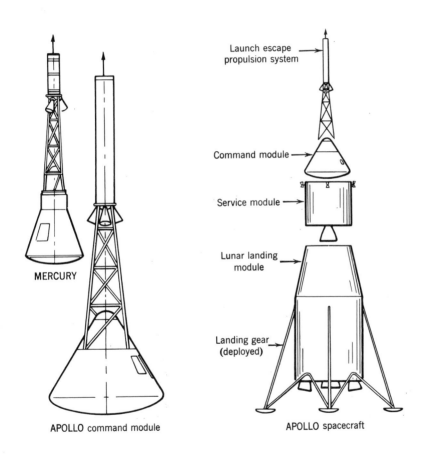

Figure 8.6. Comparison of MERCURY and APOLLO Spacecrafts. (Courtesy of the National
Aeronautics and Space Administration.)

the first United States Earth-orbital flight was made by Marine Lieutenant Colonel John Glenn, and, after three orbits, a successful reentry and recovery was made. Project Mercury was extended since Glenn's flight and completed by Major Gordon Cooper (22 orbits). Project Gemini was initiated in 1965 and spectacular 2-man flights up to 62 orbits and a "walk in space" were successfully accomplished (Major E. White).

These manned Earth-orbital flights provided the technical knowledge and operational experience with which we can ultimately make flights to the moon. During these missions planning and preliminary development will take place to provide an ultimate capability to explore other celestial bodies in the solar system. Venus may be more closely investigated in the early 1970's, first with unmanned fly-by missions and later with spacecraft that will orbit the planet. Two-planet missions also appear feasible. One such possibility would be a Venus-Mercury exploration. A Venus orbit could be followed by a flight to the vicinity of Mercury before returning to Earth. A two-planet mission has the advantage of exploring two planets without using appreciably more energy than is necessary for a single planet.

After Venus missions in the mid- or late 1970's, Mars-orbital flights will take place, followed by excursions to the surface of Mars from Mars-orbital flights. Such missions would capitalize on the rendezvous experience gained during lunar flights and the earlier Earth-orbital flights. A typical lunar mission and its spacecraft are described in Chapter 9.

Design Requirements

A large number of detail requirements must be satisfied during the design of a spacecraft. For manned spacecraft many of these details have to do with the survival and comfort of the human occupants. For both manned and unmanned spacecraft the basic structure must be designed to withstand the loads and heating produced by the flight conditions. Heating tends to decrease the strength of the materials at the same time that high loads are experienced.

As an illustration of the magnitude of heating and deceleration, Figure 8.7 shows how the velocity, deceleration, and heating of a Mercury spacecraft vary with altitude during re-entry into the Earth's

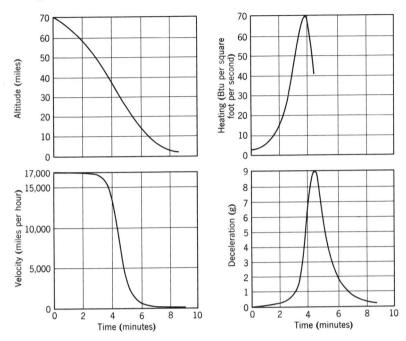

Figure 8.7. Re-entry Conditions of MERCURY Spacecraft. (Reprinted with permission. Copyright (C) 1960 by Scientific American, Inc.)

atmosphere from an Earth-satellite orbit. The initial velocity at re-entry is approximately 17,000 miles per hour. As the altitude decreases, the denser atmosphere causes the velocity to decrease. At an altitude of about 35,000 feet the velocity has decreased to just above 12,000 miles per hour. The maximum deceleration of 9 g's is reached at this point. Slightly before this, the maximum heating rate of 70 Btu per square foot per second is experienced. The basic structure and all components of it must be designed to withstand the loads produced by the 9-g deceleration. In addition, the spacecraft must be capable of resisting collisions with the tiny meteorites that are encountered in space. Special meteorite "bumpers" have been designed with this purpose in mind. However, the small meteoroids may be too small to do any damage and the large meteorites may be encountered very infrequently. Special loads must be considered for the condition in which one spacecraft is expected to rendezvous with another spacecraft or with a space station. The loads encountered during a landing on the moon or some other celestial body and the launching loads experienced during any part of the mission are also among the design conditions to be considered.   Such conditions may be critical for certain parts of the structure but not other parts.

Taking care of the effect of heating is a particularly difficult problem.   The velocity at which a spacecraft re-enters the Earth's atmosphere from either orbital or deep-space flights is exceedingly high. This high velocity on re-entry represents a tremendous amount of energy which must be absorbed or dissipated.   To illustrate the magnitude of this energy, let us assume two cases: (a) a 4000-pound spacecraft re-entering the Earth's atmosphere from an Earth-satellite orbit at 17,000 miles an hour; and (b) a 4000-pound spacecraft re-entering the Earth's atmosphere on a return flight from another planet at 25,000 miles per hour.

Kinetic energy, the energy due to motion, can be calculated from the formula,

$$KE = \tfrac{1}{2}MV^2$$

where M = mass (= W/g) and V is the velocity in feet per second (W is the weight in pounds and g is the acceleration due to gravity in feet per second per second.)   Kinetic energy is then expressed in foot-pounds.

The kinetic energy for (a) can be calculated by substituting the values for mass and velocity in the basic kinetic energy equation

$$KE = \tfrac{1}{2}MV^2$$

$$= \frac{1}{2}\left(\frac{4000}{32.2}\right)\left(17,000 \times \frac{88}{60}\right)^2$$

$$= 386 \times 10^8 \text{ ft-lb.}$$

In this formula the fraction $\frac{88}{60}$ is used to convert the 17,000 miles per hour to feet per second as 88 feet per second is equal to 60 miles per hour.   If it is desired to express the energy in British thermal units (Btu) instead of foot-pounds, the conversion factor of 778.3 is used (there are 778.3 foot-pounds per Btu).

Therefore,

$$\frac{KE \text{ (ft-lb)}}{778.3} = \frac{386 \times 10^8}{778.3}$$

$$= 49.6 \times 10^6 \text{ Btu.}$$

The kinetic energy for (b) is

$$KE = \tfrac{1}{2}MV^2$$

$$= \frac{1}{2} \times \frac{4000}{32.2} \times \left(25{,}000 \times \frac{88}{60}\right)^2$$

$$= 814 \times 10^8 \text{ foot-pounds}$$

or, converting to Btu's,

$$\frac{KE \text{ (ft-lb)}}{778.3} = 105 \times 10^6 \text{ Btu.}$$

It is interesting to note that the kinetic energy of a spacecraft returning from deep space (case b) is roughly twice that of a space craft of equal weight returning from an Earth-satellite orbit (case a).

Considering the case with the smallest energy and calculating the amount of energy per pound,

$$\frac{49.6 \times 10^6}{4 \times 10^3} = 12.4 \times 10^3 \text{ Btu's per pound,}$$

we can readily see that this is enough energy to vaporize completely any known practical material if all of the energy had to be absorbed by the spacecraft. To understand this, it is only necessary to recall that one Btu is $\frac{1}{180}$ of the amount of heat required to convert one pound of water in ice form to steam at standard atmospheric pressure. Accordingly, 12.4×10^3 Btu's is $(12.4 \times 10^3)/180 = 68.8$ times the amount of heat necessary to convert one pound of ice to steam!

Copper has a melting point of 1975°F. Using copper as an example of the amount of heat required to raise it from a temperature of 0 to 1975°F, we would use the conventional heat equation, Q equals $mc\Delta t$, where m equals weight, c equals specific heat, and Δt equals change in temperature. From this equation we obtain Q in Btu's if m is in pounds, C is in Btu per pound per degree Fahrenheit, and Δt is in degrees Fahrenheit. Therefore

$$Q = 1 \times 0.093 \times 1975$$

$$= 183.675 \text{ Btu's,}$$

or only 183.675 Btu's are required to raise one pound of copper from zero degrees Fahrenheit to the melting point. We can readily imagine what would happen if the pound of copper had to absorb 12.4×10^3 Btu's of heating!

Fortunately, the entire energy need not be absorbed by the space-craft. As it passes through the atmosphere, it is preceded by a shock wave which is caused by the spacecraft tending to compress the air. Molecules of air striking its forward surface rebound at high velocity and collide with other molecules resulting in heating. The shock wave extends laterally far beyond the spacecraft, and a wake of heated air is left behind which may contain as much as 99 per cent of the heat. The high temperature generated ionizes a layer of air around the spacecraft, which, however, does not tend to increase the temperature of the spacecraft through radiation. To absorb the heat that is transmitted to the spacecraft, the *ablation method* is most generally used. This method utilizes a material that absorbs heat as it changes from one physical state to another of a lower density, for example a solid to a liquid, a solid to a liquid to a gas, or directly from a solid to a gas. The last change is called sublimation.

The ablation process must take place uniformly over the surface of the spacecraft. Other characteristics desired in an ablation material are low thermal conductivity, low density, high latent heat of fusion, and high viscosity. Many plastics have very good ablation characteristics.

Other common methods of heat protection are heat-sink, transpira-tion, and regenerative or radiator cooling. Although some of these methods have advantages over the ablation method, in general the disadvantages more than offset the advantages.

In the *heat-sink* method a material that absorbs heat by conduction is used. Ideally, the material should have a high thermal conductivity, a high thermal capacity, and a high melting point, together with a low surface temperature gradient and a high reflectivity. Early ballistic missiles used this method for the heat protection of the nose cones.

The *transpiration* method of cooling consists of forcing a fluid through pores in the surface material. The fluid passing through the pores cools the surface material and then forms an insulating layer between the surface material and the heat source. The pores can be produced mechanically, or a porous material may be used. Important characteristics are a high effective heat capacity of the fluid and a high heat transfer coefficient between the fluid and the metal.

In the *regenerative or radiator* cooling method a liquid is circulated in a jacket or in tubes beneath the surface to be cooled and then passed through a heat exchanger and re-used.

Transpiration and regenerative cooling methods are in general unsatisfactory for spacecraft re-entries as high heat fluxes are encountered. These methods are not capable of absorbing heat rapidly without exhorbitant weight penalties.

Although the heat-sink method is satisfactory for relatively low heat fluxes, heat-sink materials are usually not satisfactory for heating over a long period of time. It is difficult to find a material possessing simultaneously a high thermal conductivity, a high thermal capacity, and a high melting point.

The methods that depend on the flow of fluids, such as in transpiration or regenerative cooling, require complex pumping equipment which adversely affects cost, reliability, and maintenance.

At present, ablation appears to be the best method for cooling spacecraft during re-entry from the standpoint of over-all efficiency.

8.3 SPACECRAFT SUBSYSTEMS

It was previously noted that a spacecraft consists of the payload and of several additonal subsystems; the latter provide electrical power on board, they perform the necessary functions to place the payload on target, they provide communications, life support, etc. A short description of what each of these spacecraft subsystems is expected to do follows, along with a discussion of the major subsystem factors.

Propulsion

During the launch of most space vehicles several primary stages of propulsion have been used and jettisoned. However, for most space missions it is necessary to have a small propulsion capabilty in the final stage, that is, the spacecraft itself. Thrust for the spacecraft may be necessary after launch and during the initial part of a space flight to maneuver the spacecraft into the correct plane, orbit, or trajectory. It may be necessary to change the velocity of the spacecraft during flight in order to correct guidance errors. Near the destination the flight plan may require a retrothrust to reduce velocity sufficiently to go into orbit around a celestial body and finally to reduce the velocity enough to land softly. For some missions it is necessary to have sufficient fuel and propulsion capabilty to launch again after landing on a celestial body. Chemical propulsion will be the primary means for at least another ten years, although other types of propulsion are showing sufficient promise for some interplanetary space flights of long duration in the future. Some types that develop only low levels of thrust may be extremely useful if the thrust can be delivered over a long period of time. Types undergoing laboratory experimentation at the present time are plasma jet, ion, electrothermal, and electromagnetic propulsion, and also nuclear engines; these are described in Chapter 7.

Guidance

Guidance of a spacecraft (see also Chapter 4) can be divided into three phases: launch, orbital or midcourse, and re-entry or terminal. In a spacecraft we are primarily concerned with the last two phases of guidance, although it is necessary that the launch-phase guidance also be accurate.

Launch-phase guidance must be such that the spacecraft is placed on the desired path at the desired velocity at the time of final thrust cutoff. Most launch vehicles have more than a single propulsion stage. The igniton, cutoff, and dropping of each propulsion stage may be preprogrammed and automatically controlled on the basis of deviations of velocity and position from an optimum path. Or, the path may be controlled by commands from the ground, based on tracking reports. Radar, radio, or inertial guidance systems may be used. Control may be accomplished by any method that can change the direction of the thrust on command or by aerodynamic surfaces if the space vehicle is still in the atmosphere. There are several methods by which the direction of thrust may be changed: swiveling of the entire rocket engine, deflection of vanes in the exhaust, deflection of rings around the engine nozzle circumference, separate rocket control nozzles, or by liquid injection thrust vector control, as used on the solid booster phase of the Titan III.

During the launch phase the entire space vehicle is guided. Firing the final propulsion stage requires great precision to obtain the correct velocity. Usually small vernier rocket engines are used to obtain the last small increment of velocity to send the spacecraft on the desired trajectory or orbit. If a perfect circular orbit of radius r is desired, the velocity vector must be normal to the line passing through the center of the body about which the circular orbit is desired. The velocity must be exactly equal to

$$V = \sqrt{g_0 r_0^2 / r},$$

where g_0 is the acceleration of gravity at the surface of the body, r_0 is the radius of the celestial body and r is the distance from the center of the body to the spacecraft. If the velocity is greater or less than

$$\sqrt{g_0 r_0^2 / r},$$

the spacecraft will go into an elliptical orbit. If the velocity is greater, the perigee of the ellipse will be at the injection point. If the velocity is less, the apogee of the ellipse will be at the injection point.

Orbital or midcourse guidance is concerned with correcting the orbit or trajectory if it is determined that there is an error from the launch phase. After the spacecraft is in space and is on essentially the correct path, only a few pounds of thrust are necessary to correct the direction of its flight path. Small ion rockets may be developed in the next few years to the point where they may be available for such small changes in velocity. At present, the associated electrical power equipment required is too heavy for space flight. Low values of thrust may be used for correction of attitude, evasive action against meteorites or other spacecraft, and terminal guidance for rendezvous or interceptor operations.

Re-entry or terminal guidance is required for two reasons: control of the spacecraft attitude on re-entry and control of its direction. Control of the attitude of the spacecraft is necessary to ensure that it will re-enter with the proper surface forward. If this could not be done, a surface might be forward which was improperly protected against the high heat of re-entry. Control of the direction of motion of the spacecraft is important from the standpoint of controlling the

angle of re-entry. Controlling this angle will control the amount
and rate of heating at re-entry and the landing point. Too shallow
an angle can allow the spacecraft to skip out of the Earth's atmosphere
and perhaps not return. Too steep an angle might allow the heating
to get too high for the protective shell or the occupants.

Attitude Control

There may be several times during the mission of a spacecraft
when it will be necessary for the spacecraft to be pointed in a particular direction. For example, when the spacecraft is near another
celestial body, it may be necessary to orient the spacecraft so that
the equipment required for observations will operate properly. Generally, there is an optimum attitude for the antenna to be most effective. If solar cells are used for the generation of auxiliary electric
power, there is a best attitude of the spacecraft for this function
to be performed properly, that is, the cells must look at the sun.
Re-entry of the spacecraft into the atmosphere of the Earth or other
celestial body makes it necessary to have the correct surface of the
spacecraft forward, so that high re-entry heating will take place
on the surface of the spacecraft designed for high heating. In case
additional thrust is required to change the flight path during flight
or if retrothrust is necessary to initiate re-entry, the spacecraft must
be properly oriented so that the thrust produced is in the right
direction. Spacecraft whose missions involve making rendezvous
with other spacecraft or space stations must have precise control
over their attitude at the time physical contact is made. The attitude of a spacecraft may be rather easily and simply controlled
by directing the reaction from a compressed gas exhausted through
a nozzle. Such a reaction jet can be coupled with a sensing device
so that the correct attitude may be obtained at the proper time.
Roll, pitch, and yaw of a spacecraft may be easily controlled and
the control may be completely automatic, remote-manual, or direct-
manual.

Instrumentation

The instrumentation for a spacecraft is a highly critical subsystem:
control instruments must measure the various key factors that con-

tribute to the operation and performance of a spacecraft. In addition, the payload contains the primary instruments necessary to measure and record the scientific data for which the space mission was originally designed.

Communications

Communications are extremely important in manned spacecraft. Commands may be given to the astronaut and, if he does not understand a command, he may by voice communication request that it be repeated. Voice communication may be used for emergency instructions if it is apparent that something is wrong with either the vehicle or its control or the astronaut.

Both high and ultrahigh frequencies were used in the Mercury spacecraft for voice communications. These two voice links were operated simultaneously. There were also two links, both in the ultrahigh-frequency band, to operate the telemetered information from the spacecraft to the Earth's surface. The telemetry link with the highest frequency could be keyed by the pilot to provide a backup for the voice communication. There were two identical command receivers through which three functions could be initiated from the ground: These functions are (1) resetting the retrotimer, (2) firing the retrorockets, and (3) aborting the mission. Voice communication could also be received by the command receivers. This could be done simultaneously with the ultrahigh- and high-frequency links when the spacecraft was within range of the command transmitter (see Chapter 6 for additional details).

Life-Support Equipment

A life-support system is one that provides the occupant or occupants of a spacecraft with a suitable atmosphere and food and water for the duration of the space mission. A means must also be provided for taking care of normal bodily functions, exercise, work, and sleep. The environmental control and life-support system varies considerably in concept with the duration of the space mission and the number of persons aboard the spacecraft. For example, for short flights, stored oxygen may be carried, whereas for long flights it may be desirable to use a regenerative system. The Mercury system, which was designed for relatively short flights, provides the occupant with a suitable atmosphere and cooling through two circuits, one for the cabin and one for the pressure suit of the occupant. The cabin circuit provides cooling. In addition to cooling, the suit circuit removes carbon dioxide, CO_2, water, H_2O, and odors, and replenishes the oxygen supply. Pure oxygen is furnished at a pressure of 5 pounds per square inch. The CO_2 is removed by absorption in lithuim hydroxide, odors are removed by adsorption with activated charcoal, and H_2O is removed by condensation and then absorption by a vinyl sponge. The water is periodically squeezed from the vinyl sponge into a condensate container and then used as a coolant for both the suit and cabin circuits, after passing through a heat exchanger. The pressure suit is left deflated unless the cabin pressure fails. These and other life support aspects are described in Chapter 5.

Recovery Aids

A number of features can be incorporated in the design to aid in the search and recovery of a spacecraft after landing back on Earth. These features will vary somewhat, depending on whether a water, land, or air-snatch recovery is planned. Whatever method is chosen, a means must be provided for decelerating the spacecraft and reducing the impact shock loads to acceptable values. Deceleration can be accomplished most easily by means of parachutes, once the spacecraft is in the atmosphere. A small drogue parachute can be activated first to reduce the velocity from supersonic to subsonic speeds; then a large parachute can be deployed to slow the spacecraft to a velocity that will permit a low impact velocity for water or land. A water recovery is the most common.

Special radar beacons can be carried that can be activated after the main parachute is deployed during descent. Also, two-way emergency voice communication systems can be carried, using both ultrahigh frequency and high-frequency transceivers. The antenna used during the space flight can be jettisoned on deployment of the parachute and the ultrahigh-frequency links transferred to a monopole antenna. On contact with the water, the parachute can be jettisoned and a high-frequency antenna deployed by a helium-filled balloon. Flashing lights and a radio beacon can be used to help locate the spacecraft. A water-activated battery can be used to turn on the lights and beacon. A dye marker, designed to eject automatically when the spacecraft makes contact with the water, is useful as a visual aid. Additional features that may be employed prior to impact are the ejection of radar chaff and a SOFAR bomb (sound fixing and ranging). The chaff can aid both surface and aircraft in locating the spacecraft. The SOFAR bomb is detonated after sinking to a predetermined depth and then gives off signals that enable listening stations to determine the location of the spacecraft by triangulation.

The events that take place in sequence during the recovery operation to locate and then recover the spacecraft can be automatically programmed. An accurate and reliable timer can be used that is activated by pressure or deceleration. Once the timer is started, the various events that must take place during the recovery operation take place automatically.

Auxiliary Power

To provide a source of electrical power for the many items of equipment and instrumentation that must be carried on a typical space mission, an auxiliary power unit must be carried. This unit must have a long life, be highly reliable and low in weight. Various types of units can convert primary energy (solar or nuclear) to electrical energy, or batteries may be carried to obtain electrical energy directly. The type of auxiliary power unit selected will depend on the requirements for the particular mission. Isotopic auxiliary power has already been used as early as the Fall of 1963.

CHAPTER 9

The Next Decade of Astronautics: Manned Exploration of Our Solar System

Kurt R. Stehling

Electro-Optical Systems, Inc.,
A Subsidiary of Xerox Corporation

Contents

The Next Decade of Astronautics:
Manned Exploration
of our Solar System

9.1 THE ROLE OF MAN IN SPACE

The projection of man into the hostile world beyond the narrow confines of our two-dimensional existence at the bottom of the atmospheric ocean will begin one of the most magnificent epochs in man's history and his conquest of his environment. Projecting man into space is not an unreasoned or ill-considered venture by the United States or the Soviet Union. Leaders in these countries, both in the technological and political communities, have seen fit to support major programs of space technology involving manned journeys into orbits around the Earth, to the moon, and perhaps even beyond. They have done this not because of a sudden burst of enthusiasm for astronautics but because of their reasoned considerations that man in space represents a technological status symbol for their respective nations and can "carry the flag" to new domains in the vast domain of space, now that man has thoroughly explored the Earth.

The populations of the two great national contenders for world supremacy, the United States and the Soviet Union, have enthusiastically supported these manned programs. Indeed they have been ahead of their leaders in calling for major manned efforts. Space technologists and astronautic experts are realizing more and more the inadequacies of space instrumentation and machinery when operating alone, without the guiding hand of a man, in an environment in which no repairs can be made and in which complicated functions cannot be attended to. What man builds does not necessarily mean that man can make reliable. When it is difficult to make even simple mechanisms for daily use (of which millions may have been built) reliable so that one or two years can be expected without interruption for repairs, why should we expect remotely controlled mechanisms, consisting of tens of thousands of electrical and electromechanical, electro-optical and other parts to operate efficiently and reliably for months, if not

315

years, in an inimical domain and without years of background experience for an apparatus such as a spacecraft?

The role of man, then, from the standpoint of advanced scientific research and development and from geopolitical or astropolitical standpoints is assured. The problem remains of providing man with a suitable artificial environment to allow him to exist in the vacuum of space under the hazards of radiation, micrometeor impact, and zero gravity. He must maintain himself not only to stay alive but to attend to scientific and technical apparatus. Ultimately he must leave the sheltered metal womb of his spacecraft to wander about on the fiercely hostile terrain of the moon and, later, a probably no less hostile firmament on the nearer planets.

9.2   THE MOON—OUR NEAREST NEIGHBOR IN SPACE

When President Kennedy, in 1961, announced that this country "would land a man on the moon in this decade," he did so partly in response to the Soviet challenge—a challenge consisting of an orbital flight by Gagarin a few months previously.* He was advised by the National Aeronautics and Space Administration, which had set up a committee to investigate what could be done by man in space. This committee recommended that a lunar landing would be feasible and practical within a decade. However, man's landing on the moon was really assured at the moment that Project Mercury, the manned Earth-orbital project, was announced. Just as the Bleriot flight across the English Channel before World War I was the precursor of the crossing of oceans with giant jets, so can we be assured that the relatively modest efforts of ballistic rockets with Shephard and Grissom, and orbital flights with Glenn, Carpenter, etc., Shirra, will be succeeded by deep-space penetration around and finally onto the moon, then to the nearer planets, and more particularly, Mars, which has probably the least dangerous environment of the Earthlike planets.

When the lunar landing program was announced, it soon became the major NASA project, gobbling up at least 75 per cent of the operational budget of that agency. The experience of the Mercury

---

* See quote at end of Chapter 2.

project and design studies done at its Langley, Virginia, facility of the National Aeronautics and Space Administration, showed that a spacecraft looking very much like the blunt-nosed, bell-shaped Mercury could be used to advantage for carrying more than one man, not only into orbit but far up into space, and with subsequently higher re-entry speeds into the Earth's atmosphere than were achieved by Mercury. From many design studies suggested by industries, and contracted by the National Aeronautics and Space Administration with universities, research foundations, and the aforementioned industries, came by late 1961 and early 1962 a fairly clear picture of what a lunar spaceship should look like. Apollo as the project was named, was placed under specific managerial direction at the National Aeronautics and Space Administration, and the North American Aviation Corporation was finally awarded the contract for the building of this space-craft. Superficially it looks somewhat like the Mercury capsule in that it has a blunt convex bottom, with barely enough space for three men sitting side by side. The blunt shape is used to make the atmos-pheric re-entry problem of the capsule easier. Actually, some capsule space had to be sacrificed by going to this shape instead of a dart, spear, or needlenose. Furthermore, an exact landing place cannot be easily determined with such a re-entry body. A sharp-nosed machine would have given a more controlled or maneuverable re-entry at the cost of proceeding through the atmosphere much more quickly; also the criteria for reentry, that is, the location of the re-entry point, would have been much more critical. Thus, if such a capsule came back from the moon at a speed of about 7 miles per second, the pilots and the guidance and control systems would have to be far more accurate in their path determination than is needed with a blunter shape, although, once slowed down enough in the atmosphere, they could glide to a convenient landing site.

This does not necessarily mean that the great space vehicles of the future will all have blunt shapes or even be shaped remotely like the planned Apollo or Gemini capsules. By the mid-70's of this cen-tury, we will surely have learned enough about the techniques of re-entry and heat control, and hypersonic aerodynamics to permit us to build manned spacecraft with shapes and contours entirely different from those we visualize now and more suited for their deep-space missions and landings at predetermined spots on earth. Streamlining, or a bullet shape, is not needed, of course, in the vacuum or space

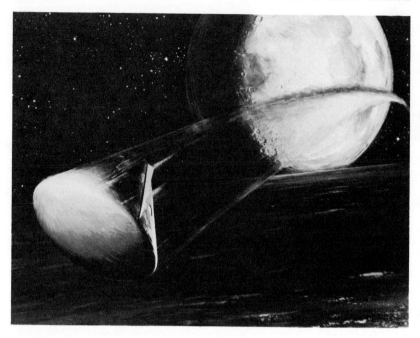

Figure 9.1. Artist's Concept of Re-entry of APOLLO Command Module. (Courtesy of National Aeronautics and Space Administration.)

because there is no resistance from any atmosphere; there is, however, a second problem, namely that of collision with dust or micrometeors. What holds true for aerodynamic resistance holds true to a lesser extent for a flight through dust and rock particles in space. A vehicle which presents a low frontal cross section would have less probability of destructive impact than one with a blunt, large-diameter nose.

Unless major events force a change of plans, it is reasonably certain that the flight to the moon anticipated for the end of this decade will proceed in the blunt-nosed re-entry space capsule now envisioned (see Figure 9.1). It may be well to recall at this point some of the fascinating aspects of this lunar mission.

Project Apollo

It is rather awe-inspiring to consider that by the end of this decade two Americans will land on the moon and spend at least a day on the lunar surface.

This mission—Project Apollo—is planned for 1970, and it calls altogether for a group of three astronauts. These men will embark at Cape Kennedy in Florida and travel from there toward the moon; after a journey of nearly three days at an initial speed of some 25,000 miles per hour they will be in the vicinity of the moon. When they reach a position approximately 100 miles from the surface of the moon, they will execute a maneuver that will place their craft into a lunar orbit. From this parking orbit, two astronauts will descend to the moon in a separate craft.

In spite of the many achievements of space travel during the last few years and in spite of the many elegant engineering accomplishments described in the previous pages, it remains a rather fantastic adventure to contemplate the descent of these two men on the moon. Consider two Americans, who will within the next few years emerge from a small craft, clad in space suits and equipped with cameras and various instruments, to explore the surface of the moon! Imagine, if you can, that these men will spend a full day exploring the moon, collecting rock samples in the fashion of prospectors, measuring temperatures, and in tourist fashion snapping pictures of their surroundings and of each other gazing about the lunar terrain! The landing will be accomplished on the side of the moon which faces the Earth, which will accordingly be in plain sight of these lunar tourists. Radio communications between these men and many tracking stations on the surface of the Earth will be maintained continuously. Consider the distance—nearly a quarter of a million miles—over which these men will communicate with their home base: The distance is so great that radio signals, traveling at the speed of light, will be delayed by nearly one and one half seconds between the time of broadcast and the time of reception. If a particular message happens to be a question to which a simple "yes" is required as an answer, the questioner must therefore wait almost three seconds of elapsed time before he receives this short answer to his query! Surely, this is no great inconvenience, but it does indeed underline the great adventure of the lunar journey.

The actual experiments that the two lunar explorers will carry out have not yet been defined in any detail. At the moment it is merely envisioned that they will spend a short period of approximately one day on the lunar surface and that they will then launch their landing craft back to the parking orbit in which the third team

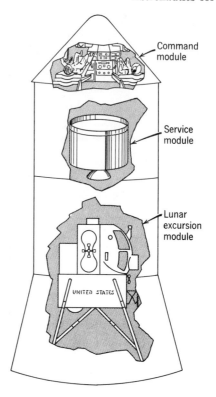

Figure 9.2.   Artist's Concept of Three-Module APOLLO Spacecraft.

member is orbiting in the mother spacecraft.   After joining him on board that craft, all three will return to Earth (see later for details). It is also planned that subsequent landings within Project Apollo will permit far greater excursion times on the lunar surface.   In order to provide facilities, supplies, and instruments, for these extended lunar visits later on, it was planned at one time to presupply such a lunar team with packages delivered prior to their arrival by separate and direct lunar supply missions from the Earth.   Such supplies could be placed on the moon by an automatic lunar landing craft, somewhat similar to the unmanned lunar mission of the Surveyor.   However, this plan may be shelved until the second or third landing.

The information which will accrue to us even from the briefest of landings of the first lunar party will certainly exceed in fascination that which the greatest explorers of all time have brought home from their distant journeys across the seas and to the poles of the Earth. Similarly, the sheer adventure of landing on the moon, exploring its terrain, and returning to the Earth must forever after remain a tale of adventure greater than any our previous explorers were ever able to tell. Let us examine now in some detail the present plan for this complicated mission Apollo.

The spacecraft that will be launched from the Earth will consist of three distinct elements, which are called modules (see Figure 9.2):

1. The uppermost module in the spacecraft is the *command module*. This is the cabin in which the three astronauts will live during and after launch until they reach lunar orbit. This command module will also be their home on the return trip from the lunar orbit to landing on Earth.

2. Directly beneath will be a large section containing auxiliaries, power units, and supplies—the *service module*. This module will remain attached to the command module until the astronauts return to Earth.

3. The bottom part of the three-module spacecraft is the *lunar excursion module*. This is a space cabin for the two astronauts which will depart from the lunar orbit and descend on the moon. The lunar excursion module will consist therefore of a two-man capsule with propulsion units that will permit them a descent to the moon and a soft landing there. The module will also contain propulsion power to reascend from the moon and join the command module in the lunar orbit, and it will contain an extensible landing structure which will serve as a launcher for the lunar departure.

The sequence of launching from the surface of the Earth and acquiring a lunar orbit, of descending therefrom to the surface of the moon, and of repeating these maneuvers in the reverse order (to return from the moon to the lunar orbit and to proceed from there back to Earth) entails several complicated maneuvers, some of which relate to the launch vehicle. The launch vehicle serves only the function of propelling the three-module spacecraft to the vicinity of the moon. However, the sequence of the mission in the order just described depends on the power available in the launch vehicle. For example, if all three astronauts were to land directly on the moon (in their three-passenger command module) and if they were then to return directly from the moon to earth, a much larger spacecraft would

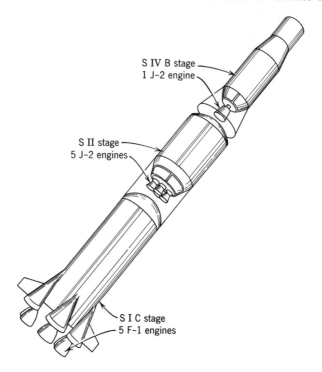

S IV B stage
1 J-2 engine

S II stage
5 J-2 engines

S I C stage
5 F-1 engines

Figure 9.3. SATURN V Launch Vehicle.

be necessary and a launch vehicle would be required with nearly twice the rocket power necessary for the more complicated mission. Accordingly, Project Apollo has been designed in the sequence of first acquiring a lunar orbit and subsequently providing descent capability for only two men in order to conserve on rocket power and thus depend on a launch vehicle that indeed can be built within the next few years. This launch vehicle—the Saturn V—is by no means a small rocket. Some of its dimensions and deployment functions are as follows:

THE SATURN V LAUNCH VEHICLE

The Saturn V is a three-stage, liquid-propelled rocket vehicle, which will provide a total thrust of nearly 9 million pounds (see Figure 9.3).

The first stage contains five engines (powered by kerosene and liquid oxygen) produced by Rocketdyne, a division of the North American Aviation Company, and designated F-1. Each of these engines yields a thrust of 1.5 million pounds, so that the five-engine cluster will have a first-stage boost of 7.5 million pounds. The first stage is 33 feet in diameter and stands 140 feet tall. The propellants in its tanks weigh 4.5 million pounds! These engines are currently undergoing tests and apparently their development will proceed on schedule from now on.

The second stage of Saturn V will yield a million pounds of thrust provided by five liquid hydrogen/liquid oxygen engines; these engines are also manufactured by Rocketdyne and are designated J-2. These engines are now in development, and current testing is sufficiently encouraging to anticipate no major setbacks. The entire second stage is 82 feet tall, and its diameter is the same as that of the first stage.

The third stage of Saturn V has a somewhat reduced diameter (approximately 22 feet) and will be powered by a single J-2 engine which delivers approximately 200,000 pounds of thrust.

With the spacecraft on top, the *entire* space vehicle will stand nearly 350 feet tall; at launch this vehicle will weigh nearly 6 million

Figure 9.4. Comparison of SATURN Vehicles. (Courtesy of National Aeronautics and Space Administration.)

pounds! The Saturn V launch vehicle is capable of providing escape velocity for a 45-ton spacecraft; it could place more than twice that weight into an Earth orbit (about 240,000 pounds) (see Figure 9.4).

THE SPACECRAFT

The spacecraft will consist of the three modules already mentioned briefly. The details of these modules, as presently envisioned are as follows:

The *command module* will be some 13 feet in diameter at the base and stand approximately 12 feet tall; its weight will be approximately 10,000 pounds. The crew compartment will provide tight but comfortable space for the three astronauts. They will be able to sleep on couches, work at tables, and eat, keep records, and communicate from appropriate stations on board. The module will contain windows to permit direct observations of the surroundings. The module will also contain a large number of instruments and controls, and the life-support equipment is at present envisioned to permit the astronauts the comfort of a cabin without requiring the additional protection of space suits. However, an air lock will be provided so that pressure-suited crew men can exit into space. It is interesting to note that some of the auxiliary power for use in the command module will be provided by fuel cells (see Chapter 1). Some interior views of the command module are shown in Figure 9.5.

The *service module* will be more than twice as large as the command module. While built to the same diameter of 13 feet, it will be some 23 feet high and weigh perhaps 50,000 pounds. The service module will contain the fuel and rockets for maneuvering the spacecraft into a lunar orbit after the entire spacecraft has traveled to the vicinity of the moon, following the initial launch from earth. Similarly, the rocket power on board the service module will be used to start the command module on its homeward journey from the lunar orbit, after the two astronauts return from their lunar excursion. The service module will be jettisoned after the command module is accelerated back toward earth. A view of the service module is shown in Fig. 9.6.

The *lunar excursion module* is the last unit in the spacecraft (see Figure 9.6). It is a two-man space capsule that will be detached from the other modules after two crewmen have entered it (subsequent to achieving lunar orbit). The lunar excursion module will permit

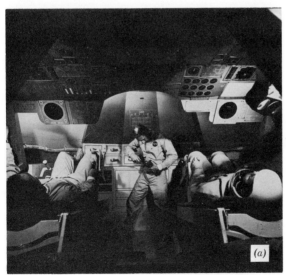

Figure 9.5. Details of APOLLO Spacecraft: Mock-up of Exterior and Interior of Command Module. (Courtesy of National Aeronautics and Space Administration.)

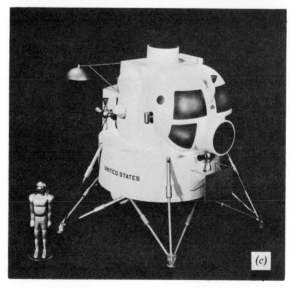

Figure 9.6.   Details of APPOLLO Spacecraft.   Mock-up of Service Module (*top*) and Lunar
Excursion Module (*bottom*).   (Courtesy of National Aeronautics and Space Administration.)

the descent of the two crewmen to the surface of the moon by application of retrorocket power (i.e., braking power). This rocket power will also permit the astronauts to hover closely above the surface of the moon to inspect in detail their landing site and to descend there gently. During final descent a five-legged landing structure with hydraulic shock absorbers will be extended to support the craft on the lunar surface. In addition to providing the crew compartment and the retrorocket power for the lunar descent, the lunar excursion module will also contain the necessary relaunching equipment, permitting the two crewmen to reascend from the moon and join the orbiting command module at the end of the lunar excursion; the launch gear will in fact, be built into the landing structure and will be left on the moon.

THIS MISSION

In the light of this particular design of the three-module spacecraft and the particular arrangement of the three-stage launch vehicle, the entire mission plan for Project Apollo will proceed according to the following sequence (see Figure 9.7):

The launch from earth will proceed from ignition through burn-out of the first stage and its subsequent jettisoning, to an ignition of the second stage and its subsequent jettisoning after burnout. At that point the third stage and the spacecraft will be in a low Earth orbit. The intermediate step of an Earth orbit is an arrangement of convenience (i.e., it permits the use of simplified guidance and control units compared with a straight Earth-to-moon trajectory). At the appropriate time in this low Earth orbit, the third stage will be fired and the craft will proceed on its lunar trajectory. After the third stage is burned out it will be jettisoned and the spacecraft will travel toward the moon. At the time of third-stage burnout the ascending craft will be at its highest speed—approximately 25,000 miles per hour.

The spacecraft will arrive in the vicinity of the moon after nearly three days have elapsed since launch. During this period the spacecraft will be in free fall and the travelers will feel weightless.

Lunar Arrival. When the craft approaches the moon, the rocket power in the service module will be employed to turn the spacecraft 180°, so that it will travel toward the moon in a tail-forward position. When the craft has approached within approximately 100 miles above

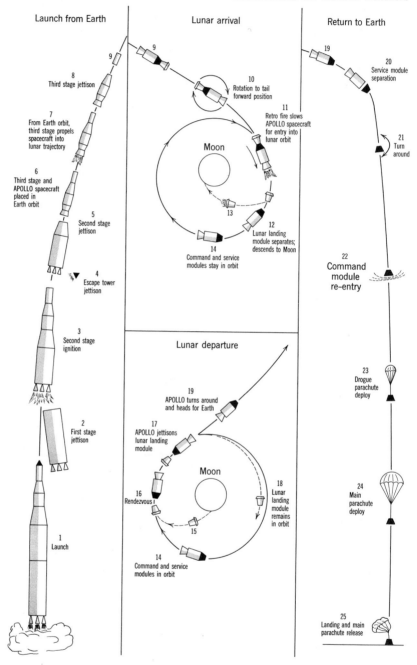

Figure 9.7.   Sequence of APOLLO Mission Events.   (Courtesy of National Aeronautics and Space Administration.)

the lunar surface, a rocket in the service module will be fired, and the retrothrust* will be used to slow down the craft sufficiently to achieve lunar orbit. When lunar orbit is achieved, another maneuver of the spacecraft modules will be carried out. This consists of detaching the lunar excursion module from the other two elements of the spacecraft, turning them through an angle of 180 degrees (so that the lunar excursion module will be juxtaposed nose-to-nose with the command module), and rejoining the three elements in their new position. This will provide a direct connection of the command module and the lunar excursion module through which two of the crew members will enter (see Figure 9.8). Subsequently, the lunar excursion module will be detached, and by application of further retrorocket power on board the lunar excursion module, the latter will descend on the lunar surface.

The *lunar departure* by the two astronauts will proceed in the lunar excursion module; its bottom structure will be equipped with sufficient rocket power to launch the cabin portion from the surface of the moon into the vicinity of the command module (in which the third crew member will still be executing an orbit some 100 miles

* Retrothrust is the term employed for (rocket thrust) forces applied counter to the direction of flight; since the craft had previously been turned into a tail-forward position, the rocket thrust will now act in this fashion.

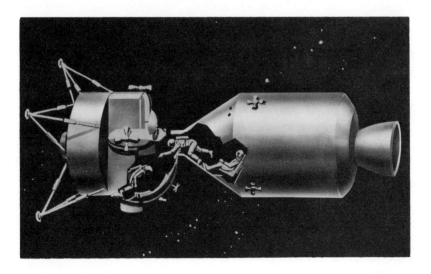

Figure 9.8. Transfer of Two Astronauts from Command Module to LEM. (Courtesy of National Aeronautics and Space Administration.)

Figure 9.9.   Artist's Concept of First Lunar Explorers.   (Courtesy of National Aeronautics and Space Administration.)

above the lunar surface). After the lunar excursion module has rendezvoused with the command module, the two moon voyagers will transfer into the command module, and the lunar excursion module will be jettisoned.

To *return to Earth,* the remaining (two-module) spacecraft will be turned 180 degrees, and the main rocket power of the service module will launch the craft into an Earth-bound trajectory. On approaching Earth, a speed of 25,000 miles per hour will again be attained. The service module will provide rocket power in the final adjustments of the homing flight path, after which it will be separated and jettisoned. Subsequently, a turn-around maneuver by the command module will be executed, so that its blunt-nosed cross section will face the atmosphere on re-entry (see Figure 9.1). At some 60,000 feet above the surface of the Earth a small parachute (a drogue chute) will open and stabilize the craft. When the craft has descended to an altitude of about 10,000 feet, the main parachute will deploy, and the command module will be sufficiently slowed thereby to permit a gentle landing on the surface of our home planet Earth.

Returned safely to earth, the first explorers of the moon and their successors in subsequent missions within Project Apollo will for a long time to come bring with them some newly gained information—scientific and human—of truly magnitudinous impact. But even at that great moment, some men will already look beyond the achievement of lunar landings and will quickly use the new data and experience of the lunar voyagers to prepare for a far longer journey:

9.3   THE MANNED EXPLORATION OF THE PLANETS

We can anticipate the eventuality of man's landing on the nearer planets. Although such a venture may seem farfetched and improbable, it must be remembered that as late as January 1961 there was no serious consideration given in the United States to a manned lunar landing; the notion was discouraged within the highest councils of the National Aeronautics and Space Administration and the Department of Defense, although several studies had been done by farsighted individuals. All that was expected at that time, within fifteen years, was a circumlunar flight—this project at that time being called

Apollo, which later, of course, became a broader project, namely the actual lunar landing. We can speculate in the mid-60s of this decade on the possibilities of a planetary landing. What problems should we expect to see and what are the probabilities of their being overcome?

First of all, it is obvious that large amounts of energy are needed to transport an object from the Earth to a nearby planet. This is axiomatic. Second, guidance and/or steering accuracies must be almost unimaginably precise. We have a similar situation with long-distance air transport. Thirty years ago it was quite an achievement for an airliner to fly 600 miles nonstop and arrive exactly at the point of its destination without corrective maneuvers. Today, flights from the West Coast of the United States to a point in Europe are daily occurrences involving distances of 4000 to 6000 miles, and the aircraft arrives at its destination within a tolerance of only a few hundred yards from the prescribed flight path. These achievements have been made possible by the building of bigger, longer-range, and faster aircraft, which carry large amounts of new guidance and navigational gear and which use celestial, radio, and inertial techniques.

The Booster Power Problems

In a similar manner, the great space ventures of the future will be made possible by the development of great rocket boosters capable of carrying ten times, if not one hundred times, the weight of presently planned boosters such as the Saturn V. There have been many discussions about the use of nuclear energy in rendezvous for increasing the space payload-carrying capability of any given booster. We can discuss this approach later; but it can be said now that the use of nuclear energy and/or rendezvous and similar stratagems do not obviate the need for higher-energy, longer-duration rocket vehicles that can carry massive payloads into Earth orbit and then into space. There are three directions in which larger booster technology can develop.

Liquid Propellant Boosters

The first approach is the uprating, or size increase of a given liquid propellant booster, such as the aforementioned Saturn V. That is, instead of using five giant F-1 engines, as many as 12 could be used. This is a possible approach, but unfortunately it would not result in a large increase in payload, although very large sums of money would be spent in developing a new booster vehicle. What is really needed is something that can give a payload increase of about twenty to fifty times. Such an increase, if it is to be achieved within the next 20 years, might be achieved by the use of solid propellant boosters.

SOLID PROPELLANT BOOSTERS

The technology of solid propellant development has been peculiarly possible and efficient in the United States and rests squarely on the fine chemical industrial complex that this country has built up. There are presently under development early prototypes of very large solid rockets with diameters of more than 20 feet. These monsters, expected to be 100 to 150 feet long, may develop thrusts upward from 20 million pounds. A cluster of four such solid giants with suitable upper stages should be able to project into Earth orbit about 2 to 5 million pounds, depending on the energy possessed by the upper stages. It must be remembered that the giant space ventures of the future which will lead to a planetary or lunar base will probably begin in Earth orbit and then be projected by other propulsion units out into space. This scheme need not necessarily be a rendezvous, but it may act as a staging or arena, just as ships crossing the ocean used to stage or preassemble in the harbor before crossing the ocean in a convoy. If we find that we want more than 5 million pounds in orbit (which means about 2 million pounds to escape) and if we find that a Martian mission will need more than 2 million pounds of spacecraft—perhaps three or four times as much— then we will have to go to another scheme, namely nuclear blast energy.

NUCLEAR BLAST ENERGY

Scientists have, for some years, speculated on the possibility of using the direct effect produced by nuclear blasts acting against the bottom of a massive vehicle. This scheme differs from the so-called "Rover" approach, in which a working fluid, such as hydrogen, is pumped in gaseous form through a red hot nuclear reactor, heated, and then expanded to produce thrust. The nuclear blast scheme (sometimes called "Orion") depends on the ejection of small atomic "bombs" from the rear of a giant space rocket, with each bomb exploding, say, a second or two apart. A giant series of pulse forces act against the vehicle, projecting it upward. Calculations have shown that payloads on the order of 2 million to 100 million pounds should be readily achievable, provided that the enormously difficult problem of directing the nuclear blasts into the proper area can be solved. There are some side problems such as the radiation fallout produced by these atomic bombs, etc. However, despite formidable practical and even some theoretical difficulties, the scheme does not look totally unfeasible and is being kept alive by various study contracts, funded mainly by the military. This nuclear scheme may someday have a place in space travel with the same relative position to present-day rocketry as steam vessels had to sailing vessels.

We see, then, that future space travel, especially to the nearer planets or for the establishment of large lunar bases or colonies on the asteroids or on satellites of the planets, or on the planets, will be made possible only by the development of giant new rocket vehicles. Although at first glance it would seem that giant rockets are the only answer to deep-space exploration by man, it must be remembered that there are limitations in money and facility that may, at least for the next few decades, prevent this country from building a booster beyond that of the Saturn V. The cost of launch facilities for a rocket of the Saturn V type are about one billion dollars for two launch pads. It has been estimated by the National Aeronautics and Space Administration that pads for a "Nova" launch vehicle (about eight times the size of the Saturn V) would cost 2 billion dollars *each*. Furthermore, the launch facilities and the geographical restrictions would prevent the building of such pads in the United States. Ironically, then, we have a situation in which the size of the Earth is beginning to be limited, and there is just not the land area available to launch colossal boosters of the post-Saturn-V type. Several proposals have been made for sea launching of rockets and while it has been done and will be done with smaller rockets up to the Thor size, it is not likely to prove practicable for very large boosters. Platforms and attachments and all the electronic and other physical gear would drive the price of such floating or anchored platforms into the billions.

The question that will face this country and perhaps the Soviet Union is this: if, on the one hand, we wish to undertake manned exploration beyond the moon or even to set up a lunar base or colony and, on the other hand, we have limitations in money and facilities for the building of the necessary boosters, must we abandon our dreams and notions of deep-space exploration? Well, as already stated, we can get by with certain stratagems, to a point, by the building of large solid booster rockets that will require no new facilities beyond those for the Saturn V rocket, or by the addition of certain solids strapped to the outside of a large liquid booster.

We will have to consider nuclear blast energy out of the question for the moment as something that can be obtained only after several decades of development. But the building of solid boosters or the addition of solid rockets to a liquid booster gives only about a 30 per cent increase in orbital payload above that of the Saturn V. This would mean an increase from 200,000 pounds in a 300-mile orbit to about 260,000 pounds. Although this is a sizable gain, it is by no means enough for the kinds of payload that will be needed for a Mars expedition, say. To transport six men to Mars and back, a journey that will take about two years if no time is spent on Mars (i.e., if only a fly-by of Mars is contemplated), would require a payload of at least one million pounds in Earth orbit, leaving about 600,000 pounds for escape to Mars after departure from Earth orbit. And even that payload is really barely marginal, and assumptions of no en route velocity correction or trimming are made and also many assumptions on life sciences' development for the survival of men in a closed system or capsule, are made.

Multiple Rendezvous

If we want to undertake a Mars expedition, how will we get the one million pounds or so into Earth orbit without the building of a new booster? First, it must be remembered that it is more practical to talk in terms of weight in Earth orbit than escape weight, because of various trajectory factors. A rough rule of thumb is that about two thirds of any given Earth-orbital weight can be projected as final payload from Earth orbit into deep space. One answer to the dilemma of large payloads in orbit (or into deep space) is the use of the *rendezvous* technique. This is by no means a new concept. Von Pirquet, a famous Austrian scientist and engineer, interested in rocketry since the early part of the century, published during the late 1920's several learned papers and articles dealing with the question of Earth-orbit rendezvous. His theory and suppositions have been supplanted by very little new material, and in essence his original concept is still true. This was, first, that any given rocket would transport a payload into Earth orbit. The payload it sends into orbit would stay in orbit, and is then gradually added to by other payloads fired up in a similar manner.

These payloads could consist of material for men, or the men themselves, in capsules, and propulsion modules or packages which would be coupled to these capsules in orbit. Gradually a composite spacecraft would be built up which would have the ability to support men for long periods of time. The escape spacecraft would have the ability to stabilize itself in correct attitude in orbit and deep space, and would have enough propulsion capability to escape tangentially from Earth orbit into deep space. After the space mission was achieved, it would return to Earth orbit and descend to Earth.

On paper, the technique looks feasible and the orbital mechanics of it have been worked out with great thoroughness. So far, the United States has not done any practical experiments leading to rendezvous capability. The great problem that faces the astronautical engineer is the question of firing rockets at suitable intervals so that their payloads will indeed approach the one already in orbit without lengthy and propellant-consuming orbital approach maneuvers. Now, in the endless domain of space, with billions of cubic miles of space available, it is almost a needle-in-a-haystack proposition to aim one payload at another and expect it not only to get close but actually to couple. Much thought has been given to the practicalities of physical rendezvous. It has been found that for saving propulsion energy it is necessary to fire successive rockets within narrowly defined periods of time, varying from a few minutes to two or three hours. The narrower the time slot or "window" used, the more accurately can successive payloads be bunched toward each other, and the lower the demand on further propulsion trimming in orbit. On the other hand, the demand on the launch vehicle becomes extraordinary, what with all supporting crews and ground servicing equipment being at the ready and operating in unison and correct sequence. It requires about 20 men to launch even a small solid rocket and it requires hundreds to launch a machine the size of the Saturn I or V. Complicated fueling techniques and electrical check-outs have to be performed, and hundreds of operations related to readying the rocket are necessary. Studies have shown so far that it is easier on the over-all operation if the launch "windows" for rendezvousing rockets are widened to, say, several hours or more so that the excessive demand on the synchronization of the ground servicing facilities are reduced. Even so, it is an extraordinary achievement, at least for American rocketry, to launch within a window of, say, one hour. At any rate, if the windows are opened up, then a special propulsion capability is needed in orbit for each payload so that maneuvering can be done and the payloads brought close to each other. Then, by microwave radar and optical seeking techniques, they would come together as a physical unity.

The National Aeronautics and Space Administration and the Defense Department are planning, during the next decade, large numbers of experiments in rendezvous; NASA's biggest effort in this technique involves Project Gemini (see Chapter 2). Then, after this early rendezvous technique is brought along, the Apollo capsule will be rendezvoused with various of its subcomponents, such as the mission module and the lunar excursion module (LEM). The Defense Department is also studying rendezvous and will experiment with this technique for the establishment of its manned orbital laboratory (MOL). So we see that rendezvous techniques are being explored and it is recognized that they will give considerable extra capability for any given launch system. This technique is similar to the refueling of bombers or other military aircraft to extend their ranges from a few hundred (or a thousand) to several thousand miles without having to land in the interim. Naturally, when more than one space rendezvous has to be attained, the complications increase rapidly, and there are those who say that it will be almost impossible to make more than two or three orbital rendezvous, even in the future.

However, despite certain doubts and worries about the technical feasibility of multiple rendezvous, it is unquestionably the only technique that will permit deep-space exploration without building giant boosters, as stated earlier. Therefore, such a technique must be evolved and a measured consideration of its possibility must show that there is presently no technical obstacle that should make this technique impractical. By the early 1970's the coupling of spacecraft in orbit, the transferring of men and materiel, and the integrating of spacecraft in Earth orbit and also lunar orbit (a special form of rendezvous not suited for long-distance missions, but only to descend to the moon) will be almost weekly occurrences.

Now, if we assume that the United States is determined to go beyond casual lunar exploration and enter the darker and vaster domain of deep space toward the nearer planets, Venus and Mars, and if we assume that a workable rendezvous technique will be built up by the early 1970's to permit us to launch spacecraft weighing hundreds of tons toward these planets, is that all we need to consider presently in the way of needed technical development? The answer is and must be no.

The Targeting Problems

Reaching the planets with men is largely, but by no means all, a matter of propulsion or propulsive power. Even a casual look into the sky will show that the planets are mere dots overhead, and when we aim for such planets we must remember that we are aiming at a point in the sky rather than at a planet four or five thousand miles in diameter. That is to say, our guidance accuracy must be of a fantastic order of accuracy to allow a spacecraft to wander from the Earth to a planet which could be 150 million miles away, and impact or orbit about this planet. There is presently no guidance system in existence or one that is conceivable that can give such an "injection" guidance accuracy for a spacecraft leaving Earth orbit like a slingshot and flying out into space to be aimed correctly at the planet, without midcourse correction.

Such correction is mandatory, and all studies done presently by large aerospace companies and other institutions in this country show this. That is to say, some kind of propulsion capability must be built into the spacecraft to permit constant trimming and correction by the pilots as they approach the planet over many months travel time. We ignore for the moment the question of having major propulsion capabilities to permit the spacecraft to slow down near the planet and orbit around it, and perhaps to land itself or a segment of itself on the planetary surface. Now, it is most expensive (actually hundreds of thousands of dollars per pound) to fly any payload to a near planet. Therefore anything taken along must be completely rational. Any redundancy that exists must be for the sake of reliability; that is, the food and oxygen supplies and auxiliary equipment must all be carefully checked and evaluated so that their function is not overextended and the men do not carry "dead" payload, so to speak. Similarly, not only must structural and auxiliary weights and equipment be of the lightest kind, but the propulsion elements must work at very high efficiencies so that the maximal thrust can be derived for a given volume and weight of spacecraft. Furthermore, the problems of storing propellants for a rocket in the vacuum of space—with intense sunlight heating the spacecraft to perhaps 200°F on one side, while the temperature of empty space at absolute zero obtains on the other side—must be considered. Even liquids that can be stored in containers for months at a time on Earth, such as nitrogen tetroxide and hydrazine or similar propellants, would gradually begin to seep and leak. Furthermore, we do not know the influence of space radiation, even very mild radiation, upon such propellants with time. It might be feasible to shield men from such radiation, but because of weight limitations it would not be feasible to shield an entire spacecraft and associated propulsion systems. Thus, propulsion systems such as we know them now would probably be impractical for deep-space penetration, and we will have to go to advanced systems, one of the most promising of which is "electric" propulsion. Here we convert the kinetic energy of electrically charged particles, accelerated through an electric field into thrust rather than converting hot gases in a rocket chamber into thrust by the acceleration and expansion through a nozzle.

Propulsion for Future Journeys

It is one of the major plans of the United States, both in the defense and civilian space arenas, to develop electric propulsors of adequate capacity to allow us to conduct space missions of the future, although presently such electric propulsors are not tied to given projects. However, we are at least developing the technology to permit us to design such things for actual space use in the early 1970's. These nonchemical propulsors are described in Chapter 7.

The important point to remember in this discussion is that we have ways and means of building and using propulsion systems far more efficient than possible with chemical propulsion (i.e., giving "more miles per gallon") but at the cost of reducing thrust levels so that these electric rockets can be used mainly for midcourse steering and trimming, rather than for primary propulsion, as would be used for leaving from the Earth's surface. The AEC and NASA are proceeding busily with the development of various compact, high-intensity nuclear reactors for electric propulsion and also for an associated scheme of nuclear-thermal propulsion. The latter, may also prove to be an important element in deep-space usage, although its specific impulse (optimistically) should not exceed about 800 seconds, if the project is developed at all during the next decade. Rover is the name given to the NASA-AEC development of a reactor that will heat hydrogen internally and then blast it through a rocket nozzle, just as hot gases are blasted from a chemical nozzle. Oddly enough, even though NASA has a substantial program in Rover and although a possible (but not planned) use of Rover will be for lunar "shuttle" operations and possibly for deep-space operations, its part in the future vehicle and propulsion technology in this country is not clear. The reason is that the technical difficulties of trying to make reactors operate at many millions of watts and at temperatures of 5000 to 6000°F are so tremendous that the United States may not find it practical or economical to proceed too far down the road with the Rover concept, and use it instead for certain near-Earth operations in which relatively small payloads are desired. A similar situation happened with the aircraft nuclear-propulsion project (ANP) in which it was found that other techniques were able to let airplanes fly for long distances and durations and in which the technical difficulties of the ANP were so great that it was not felt warranted under any circumstances to continue with them. There are no long-range plans at present either to continue or to cancel the Rover concept. The picture that electric propulsion will and must play for deep-space penetration is clearer. The latter is critically dependent on the development of lightweight, reliable nuclear reactors, capable of operating for *years* without breakdown and producing hundreds of thousands of kilowatts of electricity. Also, methods must be found to shield men from the intense nuclear flux emitted by the electric propulsion reactors (Snaps) or the Rover reactor.

However, as long as men's aspirations and ambitions drive them to the desire for exploration of the cosmos, they will find ways to pay for and engineer the machines necessary to translate these ambitions into reality. By the early 1970's, man will have stepped onto the first nonterrestial firmament in his 100-million-year history on Earth. He will return, with the dry dust of a dead world on his person. He will have seen the Earth as just another heavenly body near the horizon of his lunar world. But strange and startling as that experience will be, it is only the first step toward an endless reach into the Solar System and the mighty Universe beyond. Some day great argosies of space vessels powered by monstrous photon or light beam jets will disappear into the black void toward the nearer stars, moving within the fantastic domain of the four-dimensional space-time continuum of Dr. Einstein—perhaps to other stars and planets where these space travelers may yet find another world of sentient (and hopefully wiser) beings.

CHAPTER 10

Astronautics in High School Science Instruction

Arthur L. Costa

National Aeronautics and Space Administration

Contents

Astronautics in High School Science Instruction

10.1 TEACHING THE SPACE SCIENCES

In 1957 the world was plunged into the Age of Space. The effects of this new era are profound, overwhelming, and unpredictable. For educators the impact of the Space Age has given impetus to a gross re-examination of curriculum construction and educational practices. Young people are being caught up in the wonder and excitement of the Space Age. The explosion of knowledge is placing greater demands on educators and scientists to identify what is worth knowing.

With the myriad of possible learnings to be included in the school curriculum today, the planning and organizing for instruction becomes a complex task. The identification of subject matter which will lead to durable, economical, and productive knowledge is a challenge in itself.

The sciences related to the exploration of space can become a valuable part of the curriculum. This chapter is intended to clarify briefly their place in teaching science and to present an extensive list of available resources for teaching astronautics.

Why Include Astronautics?

Good planning precedes good teaching. The selection of content areas and subject matter is the heart of good teaching. Deciding what to teach is vital to the attainment of the educational objectives set by the student, the school, and society.

How does the study of astronautics contribute to these objectives? What criteria should be used to determine what should be included in the curriculum? How does a teacher know if a study such as this is worthwhile? Why teach astronautics?

MEETING SOCIETAL NEEDS

At no time in the history of the United States has there been such emphasis on science and technology. The processes and the products of scientific endeavor have enhanced our society to ever-increasing heights. Scientific processes are being employed beyond the laboratories of scientific research centers. We find such processes as testing, experimenting, researching, predicting, and evaluating in the various fields of city planning, architecture, advertising, and politics. The applications of science have contributed to greater ease of transportation and communication, improved health standards and longevity, and to increased amounts of leisure time. These benefits have become accepted in homes, industries, and institutions to such a degree that modern man would be at a loss without them.

As participating members of a democratic society, the citizenry has not only a right but a responsibility to understand their government's role in the economic and social implications of scientific endeavor. The ability to make intelligent decisions depends on the extent to which an individual comprehends and appreciates the nature and effects of scientific inquiry. For even the layman, some knowledge of this subject contributes to his fascination, understanding, and appreciation as he encounters scientific progress being reported in the news and mass communication media and as he realizes and supports the benefits accrueing to him in daily life.

The role of education today, then, is to prepare our young people to live in, adjust to, and improve on our society—a society heavily dependent upon and enhanced by science and technology. Our students, therefore, need to be equipped with understanding, attitudes, and skills that will help them to participate in and contribute to their society. In order to prepare them for living in the Age of Space, the teaching of science *must* include astronautics.

PREPARING FOR CAREERS IN SPACE SCIENCE

Some students will be contributing directly to the fields of space research which demand a depth of knowledge in the sciences and mathematics as well as skill in scientific research. Others will be working in related fields calling on technical, professional, computational, and artistic skills. The number of people employed in the aviation-aerospace industry is rapidly increasing and has already surpassed that of the automobile industry. With this tremendous increase it is difficult to identify or to classify the types of specialties that will be required.

What are the opportunities for students today to pursue a career in astronautics? Students may wish to become better acquainted with the requirements and opportunities in a space-related profession or career. Working with teachers and guidance counselors and contacting various industries in or near the community may give students a clearer picture of the prerequisites for entering such a field. Some students may wish to interview parents, relatives and interested members of the community who are presently engaged in astronautics to determine their roles in the exploration of space. Other students may write to various industries and agencies outside the community for information regarding needs and qualifications of various positions.*

Developing Appreciations

The exploration of space is a cooperative venture. Students must be helped to realize the tremendous amount of talent needed from the mathematical, biological, and physical sciences as well as the fields of technology and administration. Students may develop this appreciation by following the progress, for example, of manned space flights and by identifying the roles of the team members involved. These include the individual contributions of physicians, scientists, and mathematicians. It involves the participation of groups of specialists in several fields of systems integrations, electronics, communications, life-support systems, etc.

The exploration of space is an international venture. Many nations of the world are involved in satellite tracking systems, scientific space projects, and weather, navigation, and communication satellite programs. The knowledge which is gained and applied through the exploration of outer space will have an impact on all nations of the

---

* Further information may be obtained from such governmental agencies as the National Aeronautics and Space Administration and the U.S. Bureau of Labor Statistics in Washington, D.C., and from universities and scientific and technological societies. The following books may be helpful:

C. Adams and W. von Braun, *Careers in Astronautics and Rocketry.* New York: McGraw-Hill, 1962.

Otto Binder, *Careers in Space.* New York: Walker and Co., 1963.

Lawrence Ely, *Your Future in Aerospace Technology.* New York: Space Products 1962.

Lynn Poole and G. Poole, *Scientists Who Work For Astronauts.* New York: Dodd-Mead, 1963.

Lewis Zarem, *Careers and Opportunities in Astronautics.* New York: Dutton, 1962.

world and is being shared to the greatest practicable extent. Our scientific and technological progress is also being observed by many nations of the world. The ultimate effects on international relations will play a large part in human destiny.

Students may wish to research and record the achievements of other nations as well as their own. They will find that many other countries cooperate with the United States in the exploration of conditions in space and in the use of the knowledge obtained.

The exploration of space is an interdisciplinary venture. The contributions of the many scientific fields of inquiry are required. Furthermore, new scientific fields of study have emerged which relate various disciplines such as bioelectronics, lunar geology, and astrobiology.

Thus mankind has entered into a most profound endeavor. The wonder, the excitement, and the magnitude of this enterprise can contribute to the student's appreciation of his age and his environment.

CAPITALIZING ON STUDENT'S INTEREST

The Age of Space has captured the imagination and fascination of young and old alike. Students *are* interested in astronautics. To the young people of today even the adventures of yesterday's science-fiction seem prosaic compared to the real accomplishments, projects, and plans of modern space research. As Dr. Robert Goddard said, ". . . the dreams of yesterday are the hope of today and the reality of tomorrow."

Of all the space-related research projects none has captured the interest and imagination of our young people as much as manned space exploration. Probably there is a degree of self-identification with another fellow human orbiting the Earth or venturing to the moon. One cannot help wondering, "How would I feel if I were up there?"

Students may be concerned with such questions as: How does the astronaut obtain an adequate food supply? What effect has weightlessness on such physiological functions as respiration, circulation, metabolism, and digestion? How are body wastes eliminated? What are the effects of great amounts of acceleration and deceleration during blast-off and re-entry? What protective measures are used to guard against radiation in space? How does the astronaut cope with the psychological effects of isolation, disorientation, and fear? What would happen if we lost track of the spacecraft? Many of these same questions challenge scientists and engineers today.

Student's questions serve as one of the indicators in determining what to teach. Their interests, their motivations, and their depth of understanding are reflected in the questions they ask. These can assist the teacher in selecting and sequencing learning opportunities toward the development of space-related concepts. Questions of students should also serve the teacher as the basis for individual study and research projects in the classroom, the library, and in the laboratory.

For example, students' curiosity about the biological necessities of man in space can lead to the development of a greater understanding of physiological principles. Determining what are the needs of man for existence on earth will help students to identify what needs to be taken into space for survival. Can students determine how much oxygen is consumed by a man in one day? How much oxygen would an astronaut need for three days of orbiting the Earth, or for a trip to the moon and return? If he were to approach the speed of light, would time pass more slowly and therefore less oxygen be needed? How should the oxygen be carried aboard the spacecraft? What might be some other means of transporting or obtaining oxygen? What is the effect on the metabolism when pure oxygen is breathed?

Learning Scientific Laws and Principles

By virtue of its interdisciplinary nature and its fascination, astronautics is a convenient and valuable medium for teaching science concepts. Through a study of astronautics many learning opportunities may be presented in which students confront, assimilate, and apply scientific laws and principles. Thus science concepts can be initiated, re-enforced, extended, and enriched.

DISCOVERING NEW CONCEPTS

A study of astronautics is sometimes the first means by which a student meets and confronts unfamiliar fields of science.

Probably one principle unique to the study of astronautics is an understanding of motion in space. Kepler's laws apply equally to natural as well as to man-made satellites. An investigation into the nature of ellipses, parabolas, and hyperbolas may help the student to understand the paths of various objects in space.

Another example of a principle which can be illustrated through astronautics is that of the electromagnetic spectrum. By detecting and interpreting the various wavelengths of the radiation coming to Earth, man has been able to probe many aspects of celestial bodies including their distance, temperature, movement, and structure. Thus man has been able to speculate more productively about the origin and future of the Universe.

EXTINGUISHING MISCONCEPTIONS

What is space? How often such replies as this are heard: "Space is empty." "Space is the absence of everything." The teacher must be alert to the identification of misconcepts held by students. Teaching toward extinguishing misconcepts is often a necessity. A study of the sun's radiation can contribute to a student's understanding of the electromagnetic spectrum as well as to his discovery that space is not empty but rather that it is filled with energy in the form of rays and particles. An investigation of the protective measures in spacecraft to guard man against the danger of meteoroid impacts, a study of the effects of erosion by interplanetary dust particles, or an exploration of the tektite theory may help students to realize that space *does* contain matter. Space is far from being empty. We are in space!

Many people still think a rocket moves because its escaping gases push against the air behind it. This is not unusual when we stop to think that the types of propulsion with which we are most familiar do need some medium to push against. When we walk we push against the floor. A ship's screw pushes against water. A study of Newton's third law can extinguish this misconcept.

Furthermore, the scientific exploration of space has caused us to re-examine many of our time-honored rules of thumb, only to find them lacking and inadequate. The misconcept of man's requirement for "natural" foods, the intuitive impressions of the consequences of weightlessness, and the indiscriminate fears of the effects of radiation can serve as good examples of how scientific concepts and quantitative data must constantly be applied.

REINFORCING PREVIOUS LEARNING

Man in space is like a fish out of water—he has left his natural environment. Man must, therefore, take part of his environment with him, since he cannot accommodate himself to conditions in space and he does not wish to perish. In the airless, weightless environment of intense radiation, glaring light, searing heat and frigid cold, man must survive.

A space capsule, a space station, or a moon base can serve as an example of a closed ecological system if it is designed for long-term occupancy. The learning of ecological principles can be dramatically reinforced when applied to man in space. Students may wish to construct a model of a closed ecological system which might be used in space. Can they devise a system to employ the same or similar cycles of the Earth's closed system? For example: plants make sugar ($C_6H_{12}O_6$) from raw materials (H_2O and CO_2) with the aid of light energy from the sun. Man consumes sugar, converts it to CO_2 and H_2O, releasing energy. The cycle is then repeated. Can students construct living laboratory systems in which these cycles occur? How might plants be grown in such a system? Which plants would be suitable? Could they be grown in such quantity to supply food *and* oxygen for a space crew? How much will it take? Could the same cycles be accomplished by using nonliving chemical reactions rather than relying on living organisms? What other ecological fact including temperature, pressure and humidity must be taken into account in providing man with a favorable environment in space?

Similarly, the search for extraterrestrial life is calling on biological principles to detect the elements of life on other planets as well as to postulate some possible conditions for other forms of life.

APPLYING PRINCIPLES TO NEW SITUATIONS

Sequence and continuity serve as criteria for organizing learning opportunities. Building on, extending, and applying previous knowledge helps to crystallize scientific concepts. Astronautics provides many new opportunities to apply previously learned information, concepts, and principles.

Early in a student's science instruction, he is introduced to the nature and effects of friction. The primary school child is often found being instructed to rub his hands together to feel the heat produced. "This," he might verbalize, "is friction." Throughout the grades he confronts friction again and again as he lubricates machines, sands wood, moves heavy objects, and discovers wheels and ball bearings.

An investigation into the shapes of rockets, nose cones, spacecraft and re-entry vehicles requires the student to apply his knowledge to this new situation. Why are the Mercury, Gemini, and Apollo capsules shaped as they are? Why are the heat shields placed on the blunt end? Why is the attitude of re-entry so crucial? What temperatures will the capsule reach on re-entry? How is the heat radiated, absorbed, or conducted away from the astronauts?

UTILIZING SCIENTIFIC PROCESSES

The acquisition of scientific information alone is not an adequate goal. The student should also acquire the ability to utilize the methods and practices of science in determining how we know what we know and in confronting new problem areas. Such processes as observing, classifying, measuring, predicting, and generalizing are inherent in arriving at scientific laws, theories, and principles.

It would be impossible to describe *the* way these processes should be taught, since their acquisition is a highly individualized matter. Some students tend to be highly analytical, whereas others are almost intuitive in their approaches to problem solving. In any case, the teacher has an obligation to nurture the student's logic and strategy and to develop his ability to identify the parameters of a situation, to perceive relationships, to suggest hypotheses and test their limits, to weigh alternatives, to set up experimental conditions, to gather data, to draw and test conclusions, to predict outcomes, and, above all, to question.

Astronautics provides a medium by which science can be taught heuristically. The many unsolved problems related to the fields of astronautics lend themselves well to developing these processes in students. For example, one problem facing scientists and engineers today is in the replication of conditions in space here on Earth. Students may gain a feeling for this when they are confronted with the problem of proving a rocket's increased efficiency in a vacuum or in devising ways to simulate weightlessness for long periods of time.

By using a model wind tunnel, students can test their ideas for rocket shapes. Through experimentation, comparative heating of variously shaped rockets can be determined. Data may be gathered regarding the effects of radiation on living organisms by subjecting seeds, small animals, and eggs to various amounts and forms of radiation. Observations of behaviors, appearance, and offspring may suggest hypotheses about man's existence in space.

Astronautics reintroduces many areas of speculation: *are* there life forms in space? What *did* cause the craters on the moon? How *will* man be affected by conditions in space over long periods of time? *Can* new sources of energy be harnessed to power space vehicles? The answers to these and many other such questions may be found in the lifetime of our students. The seeds of their solution can be planted now by encouraging students to suggest and support their own hypotheses.

Integrating Learning

"Space is the place where *all* the sciences meet"—Lee DuBridge.

Probably the most valuable aspect of teaching astronautics is the fact that it draws on all the sciences. It would be relatively simple to identify and relegate the various fields of astronautics to each of the science compartments commonly found in the schools. An example might be:

Mathematics — Problems of computing satellite orbits, trajectories, momentum, thrust and velocities of rocket motors. Measuring distance, time, and size. Graphing rocket flights and distance/velocity/acceleration/time relationships. Discovering shapes, including ellipses, hyperbolas, spheres.

Physics — Problems of heating, including ablation, temperatures in space, re-entry, conductivity, radiation laws, and combustion. Problems of coping with gravity, including mass and weight, weightlessness, and gravitational fields. Optical problems, including atmospheric refraction, spectroscopy, astronomical instrumentation, and photography. Problems of radiation, including the electromagnetic spectrum, cosmic rays and solar particles, the Van Allen Belts, and ionosphere characteristics. Problems related to energy sources, including solar cells, electric propulsion, radio transmission, and telemetry.

Chemistry — Problems of designing rocket fuels, life-support systems, fuel cells, metallurgy, and recycling oxygen, water, food, and carbon dioxide. Understandings related to atmospheric, lunar, and planetary chemistry.

Biology — Problems of environmental needs, including oxygen requirements and supply, removal of wastes, and ecological systems. Problems related to protecting man against hazards of space. Problems related to existing in space for extended periods of time, including low-pressure metabolism, reproduction in a weightless state, and biogravitation. The search for extraterrestrial life. Problems of man-machine-mission integration.

Astronomy	Problems of determining conditions in space, including time-distance relationships and interpreting starlight and wave motion. Problems of observing and classifying stars and other celestial objects. Study of the Solar System and cosmology.
Geology	Problems of determining the interior and surface structure of the moon and planets. Utilization of mineral deposits on other planets.
Sociology	Problems of international communication. The economic and sociological role of government in scientific research. The impact on society, including cultural lag, population trends, industrialization, and conservation of natural and human resources. Problems of space law and international cooperation in application programs of weather, navigation, and communication.
Psychology	Problems of man in space, including fear and isolation disorientation. Astronaut training.

The unique factor of astronautics is its interdisciplinary and multi-faceted foundation. In astronautics all the sciences are called into play. The integration of man, machine, and mission can serve the teacher well in helping students to recall, seek, and organize learnings into meaningful wholes and broad understandings. Discovering concepts in one field of inquiry and applying them in another is one of the best ways to re-enforce, complement, and buttress what has been learned. Perceiving relationships among the various disciplines of science is one of our most needed skills.

Evaluating Students' Progress

What is important, however, is not the adjectives used to describe the value of teaching astronautics, but the results such teaching achieves.

Teachers, of course, will want to prepare their own measuring devices to appraise growth in students' attitudes, skills, and understanding. Many evaluative techniques should be employed to gather evidence of growth. Teachers should be alert to such behaviors as students:

—begin to explain current happenings in the space sciences, using the learnings from their classroom experiences;

—begin to design their own experimental projects centering around astronautical research;

—choose more space-related reading material from the library (see the resources listed at the end of this chapter);

—ask probing questions which display their cognition of basic science concepts and principles;

—seek information regarding career opportunities in a space-related field;

—become increasingly proficient in such problem-solving skills as observing, measuring, and experimenting;

—display increasingly more interest in various governmental and industrial space research and application programs;

—pursue assignments and projects with sustained perseverance even though they become more complex;

—carry on special interest projects outside the classroom.

In Conclusion

This discussion has been an attempt to cite the place of astronautics in the science curriculum. It relates astronautics to the criteria used for deciding what to teach. It points up the opportunities for utilizing astronautics in teaching science through the introduction, extension, and re-enforcement of concepts and broad understandings and in the practice of scientific processes.

The demonstration of interest by students and the availability of numerous and helpful teaching aids and references contribute to the enthusiasm for such a study. The need and support by governmental, societal, and industrial leaders presents an important obligation for the teacher to prepare students to live productively in the Space Age. Finally, the interrelation of scientific disciplines in astronautics creates an unusual and challenging medium with which to unify, enrich, and apply the student's understanding of and inquiry into his world in space.

10.2 RESOURCES FOR TEACHING ASTRONAUTICS

The following list is by no means exhaustive. It represents selected recent publications and sources which may prove helpful to teachers

and students in locating information and material for reference. But
any such list needs constant revision. This can be accomplished by
supplementing these materials with newspaper and magazine articles,
television and radio programs, and maintaining contact with governmental, industrial, and community agencies in your area.

General Bibliography for Teachers and Students*

* Those sources marked "T" are primarily for teacher use; those with "S" are
suitable for student use as well.

Adler, Irving, *Seeing the Earth from Space*. New York: John Day, 1962.
TS

Adams, Carsbie C., and Wernher von Braun. *Careers in Astronautics and
Rocketry*. New York: McGraw-Hill, 1962. TS

Ahnstrom, D. N., *The Complete Book of Jets and Rockets*. Cleveland: World,
1959. TS

American Assembly, Columbia University. *Outer Space: Prospects for Man
and Society*. Englewood Cliffs, N.J.: Prentice Hall, 1962. T

Anthony, H. D. *Sir Isaac Newton*. New York: Abelard-Schuman, 1960. T

Asimov, Isaac. *The Double Planet*. New York: Abelard Schuman, 1960. TS

Asimov, Isaac. *The Kingdom of the Sun*. New York: Abelard-Schuman,
1960. TS

Beard, R. B., and A. C. Rotherham. *Space Flight and Satellite Vehicles*.
New York: Pitman. 1958. T

Beau, Georges. *Springtime of the Stars*. New York: Criterion, 1961. T

Bell, Joseph N. *Seven Into Space*. New York: Hawthorn, 1960. TS

Benedict, E. T. (ed.): *Weightlessness—Physical Phenomena and Biological
Effects*. New York, Plenum Press, 1961. T

Benson, Otis O., Jr., and Hubertus Strughold (eds.). *Physics and Medicine of
the Atmosphere and Space*. New York: Wiley, 1960. T

Bergaust, Erik. *First Men in Space*. New York: Putnam, 1960. TS

Bergaust, Erik. *Reaching for the Stars*. New York: Doubleday, 1960. TS

Bergaust, Erik. *Satellites and Space Probes*. New York: Putnam, 1959. TS

Bergaust, Erik, and Seabrook Hull. *Rocket to the Moon*. Princeton, N.J.:
Van Nostrand, 1958. TS

Bergman, Jules. *Ninety Seconds to Space: The Story of the X-15*. New York:
Doubleday, 1960. TS

Berkner, Lloyd V., and Hugh Odishaw (eds.). *Science in Space*. New York:
McGraw-Hill, 1961. TS

Bernardo, James V. *Aviation in the Modern World*. New York: Dutton,
1960. TS

Binder, Otto. *Careers in Space*. New York: Walker & Co., 1963. TS

Bok, Bart J., *The Astronomer's Universe*. New York: Cambridge University
Press, 1959. T

Bondi, Hermann. *The Universe at Large*. New York: Doubleday, 1960. TS

Branley, Franklyn M. *Exploring by Astronaut: The Story of Project Mercury*.
New York: Crowell, 1961. TS

Branley, Franklyn M. *Experiments in Sky Watching.* New York: Crowell, 1959. TS

Brown, R. Hanbury, and A. C. B. Lovell. *The Exploration of Space by Radio.* New York: Wiley, 1958. T

Bucheim, Robert, and the staff of the Rand Corporation. *Space Handbook: Astronautics and its Application.* New York: Random House, 1959. TS

Caidin, Martin. *The Astronauts.* New York: Dutton, 1960. TS

Caidin, Martin. *Spaceport U.S.A.: The Story of Cape Canaveral.* New York: Dutton, 1959. TS

Calk, James, P. *The Perspective Universe.* New York: Exposition, 1959. T

Carpenter, M. S., L. S. Cooper, Jr., J. H. Glenn, Jr., V. I. Grissom, W. M. Shirra, Jr., A. B. Shepard, and D. K. Stayton. *We Seven.* New York: Simon and Schuster, 1962. TS

Clarke, Arthur C. *Interplanetary Flight.* New York: Harper, 1960. TS

Clarke, Arthur C. *The Exploration of Space.* New York: Harper, 1959. TS

Clason, Clyde B. *Exploring the Distant Stars.* New York: Putnam, 1958. TS

Coombs, Charles. *Gateway to Space.* New York: Morrow, 1960. TS

Couderc, Paul. *The Wider Universe.* New York: Harper, 1960. T

Cox, Donald, and Michael Stoiko. *Spacepower: What It Means to You.* New York: Winston, 1958. T

Cyr, Donald. *Mars Revisited.* Philadelphia: Dorrance, 1959. TS

DuBridge, Lee A. *Introduction to Space.* New York: Columbia University Press, 1960. T

Ducrocq, Albert. *Victory over Space.* Boston: Little, Brown, 1961. T

Fermi, Laura, and Gilberto Bernardini. *Galileo and the Scientific Revolution.* New York: Basic Books, 1961. TS

Firsoff, V. A. *Strange World of the Moon.* New York: Basic Books, 1959. T

Gatland, K. W., and D. D. Dempster. *The Inhabited Universe.* New York: McKay, 1959. T

Goddard, Robert H. *Rocket Development. Liquid-Fuel Rocket Research.* Edited by G. Edward Pendray and Esther C. Goddard. Englewood Cliffs, N.J.: Prentice-Hall, 1948. T

Goddard, Robert H. *Rockets.* American Rocket Society, New York: 1946. T

Godwin, Felix. *The Exploration of the Solar System.* Plenum, New York, 1960. T

Goodwin, Harold L. *Space: Frontier Unlimited.* Princeton, N.J.: Van Nostrand Searchlite Book, 1962. TS

Haggerty, James J., Jr., and John H. Woodburn. *Spacecraft.* New York: Scholastic, 1962. TS

Haley, Andrew G. *Rocketry and Space Exploration.* Princeton, N.J.: Van Nostrand, 1958. T

Hanrahan, James S., and David Bushnell. *Space Biology: The Human Factors in Space Flight.* New York: Basic Books, 1960. T

Helvey, T. C. *Moon Base.* New York: Rider, 1960. TS

Hendrickson, Walter. *Reach for the Moon.* New York: Bobbs-Merrill. 1962. TS

Howard, Neale E. *Standard Handbook for Telescope Making.* New York: Crowell, 1959. TS

Howard, Neale E. *Handbook for Observing the Satellites.* New York: Crowell, 1958. TS

Hubble, Edwin. *The Realm of the Nebulae*. New York: Dover, 1958. T

Hynek, Allen, and Norman Anderson. *Challenge of the Universe*. New York: Scholastic, 1960. TS

Jammer, Max. *Concepts of Space: The History of Theories of Space in Physics*. New York: Harper, 1960. T

Jastrow, Robert (ed.). *The Exploration of Space*. New York: Macmillan, 1960. T

Jessup, Philip C., and Howard J. Taubenfeld. *Controls for Outer Space*. New York: Columbia University Press, 1959. T

Johnson, Francis S. *Satellite Environment Handbook*. Stanford, Calif.: Stanford University Press, 1961. T

Johnson, Martin. *Astronomy of Stellar Energy and Decay*. New York: Dover, 1959. T

Kiepenheuer, Karl. *The Sun*. Ann Arbor: University of Michigan Press, 1959. T

King, Henry C. *Astronomy*. New York: Watts, 1960. TS

King, Henry C. *Background of Astronomy*. New York: Braziller, 1958. T

Kinney, William A. *Medical Science and Space Travel*. New York: Watts, 1959. TS

Kuiper, Gerald P., and Barbara M. Middlehurst. *Telescopes*. Chicago: University of Chicago Press, 1960. T

Lent, Henry B. *Man Alive in Outer Space*. New York: Macmillan, 1961. TS

Levitt, I. M. *Exploring the Secrets of Space*. Englewood Cliffs, N.J.: Prentice-Hall, 1963. TS

Levitt, I. M. *Target for Tomorrow*. New York: Fleet, 1959. T

Ley, Willy. *Rockets, Missiles, and Space Travel*. New York: Viking, 1961. TS

Ley, Willy. *Satellites, Rockets, and Outer Space*. New York: Signet, 1958. TS

Lovell, A. C. B. *The Individual and the Universe*. New York: Harper, 1959. TS

Lyttleton, R. A. *Man's View of the Universe*. Boston: Little Brown, 1961. T

Mallan, Lloyd. *Men, Rockets and Space Rats*. New York, Messner, 1961. TS

Mallan, Lloyd. *A Guide to Astronomy*. New York, Fawcett, 1958. TS

Mallan, Lloyd. *Space Satellites*. New York: Fawcett, 1958. TS

Mattersdorf, Leo. *Insight into Astronomy*. New York: Lantern, 1959. TS

Mayall, R. Newton, and Margaret W. Mayall. *A Beginner's Guide to the Skies*. New York: Putnam, 1960. TS

Mayall, R. Newton, Margaret W. Mayall, and Jerome Wyckoff. *The Sky Observer's Guide*. New York: Golden, 1959. TS

Mehlin, Theodore G. *Astronomy*. New York: Wiley, 1959. T

Menzel, Donald H. *Our Sun*. Cambridge, Mass.: Harvard University Press, 1959. T

Merrill, Paul W. *Space Chemistry*. Ann Arbor: University of Michigan Press, 1963. TS

Michael, Donald N., and others. *Proposed Studies on the Implications of Peaceful Space Activities for Human Affairs*. Washington, D.C. Brookings Institution, 1961. T

Moffat, Samual, and Joshua Lederberg. *Space Biology*. New York: Scholastic, 1960. TS

Moore, Patrick. *A Guide to the Planets*. New York: Norton, 1960. TS

Moore, Patrick. *A Guide to the Stars.* New York, Norton, 1960. TS
Moore, Patrick. *Earth Satellites.* New York: Norton, 1958. TS
Motz, Lloyd. *This is Outer Space.* New York: New American Library, 1960. TS
Motz, Lloyd. *This is Astronomy.* New York: Columbia, 1963. TS
Newell, Homer E. *Express to the Stars.* New York: McGraw-Hill, 1961. TS
Newell, Homer E. *Sounding Rockets.* New York: McGraw-Hill, 1959. T
Newlon, Clark. *1001 Questions Answered about Space.* New York: Dodd-Mead, 1962. T
New York Times. America's Race for the Moon. New York: Random House, 1962. TS
Oberth, Hermann. *The Moon Car.* New York: Harper, 1959. T
Oberth, Hermann. *Man into Space.* New York: Harper, 1957. T
Odishau, Hugh. *Space Science Serves Man.* New York: Scholastic, 1964. TS
Olcott, W. T., and R. and M. Mayall. *Field Book of the Skies.* New York: Putnam, 1954. TS
Ordway, Frederick I., III. Advances in Space Science, Volume II. New York: Academic, 1960. T
Ordway, Frederick I., III. Advances in Space Science, Volume I, New York: Academic, 1959. T
Ovenden, Michael W. *Artificial Satellites.* Baltimore, Penguin, 1961. TS
Peek, Bertrand H. *The Planet Jupiter.* New York: Macmillan, 1958. T
Pickering, James S. *Captives of the Sun.* New York: Dodd-Mead, 1961. TS
Posen, Dan Q. *Life Beyond Our Planet.* New York: McGraw-Hill, 1962. TS
Rackham, T. *Astronomical Photography at the Telescope.* New York: Macmillan, 1960. T
Reinfeld, Fred. *What's New in Science.* New York: Sterling, 1960.
Richardson, Robert. *Astronomy in Action.* New York: McGraw-Hill, 1962. TS
Richardson, Robert S., and Chesley Bonestell (eds.). *Man and the Moon.* Cleveland: World, 1961. TS
Ronan, Colin (ed.). *Changing Views of the Universe.* New York: Macmillan, 1961. T
Rush, Hanniford. *Wonderful New Book of Project Apollo.* Skokie, Ill.: Rand-McNally, 1962. TS
Russell, John L., Jr. *Destination: Space.* Chicago, Ill.: Popular Mechanics, 1959. TS
Select Commitee on Astronautics. *What's Ahead in Space.* New York: Noble, 1960. T
Sells, S. B., and Charles A. Berry, M.D. (eds.). *Human Factors in Jet and Space Travel.* New York: Ronald, 1961. T
Shamos, Morris H. *Great Experiments in Physics.* New York: Holt, 1959. TS
Shapley, Harlow. *Of Stars and Men.* Boston: Beacon, 1958. TS
Simons, David G., with Don A. Schanche. *Man High.* New York: Doubleday, 1960. TS
Smith, F. Graham. *Radio Astronomy.* Baltimore: Pelican, 1961. T
Stambler, Irwin. Space Ship: *The Story of the X-15.* New York: Putnam, 1961. TS
Stehling, Kurt R. *Project Vanguard.* New York: Doubleday, 1961. T
Stine, Harry. *Man and the Space Frontier.* New York: Knopf, 1962. TS

Stokley, James. *Atoms to Galaxies*. New York: Ronald, 1961. TS
Struve, Otto, and others. *Elementary Astronomy*. New York: Oxford University Press, 1959. T
Ten Steps into Space. Philadelphia: *The Franklin Institute*, 1958. T
Thomas, Shirley. *Men of Space*, Volume II. Chelton Books, 1961. TS
Thomas, Shirley. *Men of Space*, Volume I. Chelton Books, 1960. TS
Tregaskis, Richard. *X-15 Diary: The Story of America's First Space Ship*. New York: Dutton, 1961. TS
Wainwright, Loudon, and the Seven Astronauts. *The Astronauts*. New York: Golden, 1961. TS
Weiser, William J. *The Space Guidebook*. New York: Coward-McCann, 1963. TS
Wells, Robert. *Alive in Space: The Science of Bio-Astronautics*. Boston: Little Brown, 1961.
Welmers, Everett T. *Thrust into Space*. New York: Scholastic. TS
Wheolock, Harold J. (compiler). *Mariner Mission to Venus*. New York: McGraw-Hill, 1963. ST
Whipple, Fred L. *Earth, Moon and Planets*. New York: Grosset, 1958. TS
Whitrow, G. J. *The Structure and Evolution of the Universe*. New York: Harper, 1959. T
Wilks, Willard. *The New Wilderness: What We Know About Space*. New York: McKay, 1963. TS
Williams, Beryl, and Samuel Epstein. *The Rocket Pioneers on the Road to Space*. New York: Messner, 1958. TS
Williams, K. G. *The New Frontier: Man's Survival in the Sky*. Springfield, Ill.: Thomas, 1959. T
Woodbury, David O. *Outward Bound for Space*. Boston: Little Brown, 1961. T
Zarem, Lewis. *New Dimensions of Flight*. New York: Dutton, 1959. TS

References, Encyclopedias, Text and Source Books

DICTIONARIES, DIRECTORIES, ENCYCLOPEDIAS, AND ATLASES

Adams, Frank Davis (ed.). *Aeronautical Dictionary*. Washington, D.C.: U.S. Government Printing Office, 1959.
Besserer, C. W., and Hazel Besserer. *Guide to the Space Age*. Englewood Cliffs, N.J.: Prentice-Hall, 1959.
Caidin, Martin. *The Man-In-Space Dictionary*. New York: Dutton, 1963.
Callatay, Vincent de. *Atlas of the Sky*. New York: St. Martin's Press, 1958.
Firsoff, V. A. *Moon Atlas*. New York: Viking, 1962.
Frenot, G. H., and A. H. Holloway (ed.). *Agard Multilingual Aeronautical Dictionary*. New York: Pergamon, 1960.
Gaynor, F. *Aerospace Dictionary*. Philosophical Library, 1960.
Gentle, Ernest J., and Charles E. Chapel, (ed.). *Aviation and Space Dictionary*. Los Angeles: Aero, 1961.
Herrick, John W., and Eric Burgess (eds.). *Rocket Encyclopedia Illustrated*. Los Angeles: Aero, 1959.
Interavia ABC. *World Directory of Aviation and Astronautics*, 9th Ed. New York: Interavia.

Jones, Sir Harold Spencer, et al. *The Space Encyclopedia*. New York: Dutton, 1960.

Lee, Ben S. (ed.). *Aerospace Facts and Figures*. American Aviation Publications, 1961.

McLaughlin, Charles (ed.). *Space Age Dictionary*. Princeton, N.J.: Van Nostrand, 1959.

Merrill, Grayson (ed.). *Dictionary of Guided Missiles and Space Flight*. Van Nostrand, 1959.

Newman, James R. (ed.). *The Harper Encyclopedia of Science*. New York: Harper and Rowe, 1963.

Ordway, Frederick I., III, and Ronald Wakeford. *International Missile and Spacecraft Guide*. New York: McGraw-Hill, 1960.

Rudaux, Lucien, and G. de Vaucouleurs (eds.). *Larousse Encyclopedia of Astronomy*. New York: Putnam, 1959.

Spitz, Armand (ed.). *Dictionary of Astronomy and Astronautics*. Philosophical Library, 1959.

TEXTBOOKS

Bryan, Leslie A., and others. *Fundamentals of Aviation and Space Technology*. Institute of Aviation, 1959.

Cavanaugh, John M. *Introduction to Space Age Astronomy*. Educational Services, 1960.

Inglis, Stuart J. *Planets, Stars and Galaxies*. New York: Wiley, 1961.

Skilling, Wiliam T., and Robert S. Richardson. *A Brief Text in Astronomy*. New York: Holt, Rinehart and Winston, 1959.

Trenklein, F. E., and C. M. Huffer. *Modern Space Science*. New York: Holt, Rinehart and Winston, 1961.

SOURCEBOOKS

Brandwein, P. F., F. G. Watson, and P. E. Blackwood. *Teaching High School Science: A Book of Methods*. New York: Harcourt, Brace and World, 1958.

Joseph, Alexander, B. F. Brandwein, E. Morholt, H. Pollack, and J. F. Castka. *Teaching High School Science: A Sourcebook for the Physical Sciences*. New York: Harcourt, Brace and World, 1961.

Moreholt, E., P. F. Brandwein, and A. Joseph. *Teaching High School Science: A Sourcebook for the Biological Sciences*. New York: Harcourt, Brace and World, 1958.

UNESCO. *Source Book for Teaching Science*. New York: International Document Service, Columbia University Press.

Elementary School Science Project. *Astronomy: the Universe in Motion; Gravitation; and others*. Urbana: University of Illinois Press, 1962.

BIBLIOGRAPHIES

Aeronautics and Space Bibliography for Secondary Grades. Washington, D.C.: National Aeronautics and Space Administration, 1963.

Benton, Mildren (compiler). *The Literature of Space Science and Exploration*. Washington, D.C.: Office of Technical Services, U.S. Department of Commerce, 1958.

Bibliography of Space Medicine. Washington, D.C.: U.S. Department of Health, Education, and Welfare, 1958.

Deason, Hilary J. (ed.). *The AAAS Science Book List.* Washington, D.C.: American Association for the Advancement of Science, 1963.

Deason, Hilary J., and Robert W. Lynn. *An Inexpensive Science Library.* Washington, D.C.: American Association for the Advancement of Science, 1961.

Etep, Raymond. *A Space Bibliography through 1958.* Maxwell Air Force Base, Alabama: Air University Research Study, 1959.

Jacobus, Arnold J., and others (compilers). *Aerospace Medicine and Biology: An Annotated Bibliography.* Washington, D.C.: U.S. Department of Commerce.

Ordway, Frederick I., III (ed.). *Space Flight Literature.* Washington, D.C.: Space Publications, 1962.

Periodicals

Aeronautics Bulletin. Parks College of Aeronautical Technology, St. Louis University, East St. Louis, Illinois.

Aerospace Engineering. Institute of Aerospace Sciences, Inc., 2 East 64th Street, New York 21, New York. $5.00.

Aerospace Magazine. Aerospace Industries Association, 610 Shoreham Building, Washington 5, D.C.

Air University Periodical Index. V. Estelle Phillips (ed.). Air University, Maxwell Air Force Base, Alabama.

Amateur Rocketeer. Amateur Rocketeer, Inc., 1029 South Main, Rochester. Indiana. $4.00.

Astronautics. 599 Eleventh Ave., New York, New York. $9.00.

Aviation Age. 205 East 42nd Street, New York 17, New York.

Aviation Week. 330 West 42nd Street, New York 36, New York. $7.00.

Journal of Aerospace Sciences. Institute of the Aerospace Sciences, Inc., and the National Science Foundation. 2 East 64th Street, New York 21, New York. $20.00.

Missiles and Rockets. 1001 Vermont Ave. N.W. Washington 5, D.C. $3.00.

Review of Popular Astronomy. Sky Publishing Corporation, 49-50-51 Bay State Road, Cambridge 38, Massachusetts. $3.00.

Science. American Association for the Advancement of Science. 1515 Massachusetts Avenue N.W., Washington 5, D.C. $8.50.

Science World. 33 West 42nd Street, New York 36, New York. $1.50.

Scientific American. 415 Madison Avenue, New York 17, New York. $6.00.

Sky and Telescope. Sky Publishing Corporation, 49-50-51 Bay State Road, Cambridge 38, Massachusetts. $5.00.

Skylights. National Aerospace Education Council, 1025 Connecticut Avenue, Washington 6, D.C.

Space/Aeronautics. 205 E. 42nd Street, New York 17, New York. $10.00.

Space Age. The Space Age, Inc., Kingston, New York. Free.

Spaceflight. Sky Publishing Corporation, 49-50-51 Bay State Road, Cambridge 38, Massachusetts.

Space Journal. Space Enterprises, Inc., Nashville, Tennessee. $2.00.

Space Log. Space Technology Laboratory, P.O. Box 95001, 8520 Sepulveda Boulevard, Westchester, California.

Space Science. 4211 Colie Drive, Silver Springs, Maryland.
Space World Magazine. 250 West 57th St., New York 19, New York.

Sources of Free and Inexpensive Materials

INDUSTRIES

A. C. Spark Plugs, General Motors Division, Milwaukee, Wisconsin.

Aerojet-General Corp., Liquid Rocket Plant, P.O. Box 1947, Sacramento, California.

Aerospace Corporation, 2400 E. El Segundo Boulevard, El Segundo, Calif.

Avco Corp., 201 Lowell Street, Wilmington, Massachusetts.

Bell Telephone (call your local business office).

Douglas Aircraft Co., Inc., 3000 Ocean Park Boulevard, Santa Monica, California.

Eastman Kodak Co., Sales Service Division, Rochester 4, New York.

Estes Industries, Inc., Box 227, Penrose, Colorado.

The Garrett Corporation, 9851–9951 Sepulveda Boulevard, Los Angeles 19, California.

General Dynamics/Astronautics, P.O. Box 1128, San Diego, Calif.

General Dynamics/Convair, Material Post Office Box 2071, San Diego, California.

General Dynamics/Pomona, P.O. Box 1011, Pomona, California.

General Electric Company, Direct Energy Conversion Operation, 1950 Western Avenue, Lymon 3, Massachusetts.

General Electric Company, Missile and Space Division, P.O. Box 8555, Philadelphia 1, Pennsylvania.

Hughes Aircraft, Florence and Teale, Culver City, California.

Jet Propulsion Laboratory, 4800 Oak Grove Drive, Pasadena 3, California.

Lear-Siegler, Inc., Instrument Division, 110 Ionia N.W., Grand Rapids, Michigan.

Lockheed Missile Division, Public Relations Department, Sunnyvale, California.

Lockheed Missile and Space Company, 7701 Woodley, Van Nuys, California.

Los Alamos Science Laboratory, Los Alamos, New Mexico.

Marquardt Corporation, Public Relations, 16555 Saticoy Street, Van Nuys, California.

Minneapolis Honeywell Regulator Company, 2600 Ridgeway Road, Minneapolis 40, Minnesota.

North American Aviation, Inc., 12214 Lakewood Blvd., Downey, Calif.

Republic Aviation Corporation, Farmingdale, Long Island, New York.

Space Technology Laboratories, P.O. Box 95001, 8520 Sepulveda Boulevard, Westchester, California.

Sperry Gyroscope Company, Public Relations Department, Division of Sperry Rand Corp., Great Neck, New York.

Strofford Industries, Inc., Box 702, Devon, Pennsylvania.

Unitron Instrument Company, Telescopic Sales Division, 66 Needhom Street, Newton Highlands 61, Massachusetts.

INSTITUTIONS, ORGANIZATIONS AND SOCIETIES

Adler Planetarium, 900 E. Achsak Bond Drive, Chicago 5, Ill.

Aerospace Industries Association, 610 Shoreham Building, Washington 5, D.C.

American Association for the Advancement of Science, 1515 Massachusetts Avenue N.W., Washington 5, D.C.

American Association of Variable Star Observers, 4 Brattle Street, Cambridge 38, Massachusetts.

American Astronomical Society, Smith's Astrophysical Observatory, Garden Street, Cambridge 38, Massachusetts.

American Institute for Aeronautics and Astronautics, 599 Eleventh Avenue, New York, New York.

American Meteorite Laboratory, P.O. Box 2098, Denver 1, Colorado.

American Museum of Natural History, Hayden Planetarium, New York 24, New York.

Astronomical League, 4 Klopfer Street, Millvale, Pittsburgh 9, Pennsylvania.

Astronomical Society of the Pacific, c/o California Academy of Sciences, Golden Gate Park, San Francisco 18, California.

Cranbrook Institute of Science, Bloomfield Hills, Michigan.

Fels Planetarium, Parkway and 20th Street, Philadelphia, Pa.

Franklin Institute, Philadelphia 3, Pennsylvania.

Institute of Aeronautical Sciences, Student Activities, 2 East 64th Street, New York 21, New York.

Junior Engineering Society (JETS), 200–201 Mechanical Engineering, Michigan State University, East Lansing, Michigan.

Lick Observatory, Mt. Hamilton, California.

Lowell Observatory, Flagstaff, Arizona.

Maryland Academy of Sciences, Enoch Pratt Library Building, 400 Cathedral Street, Baltimore 1, Maryland.

Mt. Wilson and Palomar Observatories, 1201 E. California Street, Pasadena 4, California.

Museum of Natural History, Cleveland, Ohio.

National Academy of Sciences, 2101 Constitution Avenue N.W., Washington 6, D.C.

National Aerospace Education Council, 1025 Connecticut Avenue, N.W., Washington 6, D.C.

National Association of Rocketry, Suite 1962, 11 West 42nd Street, New York 36, New York.

National Geographic Society, 16th and M Streets, N.W., Washington 6, D.C.

National Science Foundation, Harvard University, Cambridge, Massachusetts.

Ohio Division of Aviation, 3130 Case Road, Columbus 21, Ohio.

QM Food and Container Institute, Chicago 9, Illinois.

Rocket Research Institute, 3262 Castera Avenue, Glendale 8, Calif.

Royal Astronomical Society of Canada, 252 College Street, Toronto 2B, Ontario.

Science Service, 1719 N. Street N.W., Washington, D.C.

Smithsonian Astrophysical Observatory, Cambridge 38, Massachusetts.

Smithsonian Institution, Distribution Section, Editorial and Publications Division, Washington 25, D.C.

World Calendar Association, 630 5th Avenue, New York 20, N.Y.

GOVERNMENT AGENCIES

Air Force Missile Test Center, Air Force Systems Command, Patrie Air Force Base, Florida.

Air University, U.S. Air Force, Maxwell Air Force Base, Alabama.

Civil Air Patrol, National Headquarters, Ellington Air Force Base, Texas.
House of Representatives, Committee on Science and Astronautics, Room 214 B,
    New House Office Building, Washington 25, D.C.
NASA Ames Research Center, Moffett Field, California.
NASA Flight Research Center, P.O. Box 273, Edwards, California.
NASA George C. Marshall Space Flight Center, Huntsville, Alabama.
NASA Goddard Institute of Space Studies, 475 Riverside Drive, New York 27,
    New York.
NASA Goddard Space Flight Center, Greenbelt, Maryland.
NASA Lewis Research Center, 21000 Brookpark Road, Cleveland 35, Ohio.
NASA Manned Spacecraft Center, Houston 1, Texas.
National Aeronautics and Space Administration, Educational Publications Branch
    (or Office of Technical Information and Reports), Washington 25, D.C.
Office of Naval Research, Department of the Navy, Washington 25, D.C.
Superintendent of Documents, U.S. Government Printing Office, Washington 25,
    D.C.
U.S. Air Force Systems Command, Los Angeles 45, California.
U.S. Coast and Geodetic Survey, U.S. Department of Commerce, Washington 25,
    D.C.
U.S. Department of Labor, Bureau of Labor Statistics, Washington 25, D.C.
U.S. Office of Education, c/o Specialist in Aerospace Education, Washington 25,
    D.C.
U.S. Weather Bureau

PUBLISHERS, DISTRIBUTORS AND EQUIPMENT SUPPLY HOUSES

Armistead and Goodman, Inc., P.O. Box 66, St. Louis 3, Missouri.
Astromurals, Inc., Washington 4, D.C.
Astronomy Charted, 35 Winfield Street, Worchester 10, Massachusetts.
Central Scientific Company, 1700 Irving Park Road, Chicago 13, Illinois.
Crowell-Collier Publishing Co., 640 Fifth Ave., New York 19, New York.
Denoyer Geppert Co., 5235 Ravenwood Ave., Chicago 40, Illinois.
Edmond Scientific Company, 101 E. Gloucester Pike, Barrington, New Jersey.
Field Enterprises, Education Building, Merchandise Mart Plaza, Chicago 54,
    Illinois.
George F. Cram, Co., 730 E. Washington St., Indianapolis 16, Indiana.
Hammond and Company, Maplewood, New Jersey.
Harmonic Reed Corporation, Rosemont, Pennsylvania.
Macalaster Becknell Company, 253 Norfolk Street, Cambridge 39, Massachusetts.
McGraw-Hill Publishing Company, 330 W. 42nd Street, New York 36, New York.
Modern Educational Aids, P.O. Box 209, Wilmett, Illinois.
Nelson Doubleday, Inc., Garden City, New York.
Perkin Elmer Corporation, Norwalk, Connecticut.
Precision Optical Company, 1001 E. 163rd St., New York 59, New York.
Questar, New Hope, Pennsylvania.
Rand McNally and Company, 8670 Le Berthon, Sunland, California.
Row Peterson Company, 1911 Ridge Avenue, Evanston, Illinois.
Sky Publishing Co., Harvard College Observatory, Cambridge 38, Massachusetts.
Slide Supply Service, Box 1031, Canton, Ohio.
Space Education and Research, 208 Commercial Building, Avon Lake, Ohio.

Space Publications, 1426 G. Street, N.W., Washington 5, D.C.
Space Science, 4211 Colie Drive, Silver Springs, Maryland.
Time Inc., Time and Life Building, Rockefeller Center, New York 20, New York.
William Frederick Press, 55 E. 86th Street, New York 28, New York.

Audio-Visual Materials

No film list can ever keep current. Many films are available through local school districts, libraries, and distribution agencies. It is advisable to investigate such sources first. The following are addresses of various agencies which make available free or low-rental films related to space. Securing their catalogue is the best way to keep up to date.

Association Films, 347 Madison Avenue, New York 17, New York.
Films are secured from the following centers of distribution: Eastern Area Exchange, Broad at Elm, Ridgefield, New Jersey; Midwestern Area Exchange, 561 Hillgrove Avenue, LeGrange, Illinois; Western Area Exchange, 299 Stevenson Street, San Francisco 3, California; Southwestern Area Exchange, 1108 Jackson St., Dallas 2, Texas:
Man in Space. Color, 31 Minutes. $12.00 Rental.
Path to Space. B/W, 28 minutes. Free.
Pioneers of Space. B/W, 30 minutes. Free.
Reaching for the Stars. Color, 13 minutes. Free.
Bell Telephone Company. Apply to your local business office for the following films:
The Big Bounce. Color, 14 minutes. Free.
Telstar. Color, 27 minutes. Free.
Voice for Mercury, A. Color, 14 minutes. Free.
Contemporary Films, 267 West 25th Street. New York, New York.
Inquisitive Giant, The. B/W, 28 minutes. $7.00 Rental.
Universe. B/W, 28 minutes. $7.00 rental.
International Screen Organization. 1445 18th Avenue, North St. Petersburg 2, Florida.
Depths of Space—Exterior Galaxies. B/W, 11 minutes. $3.00 Rental.
Milky Way, The. B/W, 11 minutes. $3.00 Rental.
Moon, The. B/W, 11 minutes. $3.00 Rental.
Solar System, The. B/W, 11 minutes. $3.00 Rental.
Sun, The. BW, 11 minutes. $3.00 Rental.
Modern Talking Picture Service, Inc., 3 East 54th Street, New York 22, New York.
Space, Science and Time. Color, 27 minutes. Free.
National Aeronautics and Space Administration. Code AFEE-3, Washington 25, D.C.
Alouette—Canada's First Satellite. B/W, 14 minutes. Free.
Areil—First International Satellite. Color, 13 minutes. Free.
Astronaut Shepard Reports on Space. Color, 20 minutes. Free.
A Voice for Mercury. Color, 14 minutes. Free
Beating the Heat. Color, 19 minutes. Free.
Before Saturn. Color, 15 minutes. Free.
Celestial Mechanics and the Lunar Probe. Color, 12 minutes. Free.

The Clouds of Venus. Color, 27 minutes. Free.
Echo in Space. Color, 14 minutes. Free.
Father of the Space Age. B/W, 18 minutes. Free.
The Flight of Faith Seven. Color, 28 minutes. Free.
Freedom Seven. Color, 28 minutes. Free.
Friendship 7. Color, 58 minutes. Free.
John Glenn Speaks to Young Americans. Color, 11 minutes. Free.
The John Glenn Story. Color, 31 minutes. Free.
The Mastery of Space. Color, 58 Minutes. Free.
Orbiting Solar Observatory. Color, 27 Minutes. Free.
Project Apollo—Manned Flight to the Moon. Color, 13 minutes. Free.
Project Echo. Color, 27 minutes. Free.
Saturn—Giant Step to the Moon. Color, 15 minutes. Free.
Saturn Propulsion Systems. Color, 15 minutes. Free.
Space for the Benefit of Mankind. B/W, 55 minutes. Free.
Steps to Saturn. Color, 22 minutes. Free.
Time and Space. Color, 27 minutes. Free.
Unmanned Spacecraft. Color, 14 minutes. Free.
X-15 Documentary. Color, 27 minutes. Free.
Louis de Rochemont Associates Film Library, 267 West 25th Street, New York 1, New York.
Exploring Space. Color or B/W, 26 minutes. $10.00–15.00 rental.
U.S. Air Force Films. Air Force Film Library Center, 8900 South Broadway, St. Louis 25, Missouri.
Beyond the Gravisphere. Color, 13 minutes. Free.
Project Echo. Color, 27 minutes. Free.
Space Communications. Color, 19 minutes. Free.
Space Guidance and Control. Color, 10 minutes. Free.
Space Navigation. Color, 13 minutes. Free.
Space Orbits. Color, 18 minutes. Free.
Survey of Astronautics. Color, 23 minutes. Free.

Index